Learning and Teaching
ARITHMETIC

Learning and Teaching
ARITHMETIC

SECOND EDITION

J. Houston Banks

George Peabody College for Teachers

Allyn and Bacon, Inc.

Boston

FIRST PRINTING . . . . MARCH 1964
SECOND PRINTING . . . . AUGUST 1964
THIRD PRINTING . . . . MAY 1965

Library of Congress Catalog Card Number

64 – 13892

PRINTED IN THE UNITED STATES OF AMERICA

Preface to the First Edition

THE MASTER TEACHER MUST MASTER HIS SUBJECT. He must enthusiastically believe in its value and feel that it is worth teaching because it is worth learning. He must have a depth of understanding of his subject that will both give him self-confidence and provide a frame of reference that will enable him to see relationships and significance beyond the immediate concern. On the other hand, the master teacher must never lose sight of the pupil's point of view. We do not expect a youngster who has just finished third grade, no matter how bright he is, to be able to teach third-grade arithmetic; we do not expect his grasp of the subject matter to be as great as that of the teacher. Yet, if the teacher's mastery of the subject matter is not to be a handicap, he must be able to transmit the fundamental experiences to the student.

Both the content and the organization of this book reflect the belief that maximum value cannot accrue from studying methods of teaching arithmetic unless the student has command of the subject to an appropriately mature degree.

Chapters Two, Four, Six, Eight, and Ten are devoted to the development of greater insight into elementary arithmetic. There is no implication that the content of these chapters, or the method of its development, should be incorporated in elementary school arithmetic. In most instances this should not be done. Following each of these chapters there is a chapter devoted to the teaching of the same aspect of arithmetic to elementary school children.

Either series of chapters can be studied in sequence without loss of continuity. The first series may be used as a text for courses in "Arithmetic for Teachers." The remaining chapters may also be used alone in courses in "Teaching of Arithmetic."

One cannot in good conscience attempt to enumerate all those to whom he is indebted for assistance. All under whom I have studied, teachers and writers, good and bad, those whom I have been privileged to teach, elementary and high school pupils, and future teachers, are responsible for whatever may be good in this book. The rest is my own doing.

J. HOUSTON BANKS

Preface to the Second Edition

IN THE FEW YEARS SINCE THE original edition was written profound changes have been taking place in the curriculum of elementary school arithmetic. There has been a decided shift in emphasis toward mathematical structure and corresponding changes in curriculum content.

Much of the material in the content chapters of the original edition was considered desirable background knowledge for the teacher. A great part of this material is now finding its way into the elementary school curriculum. It can no longer be considered desirable background, it is now essential content if the teacher expects to teach the newer curriculum.

The basic plan of the book is unchanged. The idea of parallel chapters, alternately content and method, has been preserved. The content chapters have been completely rewritten. Set theory is used to establish the properties of the natural numbers. In this edition emphasis is placed on familiar number systems first, then the abstract structure is developed. The reverse procedure dominated the first edition.

The methods chapters have been considerably enlarged and revised. Many more exercises have been included.

It is hoped that this edition will accomplish two objectives: (1). Update the book in the light of the changes that have occurred since the first edition, (2). Make the material more accessible to the reader.

J. H. B.

Contents

Learning and Teaching
ARITHMETIC

Arithmetic in
Today's Schools

THE POPULARITY OF THE TIME-WORN phrase "readin', ritin', and 'rithmetic" does not stem alone from alliteration. This is the indispensable tripod on which an education rests. Penmanship may have suffered in recent years. This is regrettable, but penmanship is an entirely different thing from ability to write if the latter is concerned with the communication of ideas. Whether Johnny can read or not, reading implies far more than mere sing-song word calling. So it is with arithmetic. Arithmetic, as conceived in the school curriculum of today, is a far cry from the rote drill on sums and products which characterized it when arithmetic and "cyphering" were synonymous. Genuine mastery of arithmetic requires, among other things, insight into its mathematical structure. Without this insight the highest order of utilization of arithmetic is impossible to attain.

1.1 STATUS OF MATHEMATICS EDUCATION

Much has been written recently concerning the status of mathematical training in America. Public attention has been focused as never before upon the kind of job the schools are doing in providing that training. The picture is not bright. Recent studies indicate that needs are not being met at any level. Not enough people are being trained as professional mathematicians; engineers are in short supply; too few people are sufficiently proficient in mathematics to supply the need for technicians. Businessmen complain that today's high school graduates are woefully weak even in elementary arithmetic.[1]

Some attribute the situation to the "modern" philosophy of education. There are those who feel the schools have fallen down on the job, that we are doing a poorer job than in the past. In all likelihood we are actually doing a better job than ever before when one considers the broadened scope of today's schools and America's acceptance of the concept of universal education, as well as the tremendous increase and diversity of the aims and obligations of education.

We find ourselves in this predicament for two reasons. First, the tragedy of America's dream of education for all lies in our complacence about the inevitable lowering of mean ability and performance. When educators refer to special education for exceptional children they usually are speaking of children with physical and/or mental handicaps. Rarely are special facilities provided for the child who is exceptionally bright. The ultimate price for such a policy may prove to be appalling.

This would not be too serious except for another American dream. The scientific, technological, and industrial achievements of recent years are too fantastic for the average citizen to realize. It would be more accurate not to call the present era the atomic age but rather the synthetic–electronic–atomic age. Progress with the atom receives the greatest amount of publicity, partially because of the accompanying dread and foreboding. But in the field of synthetics chemists can almost guarantee the construction of a molecule to any desired specifications. Electronic engineers have not only given us radar and television; automation and electronic computing machines will probably have far greater impact on our way of life.

---

[1] Henry S. Dyer, Robert Kalin, and Frederic M. Lord, *Problems in Mathematical Education* (Princeton, New Jersey: Educational Testing Service, 1956).

This rush of events, which has taken place entirely since World War II, has put a tremendous strain on the nation's scientific and mathematical manpower resources. The schools have found themselves faced with a task for which they were wholly unprepared. The great paradox of this age is the fact that as our culture becomes more and more technical—more mathematical—a continuously decreasing percentage of our population is receiving mathematical training.

The relatively small number of high school pupils who study mathematics is reflected in schools of engineering and departments of science.[2] High school mathematics is more basic to a scientific career than even the high school science course. The unpopularity of mathematics as a high school subject is, at least partially, due to unfortunate student experiences in elementary arithmetic. Thus the status of arithmetic instruction is not only an important concern in its own right, but it is also a major concern relative to the supply of specialists at all levels of educational achievement.

Recent events give promise that the situation will soon change significantly. National concern for the status of mathematics education has brought forth unprecedented action on the part of educational foundations and the Federal Government. Many diverse activities are being financed attacking the problem on two fronts: (1) curricular changes and (2) increased teacher competency.

By far, the greater emphasis has been placed upon the problem at the secondary school level. But the possibility that the core of the problem lies in the elementary school has not gone unnoticed. The School Mathematics Study Group (SMSG)[3] operates on a subsidy from the National Science Foundation which is itself a creature of the Federal Government and dispenser of public funds. The SMSG has prepared text materials in mathematics for Grades 4 to 6 as well as the junior high school years. The National Science Foundation has also financed on a small scale summer institutes for elementary teachers. At the state and local levels inservice training courses, workshops, and institutes on arithmetic are commonplace.

Many other groups are experimenting with new curricular material for the elementary and secondary schools. The University of

[2] Kenneth E. Brown, Mathematics in the Public Schools, Bulletin No. 5 (Washington, D.C.: U.S. Department of Health, Education and Welfare, 1953), p. 40.

[3] SMSG School of Education, Cedar Hall, Stanford University, Stanford, California.

Illinois Arithmetic Project,[4] the Madison Project,[5] the Greater Cleveland Project,[6] and the work of Professors Hawley and Suppes[7] are among the better known efforts at the elementary level. The University of Maryland Mathematics Project[8] is devoted exclusively to the junior high school years. Many other groups working at the secondary level include the junior high years in their efforts.

Two recent reports of national scope will doubtless have a far-reaching effect on the emerging curriculum. They are *The Secondary Mathematics Curriculum*, Report of the Secondary School Curriculum Committee of the National Council of Teachers of Mathematics and *Program for College Preparatory Mathematics*, Report of the Commission on Mathematics of the College Entrance Examination Board. Although these reports are concerned directly with the secondary school, they have significant implications for the mathematics curriculum of the elementary school.

That a new arithmetic curriculum is emerging seems inevitable. That it will give more emphasis to the mathematical concepts underlying arithmetic, to generalization, and to mathematical structure is most probable. A significant aspect of this movement is an increasing concern for better preparation of elementary teachers relative to their responsibilities as teachers of arithmetic.

1.2 A BACKWARD GLANCE

Arithmetic made its entrance into the curriculum of the Latin grammar school in colonial times because of its utility. The needs of commerce, surveying, and navigation dictated its content. Instruction consisted largely of the memorization of rules for "cyphering." Problem solving consisted of classifying by type and applying mechanical rules. Gradually the content lost contact with the practical needs of the time.

In the early part of the nineteenth century the Pestalozzian influence brought about significant changes in both content and method. One of the most influential writers of the period was Warren

[4] University of Illinois Arithmetic Project, University of Illinois, 1207 West Stoughton, Urbana, Illinois.

[5] Dr. Robert B. Davis, Syracuse University, Syracuse 10, New York.

[6] Information may be obtained from: Science Research Associates, Inc. 259 E. Erie Street, Chicago 11, Illinois.

[7] Professor Patrick Suppes, Serra House, Stanford, California.

[8] Dr. John R. Mayor, 1515 Massachusetts Ave., N.W., Washington, D.C.

Colburn. He dispensed with formal rules for solving problems. He placed great emphasis upon the disciplinary value of the subject and took the position that if it were to be of value a rule must be discovered by the learner. We see here an early forerunner of the presently popular discovery method. This period saw the rise of the academy and the decline of the Latin grammar school. During this time the major justification for mathematics in the curriculum was its disciplinary value rather than its practical usefulness.

The theory of mental discipline was not successfully challenged until about the beginning of the present century. In fact, it had become so ingrained in educational theory and practice that some educators and many laymen still take it as axiomatic. As is frequently the case, change from one extreme position was followed by an equally extreme shift in the opposite direction. The extreme utilitarian point of view will make of arithmetic or any other area of knowledge a drab and dreary experience. Those who would restrict the arithmetic experiences of the child to his transitory felt needs are both unrealistic and pessimistic. The intellectual curiosity of children and their feeling of accomplishment in learning for its own sake, unrelated to any practical application, are so consistently ignored as to be often stifled.

Our forefathers felt no need for television and commercial aviation. Even after these became available, acceptance had to await the creation of a feeling of need on the part of the public, which first had to be educated to their possibilities. So it is with the child, who cannot possibly feel the need for something of which he is totally ignorant. The feeling of need, the realization of the utility of a mathematical concept or process, must be created for him. Even so, in many cases this realization of value can hardly be achieved without prior understanding of the process. This is particularly true of mathematics. The history of the development of the subject illustrates the point. There are exceptions, but the stimulus for a major portion of mathematical development was not merely a realization of its practical value. Its utility was discovered after its creation. If necessity is the mother of invention, intellectual curiosity is the father. The fallacy of much that has passed for curriculum research in arithmetic lies in the fact that one cannot recognize a need for, and cannot use, that which he does not know exists.

The decrease of stress on its value as a mental discipline ushered in a period when arithmetic was to be restricted to the barest essentials, the need for which could be definitely proven. "Social utility" became the sole criterion for curriculum content. Teaching and learning of arithmetic were to be incidental to the other activities of the school—be that the core, the activity, the problem, the project, or simply the other broad areas of the curriculum, such as social studies or science. This point of view, though championed in many educational circles, has never received wholehearted, widespread acceptance in the classroom.

Although there is some evidence to support the theory of incidental learning of arithmetic, the most widely accepted view holds that it must be supplemented by systematic instruction. Successful learning of arithmetic which is wholly dependent upon experiences of the classroom requires the highest order of teaching skill.

In fact it is quite probable that in such exceptional cases the learning experiences merely seem to be incidental to the other activities of the classroom. We just happen to need a given bit of instruction in arithmetic at the opportune time because an expert teacher made it "just happen" that way.

The revolt against the theory of mental discipline brought about some much-needed reform. One is not required to accept utility, eventual or immediate, as the sole criterion for the selection of curriculum content in order to agree that much of the former content of arithmetic was both needless and unjustifiable. Particularly significant is the elimination of seldom-used fractions such as $\frac{196}{753}$, complex fractions, and the memorization of endless denominate-number tables. The postponement of formal instruction until Grade 3 or later has become rather generally accepted practice. This does not imply that number experiences are not utilized in the early grades, but that the theory of incidental learning and social usage is taken to have merit for this stage of maturity. The role of drill has undergone a searching critical appraisal. Perhaps the most far-reaching reform centers around the choice of problem material. There are those who condemn textbook problems *per se* as being removed from reality for the child. They would restrict problem solving to activities of the child at school, in the home, and in the community. Emphasis on real problem situations is sound, for the textbook problem can never incorporate all that is involved in solving a real problem. Nonetheless, the newer texts make a real effort to reflect the interests, activities, and experiences of children.

Present curricular trends lean heavily toward the mathematical phase of arithmetic. Concepts and skills are being introduced earlier. Relatively greater attention is devoted to the development of meanings. Inductive developmental procedures are replacing deductive explanatory methods in introducing new material.[9]

1.3 THEORIES OF LEARNING

Mental discipline is a corollary of the psychological theory of learning known as *faculty psychology*. According to this theory the mind is composed of certain faculties, such as reasoning, memory, perception, will, and the like. Exercising a faculty was supposed to strengthen that part of the mind just as exercising the biceps will build strong arms. Practice in reasoning in geometry was thought to make one a better reasoner in law. Memorizing nonsense syllables should make one more proficient in memorizing poetry. Under this theory it makes little difference what the content of arithmetic is, just so it is hard enough. Its relation to the needs of childhood or maturity is incidental.

Shortly before the turn of the present century the results of experimental psychology began to cast grave doubts upon the validity of the faculty theory. As a result of this early work Thorndike's *stimulus–response bond* theory was proposed as an explanation of the learning process. According to the bond theory a given stimulus (3 + 4) elicits a response (7) from the organism. Repetition of the stimulus–response strengthens the connection, the bond. Learning consists of strengthening the bond until the desired response always follows the stimulus. If the wrong neural connection has been established (3 + 4 = 5), the bond must be broken. The educational implications of this theory require that the learner be provided with *all* the specific skills and responses that he will need in later life. This theory gives rise to the theory of transfer of training of *identical elements*. What we have learned in one situation will transfer and be an aid in a new situation only to the extent that the two contain identical elements. It is now recognized by most psychologists that the bond theory is as sweeping an oversimplification of the learning process as was faculty psychology. The inadequacy of the theory of identical elements as an explanation of the learning process is evidenced by the fact that it was soon altered by its proponents. The most important element in the stimulus–response pattern is the

[9] For a good contrast between the two approaches see Herbert F. Spitzer, *The Teaching of Arithmetic* (3rd ed.; Boston: Houghton-Mifflin, 1961), pp. 7–11.

organism connecting them. The organism is never the same after responding to a stimulus. Furthermore, individual differences between organisms complicate the stimulus–response relationship. A given stimulus will not elicit identical responses from all organisms. Far more significant is the realization that elemental bonds do not exist in isolation; they are related parts of a total pattern.

Judd's theory of transfer admits the possibility of transference of habits, generalized skills, ideals, attitudes, and the like. According to this theory a learned response may be generalized by the learner and applied to new specific situations falling under the generalization.

In contrast with *connectionism* theories of learning, which place emphasis on the neural bond within the organism connecting stimulus and response, there have been proposed *field* theories. The impetus for field theories was provided by the *Gestalt* psychologists. According to their point of view, learning occurs when a Gestalt (or configuration) appears for the learner. It is not enough that a new situation contain familiar elements; these elements must be seen in relationship to each other as parts of an organized whole. When this is done *insight* takes place. The whole and the sum of its parts are not the same thing. Each Gestalt (whole) is an element of a larger whole. Generalization consists of extending and enlarging the configuration; in this way a body of knowledge is developed.

The reader is aware from his own experience that there are many kinds of learning. There probably is no one theory that adequately describes all learning. Furthermore, there is probably no one best method for all individuals. For some individuals memorization of the multiplication tables may be the most efficient means of reducing these number relations to automatic responses. For others, usage accompanied by reference to the facts when necessary may be the superior approach. The teacher can make no graver mistake than to assume that her pupils learn in exactly the same way she does, or that all her pupils learn in the same way. For some, a great deal of formal drill may be necessary for the mastery of a skill (strengthening bonds) while for others greater emphasis should be placed upon relating the skill to similar skills (configurational learning).

One need not subscribe to *a* theory of learning in order to develop a satisfactory set of principles relating to learning as a frame of reference for teaching. This is particularly true when various theories are viewed as complementing each other rather than in contradiction.

1. The end result of learning is changed *behavior*.

2. Learning is an *active process*. Mental activity is essential; physical activity is also frequently involved. No amount of "teaching" that consists only of telling can guarantee learning. We learn by doing, albeit the doing may be entirely mental. But the learner cannot be a passive spectator. He must be an active participant in the process.

3. The learner must have a motive for learning. Learning is *goal*-seeking. Positive, direct, immediate goals are more effective than remote goals or avoidance. It is better for the pupil to see the advantage of multiplying 7 × 13 over adding 13 + 13 + 13 + 13 + 13 + 13 + 13 than to have as his goal the avoidance of censure and possible failure.

4. *Trial* is an essential component of most learning. Trial may be for the purpose of eliminating wrong responses, or it may be to discover the relationship of the element to the whole configuration. Aimless trial, although it may ultimately produce the correct response, is not learning. The pupil who combines numbers in a problem in various ways until he gets the correct answer is not learning.

5. Complete learning includes *understanding*. Learning is not complete until the relationships of the situation become apparent and the generalized concept projected to similar situations.

6. We learn habits, attitudes, and techniques of thought as well as facts and skills. Unfortunately, in many cases the one thing which is learned most thoroughly in arithmetic is the feeling that the individual cannot learn mathematics. The habitual response to a quantitative situation is one of fear, impotence, and distaste. Checking on the reasonableness of results is a habit that must be learned. The teacher of arithmetic has no greater responsibility than the development of satisfactory habits and attitudes.

1.4 ISSUES IN ARITHMETIC TEACHING

What is the relative importance of arithmetic in the elementary school curriculum? One view holds that arithmetic should be restricted to the minimum essentials which are needed by everyone. Viewed from the standpoint of mathematical content this would include computation, both written and mental, with whole numbers. Computation with the common fractions, halves, thirds, and fourths, and the decimal fractions, tenths and hundredths, is usually conceded. This is debatable, however. Many people who cannot compute with fractions seem to get along reasonably well in spite of this lack.

If our concern is with what most people *can* use to their profit in our mid-twentieth-century society it is a different story. We consider *use* to include the interpretation of data relevant to personal, civic, and economic decisions. It also includes the understanding necessary for the use of arithmetic as a language—quantitative and relational language. From this point of view utility is an adequate criterion for the determination of minimum requirements.

There is still another view which is taking on a rapidly increasing degree of importance. Along with the many for whom the minimal requirements will be adequate there is an increasing number for whom arithmetic will be the foundation upon which a mathematical superstructure rests—mathematics through college for some, and through professional training for a few. Every research mathematician has had some kind of instruction in arithmetic. It is wellnigh impossible for the arithmetic teacher to know what the individual child's mathematical future is to be. It does not follow that the teacher should assume that all her pupils are future professional mathematicians. The special needs of this group should be met by way of enrichment activities which are not required of all. In fact, if the gifted can be identified with assurance it may be well to ignore much of the repetitive routine of the minimum requirements so far as they are concerned. They should be permitted to develop as rapidly as their capacities will permit, for they have a long way to go. To say the least, the teacher has the grave responsibility not to kill off, but to encourage, innate ability and unusual interest.

Should arithmetic be developed from the standpoint of social usage or mathematical content? At a more advanced level this question can be restated: Should we teach applied mathematics or pure mathematics? In the elementary school the distinction is neither feasible nor desirable. In the learning situation of the child this should be thought of as two aspects of the same thing. Even so, which should come first, social usage or mathematical content? Again, no definite answer is possible. It depends both on the nature of the particular situation and on the organizational structure of the curriculum. If the traditional subject matter pattern is followed, social usage might well serve both as motivation for the mathematical content to be studied and as an application of the content for the final step in the learning process. If the curriculum is built on the core concept, social usage will likely predominate.

However, regardless of the organizational pattern of the total curriculum, the mathematical structure of arithmetic cannot be ignored. To do so is to invite disaster for the pupil. Arithmetic cannot be learned adequately if its logical, sequential nature is disregarded.

Present curricular experimentation calls for a word of caution in this respect. In the recent past, social utility has been stressed to the detriment of the mathematics of arithmetic. But correct mathematics is not enough. It is just as important that the arithmetic curriculum be psychologically and pedagogically sound as that it be mathematically sound.

Can a satisfactory degree of efficiency be reached by incidental teaching alone?—Probably not. Some experimental evidence indicates that it can be done, although it requires a high order of teaching ability not possessed by most teachers. Furthermore, there is a strong suspicion that systematic instruction is merely made to appear to be incidental. If the proper attitudes toward arithmetic can be developed and maintained such a subterfuge seems pointless. There is fairly general agreement that when integrated curriculum plans are used the learning of arithmetic which is incidental to the main activity must be supplemented with systematic instruction.[10]

What about readiness in learning arithmetic? A readiness program is a learning program. Readiness and willingness are not synonymous. No amount of effort on the part of the child can replace the requisite maturity necessary to grasp an abstract mathematical concept. Readiness, however, is not all maturation. A large segment of the job of teaching consists of building readiness. The teacher who stands idly by waiting for the child to be "ready" is lazy, uninformed, or both. A large portion of the arithmetic of the first two grades should be devoted to the building of readiness for formal instruction. The

[10] Ernest Horn, "The Teaching of Arithmetic," *Fiftieth Yearbook*, Part II, National Society for the Study of Education (Chicago: University of Chicago Press, 1951), p. 18.

Paul R. Hanna and others, "Arithmetic in an Activity Program," *Tenth Yearbook*, National Council of Teachers of Mathematics (New York: Teachers College, Columbia University, 1935), p. 118.

sequential nature of arithmetic makes it obvious that readiness for a new concept implies mastery of those ideas and skills upon which it is based.

What are the relative roles of meaning and drill? One hundred percent mastery of the facts and skills of arithmetic is wasted effort if attendant meanings and understandings are missing. Without meanings there can be no understanding and without understanding there can be no application. The ultimate objective of instruction in arithmetic is the development of problem-solving ability. The child may know what you mean when he is told to multiply $\frac{2}{3}$ by $\frac{1}{5}$. "Multiply numerators to get the numerator of the result and multiply denominators to get the denominator" may be a perfectly meaningful statement for the child. He may be capable of following the instructions and obtaining the correct result and still not understand why this gives the correct result. Unless he understands the significance of what he does he cannot apply his knowledge to the solution of a problem. Understanding furthermore lends permanence to acquired skills. A process that is understood is not easily forgotten, and if it is forgotten the understanding serves as a framework for re-establishing the skill.

There are differences of opinion as to whether drill (if drill is a bad word, read *practice* or *use*) should precede or follow understanding. Undoubtedly, drill on understood material is more efficient; the child is thus more easily motivated. Complete mastery is obtainable with less drill. But to require full understanding before any drill is to ignore the fact that use broadens and deepens understanding. The use of drill before understanding does not necessarily imply that a skill which is not understood has value. Although, ideally, understanding should come first, in practice development of skill and meaning proceed together. Yet neither occurs as a result of the other. No amount of skill can insure understanding, and understanding does not eliminate the need for drill to establish the skill.

The purposes of drill are threefold. Some material, such as the basic addition and multiplication facts, must be reduced to automatic responses, almost to the level of reflex actions. At first glance memorizing the multiplication facts by "lines" might appear the most efficient means of attaining automatic responses—and this may be true for some individuals. But aside from the fact that countless children have learned through the twelfth "line" perfectly without any inkling of its meaning, many persons know the table as a whole, not as individual facts. Thus to recall 7×9, many persons who were taught this way have to think "$7 \times 7 = 49, 7 \times 8 = 56, 7 \times 9 = 63$."

Other skills such as the multiplication and subtraction algorithms should be practiced until the ideal of 100 percent accuracy is approximated and a reasonable degree of speed is established.

Varied practice in the form of application to problem situations should be provided to develop breadth and depth of understanding.

Are crutches of any value? As long as a crutch is a learning aid it is a good device and should not be discouraged. But when used excessively and too long it becomes a substitute for learning. When a first grader counts his fingers to get the sum of $5 + 3$ he is using a convenient learning aid. But if he continues to do this in the eighth grade he is simply still acting like a first grader. Crutches that are mathematically sound can be used to advantage if used with caution. The teacher must sense the time when they should be discarded and insist that they be. Other crutches should never be used; for example, *of* means *times*. "What is $\frac{1}{2}$ of 36?" implies "$\frac{1}{2} \times 36$" but the crutch becomes a stumbling block if the question becomes "36 is $\frac{1}{2}$ of what?" This is not a condemnation of word cues. It is a condemnation of their use without regard for the meaning of the cue word in the particular problem setting.

Should provision for the gifted be enrichment or acceleration? No one can prevent the gifted child from learning faster than the average or slow child. A properly conceived enrichment program is not merely a quantitative differentiation. It is quite possible for the entire class to study the same mathematical topic but as varied levels of abstraction, application, and generalization. This kind of provision for the gifted is more challenging and more fruitful than superficial mastery of material at a faster than average rate. If the choice is between letting the child explore widely and "dig deep" on the one hand or "run fast" on the other, the former is by far the wiser choice.

What instructional materials should be used in the teaching of arithmetic? This issue is usually posed in terms of the proper role of the textbook. Some people seem to feel that the textbook *is* the curriculum. Consequently, the book must be rigidly followed and all of its problems worked. If the book is mastered there is little reason to consider any other material. At the other end of the spectrum there are those who feel that the textbook is an impediment. It should be ignored; the arithmetic class should be an outgrowth of school, home, and community activities.

It is true that a textbook is merely a teaching aid. But it is an important one. For the vast majority of teachers an indispensable one. Covering the text is not an end in itself. Textbooks, as well as all other teaching materials, are of value only to the extent that they help produce the desired behavioral changes in pupils. This should be the criterion for the selection of instructional materials, anything from a classroom gadget to a field trip. The one question is—is it worth the cost; in money, in terms of teacher time and energy, in terms of pupil time and energy? One might wonder why the first consideration, money, is included. Surely it has no educational significance even though it is otherwise the *sine qua non*. Filling a classroom with junk, simply because the money is available, is absolutely no assurance of improved instruction.

What is the role of programmed learning in the teaching of arithmetic? This is, of course, an extension of the previous topic. Programmed learning materials constitute one of the most recently developed teaching aids. With the enthusiasm of a crusader, some of its advocates make elaborate claims for programmed learning. If a program and a machine to teach it can do a better job than the teacher then the teacher probably *does* need to be replaced—by a better teacher. Programmed material is doubtless an effective aid in many types of learning. But the possibility that it can ever be entrusted with the entire job is indeed remote. Programmed learning cannot be ignored or laughed off. Evidence as to its value is too strong. However, we have yet to learn very much as to its best use. Some think that its greatest possibility lies in remedial work while there are others who are just as sure that it is the ideal solution to the problem of providing for the gifted. The effectiveness of programmed learning can be no better than the program itself. There is no assurance that the avalanche of material now offered the public is of uniform quality. As we learn more about it, programmed material will probably be used to great advantage with some kinds of tasks, thus relieving the teacher for more creative activities. As we experiment with the medium it seems unavoidable that an unexpected dividend will accrue in the form of better understanding of the learning process.

1.5 GOALS OF ARITHMETIC INSTRUCTION

The program of arithmetic in the elementary school is conceded to be restricted to contributions to the *common learnings*, to be a part of general education; that is, broad nonspecialized and nonvocational education which seeks to develop those abilities, attitudes, understandings, and behavior patterns that should be common to all educable men and women. The arithmetic content should therefore have wide application, universal value, and intellectual appeal.

The general education, or common learnings, program of the elementary school should help the individual: (1) to think effectively and communicate his thoughts with clarity, (2) to know and discharge his responsibilities as an intelligent citizen in a democracy, (3) to practice healthful living habits, (4) to develop a sense of relative values, (5) to make a wise vocational choice, (6) to gain skill in the techniques of adding to one's knowledge, (7) to develop esthetic appreciation and to find self-expression in things of beauty.

The content of arithmetic should be selected with these broad objectives as a frame of reference. The possible contribution of arithmetic to their total realization far transcends immediate utility. Proficiency in the fundamental operations with integers and fractions will go unchallenged as a legitimate aim of arithmetic instruction. Yet of equal importance is a clear grasp of the basic concepts underlying the operations. The claims of arithmetic, or any other subject, on the curriculum must ultimately rest upon the probability of changed behavior in the child. The arithmetic program should contribute to the development of desirable attitudes and habits, such as orderliness of thought processes as well as of written work, the habit of checking all results, the proper attitude toward approximate data and the results obtained therefrom. The program should make provision for the development of effective application of skills to the solution of problems. This implies more than merely knowing which operation to perform. It includes such things as the gathering and interpretation of data, the recognition of the relevance or irrelevance of data, and the use of tables and graphs. The program should seek to develop intellectual independence by leading the child to discover relationships for himself, to appraise the correctness of his own results, and to make his own interpretations. Effective thinking should be improved through development of ability to maintain

sustained concentration, to generalize experience, to think analyti-
cally, to reason by analogy, to think critically, to give intellectual
curiosity free play.

The Commission on Post-War Plans of the National Council of
Teachers of Mathematics has compiled a check list containing twenty-
nine items. These items constitute the mathematical skills and com-
petencies which the Commission believes should be included in a
program of mathematics for general education:

THE CHECK LIST

1. *Computation.* Can you add, subtract, multiply, and divide effectively
   with whole numbers, common fractions, and decimals?
2. *Per cents.* Can you use per cents understandingly and accurately?
3. *Ratio.* Do you have a clear understanding of ratio?
4. *Estimating.* Before you perform a computation, do you estimate the
   result for the purpose of checking your answer?
5. *Rounding numbers.* Do you know the meaning of significant figures?
   Can you round numbers properly?
6. *Tables.* Can you find correct values in tables; e.g., interest and income
   tax?
7. *Graphs.* Can you read ordinary graphs: bar, line, and circle graphs?
   the graph of a formula?
8. *Statistics.* Do you know the main guides that one should follow in
   collecting and interpreting data; can you use averages (mean, median,
   mode); can you draw and interpret a graph?
9. *The nature of a measurement.* Do you know the meaning of a measurement, of a standard unit, of the largest permissible error, of tolerance,
   and of the statement that "a measurement is an approximation"?
10. *Use of measuring devices.* Can you use certain measuring devices. such
    as the ordinary ruler, other rulers (graduated to thirty-seconds, to
    tenths of an inch, and to millimeters), protractors, graph paper, tape,
    caliper micrometer, and thermometer?
11. *Square root.* Can you find the square root of a number by table, or
    by division?
12. *Angles.* Can you estimate, read, and construct an angle?
13. *Geometric concepts.* Do you have an understanding of point, line, angle,
    parallel lines, perpendicular lines, triangle (right, scalene, isosceles,
    and equilateral), parallelogram (including square and rectangle),
    trapezoid, circle, regular polygon, prism, cylinder, cone, and
    sphere?
14. *The 3–4–5 relation.* Can you use the Pythagorean relationship in a
    right triangle?

15. *Constructions.* Can you with ruler and compass construct a circle, a square, and a rectangle, transfer a line segment and an angle, bisect a line segment and an angle, copy a triangle, divide a line segment into more than two equal parts, draw a tangent to a circle, and draw a geometric figure to scale?

16. *Drawings.* Can you read and interpret reasonably well, maps, floor plans, mechanical drawings, and blueprints? Can you find the distance between two points on a map?

17. *Vectors.* Do you understand the meaning of vector, and can you find the resultant of two forces?

18. *Metric system.* Do you know how to use the most important metric units (meter, centimeter, millimeter, kilometer, gram, kilogram)?

19. *Conversion.* In measuring length, area, volume, weight, time, temperature, angle, and speed, can you shift from one commonly used standard unit to another widely used standard unit; e.g., do you know the relation between yard and foot, inch and centimeter, etc.?

20. *Algebraic symbolism.* Can you use letters to represent numbers; i.e., do you understand the symbolism of algebra—do you know the meaning of exponent and coefficient?

21. *Formulas.* Do you know the meaning of a formula—can you, for example, write an arithmetic rule as a formula, and can you substitute given values in order to find the value for a required unknown?

22. *Signed numbers.* Do you understand signed numbers and can you use them?

23. *Using the axioms.* Do you understand what you are doing when you use the axioms to change the form of a formula or when you find the value of an unknown in a simple equation?

24. *Practical formulas.* Do you know from memory certain widely used formulas relating to areas, volumes, and interest, and to discount, rate, and time?

25. *Similar triangles and proportion.* Do you understand the meaning of similar triangles, and do you know how to use the fact that in similar triangles the ratios of corresponding sides are equal? Can you manage a proportion?

26. *Trigonometry.* Do you know the meaning of tangent, sine, cosine? Can you develop their meanings by means of scale drawings?

27. *First steps in business arithmetic.* Are you mathematically conditioned for satisfactory adjustment to a first job in business; e.g., have you a start in understanding the keeping of a simple account, making change, and the arithmetic that illustrates the most common problems of communications and everyday affairs?

28. *Stretching the dollar.* Do you have a basis for dealing intelligently with the main problems of the consumer; e.g., the cost of borrowing money, insurance to secure adequate protection against the numerous hazards

of life, the wise management of money, and buying with a given income so as to get good values as regards both quantity and quality?

29. *Proceeding from hypothesis to conclusion.* Can you analyze a statement in a newspaper and determine what is assumed, and whether the suggested conclusions really follow from the given facts or assumptions?[11]

This is admittedly an ambitious program for the eight years of elementary school. "In some schools a few of the best students can get all this by the end of the eighth grade. Most pupils, however, would need to continue general mathematics for one or two years, in order to master what the check list calls for."[12] This is an understatement in the light of the findings of Beckman, Brown, Davis, Ohlsen, and Renner.[13] These studies indicate a need for training beyond elementary arithmetic, as it is being taught, if functional competence is to be acquired. Nevertheless, the check list provides an ideal to be sought in the elementary arithmetic program. It reflects the diversity of goals which a good program of instruction seeks to establish.

1.6 THE TEACHER OF ARITHMETIC

Preparation for teaching in the elementary school presents a truly formidable challenge. Expected competences include music, arts and crafts, science, health, social studies, literature, and grammar. The elementary teacher must be a reading specialist; must be versed in

[11] Commission on Post-War Plans of the National Council of Teachers of Mathematics, *Guidance Pamphlet in Mathematics for High School Students* (Washington: The Mathematics Teacher, 1947), pp. 4–5.

[12] *Ibid.*, p. 5.

[13] Milton W. Beckman, "The Level of Mathematical Competency and Relative Gains in Competency of Pupils Enrolled in Algebra and General Mathematics" (unpublished Ph.D. dissertation, University of Nebraska, 1951).

Robert C. Brown, "Functional Competence in Mathematics of Louisiana High School Seniors" (unpublished Ph.D. dissertation, George Peabody College for Teachers, 1956).

David J. Davis, "A Comparative Study of Achievement Levels of Twelfth Grade Pupils on a Test Designed to Measure Functional Competence in Mathematics" (unpublished Ph.D. dissertation, University of Michigan, 1950).

Merle M. Ohlsen, "Control of Fundamental Mathematical Skills and Concepts by High School Students," *The Mathematics Teacher*, XXXIX, No. 8 (1946), p. 365.

John W. Renner, "Relationship Between Instructional Provisions and Functional Competence in Mathematics in Iowa High School Seniors" (unpublished Ph.D. dissertation, State University of Iowa, 1955).

child psychology; must know intimately teaching theory and practice—and must teach arithmetic.

In no other area is the teacher's competence more significant to the progress of the child than in arithmetic. This is evidenced by the fact that arithmetic with significant frequency is voted the most liked and the most disliked subject by elementary school children. A tone-deaf teacher may be able to do little by way of music appreciation for the pupil, but this inability will not produce harmful results; subsequent instruction will not be handicapped by this lack. This is not true of arithmetic. Its sequential nature prohibits gaps in its development. Failures of an earlier teacher must be overcome before progress can continue.

Many persons believe that mathematical disability is far more frequently the result of emotional blocks than lack of mental power. An unhealthy attitude toward arithmetic may result from a number of causes. Parental attitudes may be responsible; "I don't expect my Johnny to do well in arithmetic because I never could get it" is a frequently expressed sentiment. There is also the other extreme, where the parent expects superior performance because of his own accomplishments. Repeated failure is almost certain to produce a bad emotional reaction to the study of arithmetic. Attitudes of his peers will have their effect upon the child's attitude. But by far the most significant contributing factor is the attitude of the teacher. The teacher who feels insecure, who dreads and dislikes the subject, for whom arithmetic is largely rote manipulation, devoid of understanding, cannot avoid transmitting her feelings to the children. The teacher may be able to bluff her way through many areas of learning, but not mathematics—where the final arbiter is reason, not some self-anointed authority. In mathematics, incompetence is one sin that is certain to find you out.

On the other hand, the teacher who has confidence, understanding, interest, and enthusiasm for arithmetic has gone a long way toward insuring success. It is as unreasonable to expect a good job from a person who dislikes arithmetic as to expect a good piano recital from a person who hates music.

A poor attitude on the part of the teacher is almost invariably coupled with a lack of understanding and mastery of the subject matter, thus compounding the bad effect on the child. Command of the material taught is not a sufficient condition for teaching success but it is certainly a necessary one. Many more teachers who fail as arithmetic teachers do so because of their own inadequacy with the subject than from a lack of knowledge of and skill in methods of teaching or from inability to work successfully with children.

The prospective teacher or, for that matter, teacher in service who has always liked arithmetic will find a more advanced mastery of the subject a fascinating undertaking. The indifferent and those whose experience with arithmetic has been unfortunate owe it to themselves to approach the study with an open mind. Not only can it become an interesting experience, the confidence which can be gained is indispensable to successful teaching. We must never lose sight of the fact that along with the facts, skills, and understandings of arithmetic the child is also developing attitudes, habits of work, ideals, and standards for himself, which in the aggregate have the greater total impact on the child's development.

Exercises

1 List social changes of the past twenty-five years which have served to complicate the job of the elementary school in the area of arithmetic education.

2 What change in the objectives of arithmetic instruction is implied by the widespread use of computing machines?

3 Is the influence of Pestalozzi in evidence in the schools of today insofar as arithmetic is concerned? Is this good or bad?

4 How does Van Engen (see Suggested Supplementary Readings on page 21) distinguish between *meaning* and *understanding*?

5 What are the relative roles of social utility and mathematical content in determining the arithmetic curriculum? Give arguments for and against social usage as the criterion for selection of material.

6 Discuss the contribution which Grades 1 and 2 should make to the arithmetic program of the elementary school.

7 Contrast the implications for drill of the "connectionist" conception of learning with that of "field" psychology.

8 List ways in which arithmetic can contribute to each of the seven aims of general education listed on page 15.

9 Which of the twenty-nine items in the check list on pages 16–18 do you consider to be basically applications of abstract arithmetic?

10 Which of the items of the check list should a sixth grade pupil be expected to master?

Suggested Supplementary Readings

Brownell, William A., "The Place of Meaning in the Teaching of Arithmetic," *Elementary School Journal*, January 1947, pp. 256–265.

Bruecker, Leo J., "The Social Phase of Arithmetic Instruction," *Sixteenth Yearbook*, National Council of Teachers of Mathematics. Washington: the Council, 1941. Pp. 140–156.

Brune, Irvin H., "Language in Mathematics," *Twenty-first Yearbook*, National Council of Teachers of Mathematics. Washington: the Council, 1953. Pp. 156–191.

Buckingham, B. R., "What Becomes of Drill," *Sixteenth Yearbook*, National Council of Teachers of Mathematics. Washington: the Council, 1941. Pp. 196–224.

Buswell, G. T., "The Relation of Social Arithmetic to Computational Arithmetic," *Tenth Yearbook*, National Council of Teachers of Mathematics. Washington: the Council, 1935. Pp. 74–84.

———, "The Function of Subject Matter in Relation to Personality," *Sixteenth Yearbook*, National Council of Teachers of Mathematics. Washington: the Council, 1941. Pp. 8–19.

Commission on Post-War Plans, *Guidance Pamphlet in Mathematics for High School Students*. Washington: The Mathematics Teacher, 1947. 25 pp.

———, "Second Report: The Improvement of Mathematics in Grades I to XIV," *The Mathematics Teacher*, May 1945, pp. 195–221.

Dyer, Henry S., Robert Kalin, and Frederic M. Lord, *Problems in Mathematical Education*. Princeton, N.J.: Educational Testing Service. 1956. 50 pp.

Fehr, Howard F., "Theories of Learning Related to the Field of Mathematics," *Twenty-first Yearbook*, National Council of Teachers of Mathematics. Washington: the Council, 1953. Pp. 1–41.

Hanna, Paul R., and others, "Arithmetic in an Activity Program," *Tenth Yearbook*, National Council of Teachers of Mathematics. Washington: the Council, 1935. Pp. 85–120.

Hildreth, Gertrude, "Principles of Learning Applied to Arithmetic," *Arithmetic Teacher*, October 1954, pp. 1–15.

Horn, Ernest, "The Teaching of Arithmetic," *Fiftieth Yearbook*, Part II, The National Society for the Study of Education. Chicago: University of Chicago Press, 1951. Pp. 6–21.

Johnson, J. T., "What Do We Mean by Meaning in Arithmetic?" *The Mathematics Teacher*, December 1948, pp. 362–367.

Lankford, Francis G. Jr., "Implications of the Psychology of Learning for the Teaching of Mathematics," *Twenty-fourth Yearbook*, National Council of Teachers of Mathematics. Washington: the Council, 1959. Pp. 405–430.

McConnell, T. R., "Recent Trends in Learning Theory: Their Application to the Psychology of Arithmetic," *Sixteenth Yearbook*, National Council of Teachers of Mathematics. Washington: the Council, 1941. Pp. 268–289.

Sueltz, Ben A., "Drill—Practice—Reasoning—Experience," *Twenty-first Yearbook*, National Council of Teachers of Mathematics. Washington: the Council, 1953. Pp. 192–204.

Swenson, Esther J., "Arithmetic for Preschool and Primary-Grade Children," *Fiftieth Yearbook*, Part II, The National Society for the Study of Education. Chicago: University of Chicago Press, 1951. Pp. 53–75.

Thiele, C. L., "Arithmetic in the Early Grades from the Point of View of Interrelationship in the Number System," *Sixteenth Yearbook*, National Council of Teachers of Mathematics. Washington: the Council, 1941. Pp. 45–79.

Van Engen, Henry, "The Formation of Concepts," *Twenty-first Yearbook*, National Council of Teachers of Mathematics. Washington: the Council, 1953. Pp. 69–98.

———, "Which Way Arithmetic," *Arithmetic Teacher*, December 1955, pp. 131–140.

Wheat, Harry G., "The Fallacy of Social Arithmetic," *The Mathematics Teacher*, January 1946, pp. 27–34.

Welmers, Everett T., "Arithmetic in Today's Culture," *Twenty-fifth Yearbook*, National Council of Teachers of Mathematics. Washington: the Council, 1960. Pp. 10–32.

Notation Systems

CHAPTER TWO

THE IMPORTANCE TO TEACHER OR student of arithmetic of a thorough understanding of our system of notation cannot be overestimated. The arithmetic algorithms are possible only because of certain properties of our system of notation. The algorithms cannot be understood without corresponding insight into the system of notation. In the past, scant attention was devoted to this topic in the elementary school. This could account for much of the mechanical learning of arithmetic, devoid of meaning and understanding, which has taken place. Yet one of the most remarkable attributes of the system is its simplicity compared to earlier, less efficient ones.

There is a difference between a number and its name. There is also a difference between the name for a number and a nonverbal mathematical symbol which stands for the number. "Twelve" is the name for the number of eggs one gets when he buys a dozen. We apply this same name to the symbol "12" and the symbol "XII."

Number names are chosen in a systematic fashion; so are number symbols. The two systems are quite similar but not identical. We call "23" "twenty-three," but we do not call "13" "onety-three."

"Numeration system" and "notation system" are frequently used interchangeably. However, in this book we wish to make a clear distinction between a system of number names and a system of number symbols. Accordingly, we shall use "numeration system" to mean a system of number names and "notation system" to mean a system of number symbols.

Some kind of notation system has existed since the predawn of civilization. Yet man had to devise one, just as language had to be created. It would be difficult for us to imagine what the world would be like if a notation system had never been invented. But what was primitive man's motivation for such an invention? Our innate number sense is quite limited. We can visualize a set of three or four objects without recourse to some kind of grouping. But if we attempted to identify the number of objects in a set without counting or grouping into subsets we would find that we could not go very far. Even in identifying a set of five we would probably, unconsciously perhaps, visualize either a set of three and a set of two or two sets of two and a set of one.

If our number requirements were not too great, up to fifteen, for example, we could invent a set of independent names for each number and get along quite well by counting. However, as our number requirements increased, this endless succession of unrelated names would soon become impossibly unmanageable. Furthermore, interpretation of the result of counting would be quite limited for want of a frame of reference. For example, one cannot visualize a set of 175 individual objects without relating it to something else. We can, however, visualize a single set of ten sets of ten, seven sets of ten, and five sets of one.

In this chapter we shall attempt to get a clearer understanding of our system of notation by: (1) examining other systems which employ the same grouping into sets, sets of one, ten, one hundred, and so on, but use a different symbolism to indicate how many of each kind of set; and (2) examining the same system when a different grouping, such as ones, eights, sixty-fours, and so on rather than ones, tens, hundreds, and so on, is used.

2.1 DECIMAL SYSTEMS

Basic to all notation systems is the idea of grouping. In our own system we consider the individual elements of the total set if there are no more than nine objects. If the total consists of ten or more objects we treat a set of ten, not as ten ones, but as a *single* set containing ten ones. Thus, twenty-three is considered to be *two* sets of ten and *three* sets of one. This is true of both our system of notation and our system of numeration.

A number is an abstraction, the cardinal number *five* is a property common to all sets of things that have the same number of elements as the number of fingers on the normal human hand. But when I look at my hand I do not see the number five any more than I see a *red* when I look at a rose. The word "five" is not a number, it is the name for a number. The symbols 5, V, ⫫ are not numbers, nor are they names for a number, they are nonverbal symbols which are used to represent a number. We call both the word "five" and the symbol "5" numerals.

Our system of notation, the Hindu–Arabic, is decimal; that is, grouping is done by tens. However, a much more important characteristic is the fact that it is *positional*. This means the value of each single symbol in a numeral is determined both by the symbol and by its position in the total numeral. Thus, in 303 the left-hand 3 has a position value 100 and total value $3 \times 100 = 300$ while the right-hand 3 has a position value 1 and a total value $3 \times 1 = 3$. Numbers other than ten have been used as base—notably two, five, and twenty—but for obvious anatomical reasons man has shown a decided preference for ten throughout history.

Our system of numeration, that is, system of number names, is also decimal. This is not because it is designed for use with the Hindu–Arabic system of notation. It would be equally appropriate for any other base-ten notation system and inappropriate if the base is not ten even though the system is positional. For example, if we used eight rather than ten as basic grouping number, fifteen would be written "17" rather than "15." Should this be called "seventeen" or "fifteen"?

Unless specifically indicated to the contrary, in this book we shall use the ordinary number names when referring to numbers by

name. That is, "twelve" will mean this many ////////////// regardless of
the notation system we are discussing.

2.2 ADDITIVE SYSTEMS

One of the most primitive systems of notation employs different
symbols for one, ten, one hundred, and higher powers of ten. The
highest power of ten is used as many times as it is contained in the
number, similarly for all lower powers of ten. For example, 6083 is
expressed by using the symbol for one thousand 6 times, the symbol
for ten 8 times, and the symbol for one 3 times. Thus the values of the
individual symbols are added to obtain the number. Note that the
symbol for one hundred is not used since the number contains none.

The ancient Egyptian hieroglyphic system is this kind. A
vertical staff was used to represent 1, a heel bone stood for 10, a
scroll for 100, a flower for 1000, a crooked finger for 10,000, a fish for
100,000, and for 1,000,000 a man in utter amazement at such a
number.

1	10	100	1000	10,000	100,000	1,000,000

Thus the number 23,154 would be expressed:

In this system, the role of the base ten is evident. Any symbol
may be used as many as nine times, but if ten of the particular
symbol are needed a new symbol is introduced instead.

The familiar Roman system is the simple additive type with two
additional properties incorporated. Here we have

$$1 = I, \quad 10 = X, \quad 100 = C, \quad \text{and} \quad 1000 = M$$

Inserted midway between each of these we have a symbol to represent
five of the one on left and half of the one on right.

$$1 = I \qquad\qquad 10 = X \qquad\qquad 100 = C \qquad\qquad 1000 = M$$
$$\qquad 5 = V \qquad\qquad 50 = L \qquad\qquad 500 = D$$

This is an improvement over the Egyptian method in that the

representation of the number is more compact. If we did not have the midway symbols one would express

$$1492 = \text{MCCCCXXXXXXXXXII}$$

But with their aid this is shortened to

$$1492 = \text{MCCCCLXXXXII}$$

The system as we know it includes a subtraction principle. If a basic symbol (I, X, C, M) stands to the left of the next higher one, or the left of the midway symbol (V, L, D) which represents five times as much, then subtraction rather than addition is implied. Thus

$$CX = 110 \quad but \quad XC = 90, \text{ and}$$
$$LX = 60 \quad but \quad XL = 40$$

We would not find 99 expressed as IC, nor would 95 be VC. Using the subtraction principle we get

$$1492 = \text{MCDXCII}$$

The subtraction principle was a relatively late introduction to the system.

2.3 THE MULTIPLICATIVE PRINCIPLE

The Chinese system illustrates the use of multiplication as a means of shortening the notation. Distinct symbols are used for the numbers one through nine just as they are in our system. But as with the Egyptians, distinct symbols are used for successive powers of ten, that is 10, 100, 1000, and so on. The symbols for one through nine are

1 2 3 4 5 6 7 8 9
一 二 三 四 五 六 七 八 九

Those for ten through one hundred thousand are

10   100   1000   10,000   100,000
十   百   千   萬   萬

Repetition is avoided by letting the first decade number precede a higher ordered number to indicate the number of times the higher number is taken. For example, 50 is written 𠃊 + or literally 5 times 10. The number 2573 is written

$$= 千 𠃊 百 匕 + =$$

Note the symbol 100,000 could be read "ten ten thousands." An alternate form for 10,000 is + 千 or "ten one thousands." Our system of numeration actually more closely parallels this system than it does our own notation.

two	thousand	five	hundred	seven—ty (ten)	three
=	千	𠃊	百	匕 +	=

When we recall that in the Chinese language a single symbol represents a word rather than a single letter the above symbols could be considered either number symbols 匕 = 7 or number names (匕 is Chinese for the English word *seven*). As a matter of fact, the above symbols are used in literature and another set of symbols is used in calculation. These, from 1 to 9, are

| ‖ ⫴ ⨯ ⚡ ⊥ ⚊̇ ⚌̇ ⚜

They also have special symbols for 10, 100, 1000, and 10,000; for zero the circle is used.

2.4 COMPUTATION

Addition is comparatively simple with Egyptian numerals. Let us find 236 + 187. If we place the numerals in the usual way, one over the other, the first step consists of

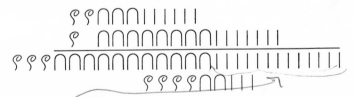

combining like symbols. Below the line we merely have the symbol for one 7 times and then 6 more times, the symbol for ten 8 times and then 3 more times, the symbol for one hundred 1 time then 2 more times. The final result is then obtained by merely converting ten of any symbol to one of the next higher symbol. If this is continued until no symbol appears more than nine times the computation is complete. There is no necessity to know that $6 + 7 = 13$ or $8 + 3 = 11$ or even that $1 + 2 = 3$. We merely have to know how to count to ten.

Multiplication is also quite simple, yet cumbersome. To find 106×23 we can adapt the usual method to these symbols. We multiply each symbol in the multiplier by each symbol in the multiplicand.

These partial products are then combined by converting ten of any symbol to one of the next higher symbol, thus obtaining

To find the partial products it is only necessary to know any symbol times ∩ equals the next higher symbol, any symbol times ∫ᵒ equals the symbol two higher, and so on.

Computation with Roman numerals is somewhat complicated by the presence of the subtractive principle. If we add $49 + 25$ the symbols which are to be subtracted can be canceled with

the same symbol which is to be added. The X before the L means "subtract 10." It is canceled with one of the X's in 25. There is no I in 25 to cancel with the I preceding the final X in 49. But it can be entered in the sum preceding the V indicating it is to be subtracted.

Multiplication with Roman numerals can become rather messy. We illustrate by finding 44×16.

$$
\begin{array}{r}
\text{X L I V} \\
\text{X V I} \\
\hline
\text{(X) L (I) V} \\
\text{(L) C C L (V) X X V} \\
\text{(C) D (X) L} \\
\hline
\text{D C L L I V or D C C I V}
\end{array}
$$

In the partial products, we have resorted to the device of circling the symbols which are to be subtracted. In the first line of partial products we have the product of I times the first factor, which is the first factor. In the second line of partial products we have the product of V times each of the terms of the first factor. Such combinations as V times L = CCL must be known. This particular example avoids many possible difficulties, such as the product of two symbols each of which is in a subtractive position. When this situation arises the partial product must be added rather than subtracted. The justification for this is established in algebra when it is shown that the product of two negative numbers is positive.

Computation with Chinese symbols presents problems somewhat similar to those encountered with our own system. However, the presence of symbols for ten, one hundred, and so on, complicates the situation. To add $608 + 537$ it is necessary to know the one digit combinations, $8 + 7 = 15$ and $6 + 5 = 11$. We must combine $- +$ (one ten) and $\equiv +$ (three tens) equal $\boxed{\text{四}} +$

$$
\begin{array}{r}
\text{六百}\qquad\text{八} \\
\text{五百}\ \text{三十七} \\
\hline
\text{一千一百}\ \text{四十五}
\end{array}
$$

(four tens) in carrying the 1 in $8 + 7 = 15$. The two symbols for ten ($+$) are not combined, they merely designate the position value of the one ($-$) and the three ($\equiv$). Similarly, when hundreds are combined 六 plus 五 equals $- + -$, but $- + -$ hundreds must be entered as $-千-百$ (one thousand one hundred).

In multiplication not only the one digit combinations but combinations indicating group size (10, 100, and so on) must be known.

To multiply 356 × 78 we must find

二百五十六
七十八
————————
二千八百四十八
二萬百千九百二十
————————
二萬七千七百六十八

$$
\begin{array}{r}
356 \\
78 \\
\hline
2848 \\
2492 \\
\hline
27768
\end{array}
$$

八 times 六 equal 四十八 ; 八 times 五 + equal 四百 ; 八 times 三百 equal 二千四百 in the first line of partial products. The 四百 and 四百 have been combined to 八百. In

the second line of partial products the multiplier is not 七, it is 七十.

We have 七十 times 六 equal 四百二十 ; 七十 times 五十 equal 三千五百 ; 七十 times 三百 equal 二萬一千. It is instructive to identify, step for step, the

steps using Chinese symbols with those using the usual symbols.

Exercises

1 Express three thousand two hundred fifty-one in: (*a*) Egyptian numerals (*b*) Roman numerals (*c*) Chinese numerals.

2 Express two thousand nine hundred forty-two in: (*a*) Egyptian numerals (*b*) Roman numerals (*c*) Chinese numerals.

3 Express one thousand one hundred one in: (*a*) Egyptian numerals (*b*) Roman numerals (*c*) Chinese numerals.

4 Write the following in Hindu-Arabic notation: (*a*) XLIII (*b*) MDCCLXXXII (*c*) CCLVII (*d*) CMXLVII (*e*) CMVI

5 Write the following in Roman numerals:
(*a*) 1959 (*b*) 2001 (*c*) 1776 (*d*) 347

6 Write in Egyptian numerals:
(*a*) 578   (*b*) 12,932   (*c*) 434   (*d*) 789

7 Which of the three systems—Egyptian, Roman, Chinese—would you prefer as a system for writing numbers (not for calculation)? Why?

8 Convert the following to Roman numerals, then perform the addition:

$$847 + 164 + 63$$

9 Repeat Exercise 8 using (*a*) Egyptian numerals, (*b*) Chinese numerals.

10 Subtract the following, using Roman numerals:

MCDXCII minus MCCLXVI

11 Multiply, using Egyptian numerals:

12 Multiply, using Roman numerals:

LXXI by XLIV

13 Multiply, using Chinese numerals:

二百四十八 by 一十二

14 In which, if any, of the systems—Egyptian, Roman, Chinese—can the number zero be written? With which of the three can decimal fractions be written?

15 Did the Romans need a symbol for zero? Explain.

16 Are Roman numerals of any value today? Why are they used rather than Egyptian or Chinese?

17 Could Roman numerals be used to write common fractions? Decimal fractions?

18 How many symbols would you need to represent 3648 in Egyptian numerals?

19 Compose an addition table using Chinese symbols for the numbers 1 to 10.

20 Compose a multiplication table for the numbers 1 to 10 using Roman numerals.

2.5 EXPONENTS AND POWERS

In the notation systems we have examined as well as in our own, 10, 10×10, $10 \times 10 \times 10$, and so forth, play an important role. These specific products, consisting of a single number called the *base* used as a factor one or more times, may be written in a most convenient form. A superscript to the right of the base number is used to indicate the number of times the base is used as a factor. The superscript is called an *exponent*. The indicated product is called a *power* of the base. Thus, $10^4 = 10 \times 10 \times 10 \times 10 = 10,000$. Ten is the base, 4 is the exponent, and 10^4 or 10,000 is the power of 10. When written in exponential form the exponent tells *what* power of the base we have. Since $1000 = 10 \times 10 \times 10 = 10^3$ we say 1000 or 10^3 is the third power of 10.

Under the above definition of an exponent any number in superscript position other than a natural number, that is 1, 2, 3, . . . , is meaningless. One might argue that zero as an exponent means that we use the base as a factor no times at all. This interpretation might prove satisfactory except for the fact that it states that something is not done, a situation which is in general unproductive. If we use anything other than natural numbers as exponents we must define what the symbolism is to mean. So long as our only guide is the earlier definition of natural number exponents we are free to define other numbers as exponents in any way we please, or to leave them undefined. However, as we shall see presently, zero and negative integers are quite as useful in connection with a study of the notation system as are the natural numbers.

Observe that by definition

$$10^3 \times 10^4 = (10 \times 10 \times 10) \times (10 \times 10 \times 10 \times 10) = 10^7$$

or in general if a, b are natural numbers

$$10^a \times 10^b = \underbrace{10 \times 10 \times 10}_{a \text{ factors}} \times \underbrace{10 \times 10 \times 10}_{b \text{ factors}} = 10^{a+b}$$

In other words, when we multiply two powers of the same base the product has for exponent the sum of the exponents of the factors.

Again, by definition

$$10^5 \div 10^3 = \frac{10 \times 10 \times 10 \times 10 \times 10}{10 \times 10 \times 10} = 10^{5-3} = 10^2$$

or in general if a, b are natural numbers and a greater than b

$$10^a \div 10^b = \frac{\overbrace{10 \times 10 \times 10}^{a \text{ factors}}}{\underbrace{10 \times 10 \times 10}_{b \text{ factors}}} = 10^{a-b}$$

We restricted the case to a greater than b in order that the difference be a natural number. If we disregard the restriction and permit $a = b$ we get $10^5 \div 10^5 = 10^{5-5} = 10^0$ which is meaningless until defined. But we know that $10^5 \div 10^5 = 1$. Therefore we define 10^0 as being 1. In fact, any number a, except $a = 0$, to the zero power is by definition 1.

$$a^0 = 1, \qquad a \neq 0.$$

When we consider a less than b the rule for division

$$10^a \div 10^b = 10^{a-b}$$

cannot be carried through with natural numbers and zero, $a - b$ is neither a natural number nor zero. However, we know from the definition of natural number exponents

$$10^3 \div 10^5 = \frac{10 \times 10 \times 10}{10 \times 10 \times 10 \times 10 \times 10} = \frac{1}{10 \times 10} = \frac{1}{10^2}$$

In general, if a and b are natural numbers and a is less than b

$$10^a \div 10^b = \frac{1}{10^{b-a}}$$

In Chapter Four negative numbers will be defined. For the present, we define negative whole number exponents as follows:

$$a^{-b} = \frac{1}{a^b}$$

Thus $10^{-1} = 1/10 = .1$, $10^{-2} = 1/10^2 = .01$, $10^{-3} = 1/10^3 = .001$, and so on.

We can now express a number as the sum of powers of ten, no power being used more than nine times.

$$347.15 = 3 \times 10^2 + 4 \times 10^1 + 7 \times 10^0 + 1 \times 10^{-1} + 5 \times 10^{-2}$$
$$404.04 = 4 \times 10^2 + 0 \times 10^1 + 4 \times 10^0 + 0 \times 10^{-1} + 4 \times 10^{-2}$$

The value of each digit in the number is obtained by multiplying the digit by the power of ten indicated by the position of the digit in the number. If we start with the one's (10^0) digit, the exponent of ten increases by one for each position to the left and decreases by one (-2 is one less than -1) for each position to the right. Thus, the position value of any digit is determined in terms of its position relative to the one's position.

Exercises

1 Evaluate the following:
(a) 10^3 (b) 4^9 (c) 6^2 (d) 8^3 (e) 7^1 (f) 13^0 (g) 6^{-3}
(h) $(\frac{1}{2})^{-2}$ (i) 75^0 (j) 83^1 (k) 3^{-2}

2 Compute the following, leaving the result in exponential form:

(a) $5^5 \times 5^4$ (b) $9^5 \div 9^3$ (c) $8^2 \times 8^3 \div 8^2$ (d) $4^2 \div 2^4$

3 Express as the sum of multiples of powers of ten:

(a) 468.23 (b) 1003.04 (c) 707.07

4 Evaluate:

(a) $2 \times 10^2 + 7 \times 10^1 + 4 \times 10^0$

(b) $6 \times 8^2 + 5 \times 8^1 + 3 \times 8^0$

(c) $4 \times 10^1 + 3 \times 10^0 + 4 \times 10^{-1}$

(d) $5 \times 6^3 + 3 \times 6^1 + 1 \times 6^0 + 4 \times 6^{-1}$

5 (a) $6(10)^3 + 5(10)^2 + 8(10)^1 + 3(10)^0$

(b) $4(10)^2 + 5(10)^0$

(c) $7(10)^3 + 2(10)^2 + 6(10)^0 + 8(10)^{-1}$

(d) $3(10)^2 + 9(10)^0 + 7(10)^{-2}$

2.6 THE ABACUS

The notation systems we have examined lend themselves reasonably well to addition and subtraction. In fact, these operations are at least as simple as with our own system except when the subtractive principle of the Roman system is encountered. But if we attempt multiplication or division the advantage of our own system becomes quite obvious. These systems were not used for computation. The computations were carried out with the aid of an *abacus*. The number symbols were used merely to record the answer.

The abacus played a rather important part in the development of Hindu–Arabic numerals. In the Orient some form of bead abacus was the most popular—in fact, its popularity remains unabated. Shopkeepers and merchants still prefer to use it in making their calculations. One of the more popular forms in Europe was the line abacus. It consisted of a series of lines drawn on a flat surface such as a table or a cabinet top. Loose counters were placed either on or between the lines. The counters we find in stores today are so called because of the early practice of using their tops as counting tables.

The lines are used to represent powers of ten: ones, tens, hundreds, and so on. The spaces between the lines represent fives, fifties, five hundreds, and so on. The use of the spaces between the lines is comparable to the use of mid-symbols (V, L, and D) in the Roman system. Three counters on the thousands line represent three thousand. Three counters between the hundreds line and the thousands line stand for three five hundreds, and can be changed to one counter on the thousands line and one on the space between it and the hundreds line. Five counters on any line may be exchanged for one in the space above. The one is "carried" to the space, thus the origin of the term "carry" in the addition algorithm. Two counters in any space may be exchanged for one on the line above. When necessary in subtraction the exchange can be reversed: this gives rise to the term "borrow." Thus, when the quantity is expressed in simplest form, there will be not more than four counters on a line and not more than one in a space.

If we wish to add 1753 + 1048 illustration (a) indicates the first step: 1753 is recorded on the abacus. In (b) 1048 has been added.

(a)   *(b)*   *(c)*

In (c) the final simplified result is shown. Five of the six counters on the 1 line are exchanged for a single counter on the space between the 1 line and the 10 line. This makes two counters in the space. They are exchanged for a single counter on the 10 line. This makes five counters there, which are exchanged for one counter in the space between the 10 line and the 100 line. The two counters in this space are exchanged for one counter on the 100 line. The final result may be read from (c) 2 *thousands*, 1 *five hundred*, 3 *hundreds*, and 1 *one*, or 2801.

Subtraction on the line abacus is, in a very real sense, a "take away" operation. To find 18,436 − 7259 we first enter 18,436 on the abacus, illustration (a). In

(a)   *(b)*   *(c)*

illustration (b) 1 *hundred* counter has been exchanged for 2 *fifty* counters and 1 *ten* counter has been exchanged for 1 *five* counter and 5 *one* counters. It is then possible to remove the counters equivalent to 7259. The final result is indicated in illustration (*c*).

On the assumption that the idea of using independent symbols for each of the numbers *one* through *nine* was already employed, it seems inevitable that someone would hit upon the idea of a symbol to indicate an empty space. Then the answer could be recorded by putting in the right *place* the symbol to indicate the number of ones, tens, and so on that there were in the final result, the zero indicating empty places.

Exercises

By means of drawings show how to perform the following computations on the line abacus:

1 3421 + 2163
2 555 + 369
3 437 + 1592 + 382
4 4342 − 2140
5 8634 − 3203
6 1734 − 296

2.7 POSITIONAL NOTATION

If in the Chinese system we omit symbols for powers of ten we have our own system, but for one thing. = 干 九 占 七 + 二 becomes = 九 七 二, which translates to 2573. The only thing lacking is a means of showing that a given power of ten (one is a power of ten, $1 = 10^0$) is missing. We need a symbol for zero.

A positional number system requires that we have a set of independent symbols for the integers one to, but not including, the arbitrarily chosen number which is to be the base. And we must have a symbol to indicate a vacant space. This place holder, zero, enables us to dispense with any symbols to indicate the positive integral powers of ten, as ten, one hundred, one thousand, and so forth. The power of ten is implied by the position occupied by the symbols for the numbers one through nine. The Egyptian ten was ∩; the Roman ten was X; the Chinese ten is +; but in the Hindu–Arabic system we do not have a single symbol for ten. The representation of ten as 10 is a compound symbol. The symbol 1 indicates that the base number ten

is to be used one time and the 0 indicates there are no additional
units. This property makes it possible to write a number as large as
we please. This was not true in the other systems we have examined.
As the numbers continue to get larger there is no end to the different
symbols needed in these systems.

The positional system is said to have the "place value property."
This merely means the value of each symbol is determined by its
position in the number, as well as the symbol itself. Thus in 22,032 the
extreme left-hand 2 represents 2 ten thousands but the 2 immediately
to its right stands for 2 thousands, while the extreme right-hand 2
stands for 2 ones. Any symbol represents ten times as much as the
same symbol in the position immediately to the right.

The following representations of the number fourteen thousand
thirty-three contrast the three kinds of systems we have discussed.
Note that all three systems are decimal.

	10,000s	1000s	100s	10s	1s
Egyptian	ʃ	ʃ ʃ ʃ ʃ		∩∩∩	| | |
Chinese	萬	四千		三十	三
Hindu-Arabic	1	4	0	3	3

In the Egyptian scheme each power of ten is indicated by a
special symbol. We indicate the number of times the power is used by
repeating the symbol that number of times. The Chinese plan also
employs different symbols for each power of ten, but the number of
times each power is used is indicated by means of the symbols for one
through nine. In the Hindu–Arabic system the numbers one through
nine are used to indicate the number of times each power of ten is
used, but there are no symbols to indicate those powers. The powers
of ten are implied by the positions of the one through nine digits.

Other systems have employed the place value principle. The
Babylonians used a positional system with sixty as base. However, in
forming the primary numbers one through fifty-nine the additive
decimal scheme was employed. The Mayan Indians of Central
America had a rather highly developed system which used twenty as
base, but they too used the additive idea to obtain their first nineteen

numbers. This was accomplished by adding dots and dashes; a dot stood for one and a dash for five.

Exercises

1 Write the third power of 10 in Roman, in Chinese, and in Hindu-Arabic numerals.

2 Express 876 as multiples of powers of 10, no power to be used more than 9 times.

3 Express 876 as multiples of powers of 8, no power to be used more than 7 times.

4 In what respects is the line abacus similar to the Roman system of notation? In what respects is it similar to Hindu-Arabic notation?

5 Draw a line abacus and show how 3652 is indicated.

6 Show how to add 1739 to the abacus described in Exercise 5.

7 Why is it impossible to have a positional number system without a symbol for zero?

8 Why is a symbol for zero not needed in the Roman system of notation?

2.8 OCTONAL NUMERALS

Man's predominant preference for ten as base undoubtedly stems from counting on the fingers. The fingers may be used as counters until they are all used. Then we have one handful, one ten, and the fingers are available all over again. The number of handfuls may have been counted by turning down the fingers. In any event, a handful of handfuls would suggest a single something. This does not require the concept of place value or a symbol for zero. It does not even require a system of notation. It is a mistake to assume that our system is unique because it is decimal. In fact it does not derive its superiority from this property, but from its utilization of the principle of place value.

The possibility of using the same positional system we now have but with a base other than ten is well known. In fact there is an organization which devotes its efforts to securing the adoption of twelve as number base.[1] Although binary, base-two, notation is not

[1] The Duodecimal Society of America, 20 Carlton Place, Staten Island 4, New York.

used, the idea of binary representation of numbers is extensively employed. This is particularly true in the construction of electronic computers. As a matter of fact, any integer greater than one can be used as number base.

Distinct symbols from zero up to but not including the base are needed. This means the invention of more symbols if the base is more than ten, and the elimination of some symbols if the base is less than ten. If eight is base the octonal number system requires the symbols 0, 1, 2, 3, 4, 5, 6, 7. In this system 10 represents eight, not ten. It is convenient to have a symbolic means of designating the base when discussing the possibility of using a base other than ten. We shall indicate the base by means of a subscript using the number name. Why could we not indicate the base by means of numerals, using the same base as used to represent the number?

EXAMPLE. $390_{(ten)} = 606_{(eight)}$

The above equality states that three hundred ninety is written 390 if ten is base and 606 if eight is base. We may verify this by evaluating $606_{(eight)}$. The 6 in the ones position represents 6×8^0 or 6 ones. The 0 in the eights position tells us we use no eights. The 6 in the eight squared or sixty-fours position tells us we have $6 \times 64 = 384$ ones. Then $6 + 0 + 384 = 390$. (If no subscript is used it is understood that ten is base.)

Consider the number 84.37. The decimal point separates the whole number 84 from the fraction $\frac{37}{100}$. But more importantly, it *labels the one's position*. Hence, indirectly, it determines the position value of each digit. It is for this reason that division or multiplication by ten or any integral power of ten merely requires a relocation of the decimal point. In 84.37 the 7 is to be multiplied by 10^{-2}, the 3 by 10^{-1}, the 4 by 10^0, and 8 by 10^1. If we move the decimal point one place to the left, or equivalently leave the decimal point where it is and shift all digits of the number one place to the right, each digit will be multiplied by a power of 10 one less than previously. This is equivalent to dividing the number by 10. In 8.437 the 8 represents only $\frac{1}{10}$ as much as before. Similarly for each digit in the number.

Consider the number 8437. The decimal point is by implication immediately to the right of the 7. Moving the decimal point one place to the left, being equivalent to division by 10, yields 843.7. Hence it is evident that dividing 8437 by 10 will give a quotient 843 and a remainder 7. If we now divide the quotient 843 by 10, the remainder is 3. Continuing in this way, it is evident that successive division by

10 will yield remainders which are the successive digits of the number, starting with the one's digit.

Now consider the number $20365_{(eight)}$. Recall that this means

$$2 \times 8^4 + 0 \times 8^3 + 3 \times 8^2 + 6 \times 8^1 + 5 \times 8^0$$

We can use the same device to mark the one's digit in any other base that we use in base ten. When the base is eight, it is properly called an *octonal point* rather than decimal point. Pointing off one place $20365_{(eight)}$ becomes $2036.5_{(eight)}$ which means

$$2 \times 8^3 + 0 \times 8^2 + 3 \times 8^1 + 6 \times 8^0 + 5 \times 8^{-1}$$

The value of each digit, and hence the value of the number, is $\frac{1}{8}$ as great as before. Hence, if we divide the number by eight, the remainder is the original one's digit. If we now divide $2036_{(eight)}$ by eight, we get $203.6_{(eight)}$. Hence the remainder on the second division is the second, or 8^1 digit. Continuing in this manner, the remainders obtained on successive divisions by eight will produce the successive digits in the base eight representation of the number, beginning with the one's digit. But the remainder obtained when a number is divided by eight, or any other number, is entirely independent of the base of notation. Twenty-five divided by eight will yield three as quotient with remainder one. This fact is true no matter how the numbers are represented. It follows that a number may be converted to a new base by dividing the number and succeeding quotients by the desired base. The successive remainders are the required digits, from lowest to highest placed.

EXAMPLE.   Express $8437_{(ten)}$ in base eight.

$$\begin{array}{r} 1054 \\ 8\overline{)8437} \end{array} \qquad \text{remainder 5}$$

$$\begin{array}{r} 131 \\ 8\overline{)1054} \end{array} \qquad \text{remainder 6}$$

$$\begin{array}{r} 16 \\ 8\overline{)131} \end{array} \qquad \text{remainder 3}$$

$$\begin{array}{r} 2 \\ 8\overline{)16} \end{array} \qquad \text{remainder 0}$$

$$\begin{array}{r} 0 \\ 8\overline{)2} \end{array} \qquad \text{remainder 2}$$

Hence,

$$8437_{(ten)} = 20365_{(eight)}$$

This may be verified by observing that

$$5 \times 8^0 + 6 \times 8^1 + 3 \times 8^2 + 0 \times 8^3 + 2 \times 8^4$$
$$= 5 + 48 + 192 + 8192 = 8437$$

The above procedure can be explained in a somewhat different manner. We first note that when we divide by 8 the remainders will always be one of the numbers 0 through 7. When we divide by 8 the quotient tells us how many full sets of 8 we can form, and the remainder tells us how many ones in excess of sets of eight make up the number. In the above example we divide 8437 by 8, giving a quotient 1054 and remainder 5. Then we know that 8437 consists of 1054 complete sets of 8 with 5 left over. Since we are trying to express the number by means of groupings of 8 the 5 left over must be expressed as the ones digit.

The second step, $1054 \div 8$, enables us to find how many sets we can form containing 8 of the sets of 8 obtained in the first step. This is the quotient 131. The remainder 6 tells us how many of the sets of 8 we could not use in forming sets of eight 8's or 64's. Then the 6 occupies the second or 8^1 position.

In similar fashion, we find from step three we can get 16 sets of 8 of the former sized sets (sets of 64) but 3 of the sets of 64 remain. Thus, a 3 is placed in the next or 8^2 position. The fourth step, $16 \div 8$, shows that the 16 sets of the previous step may be grouped into 2 sets eight times as large with none of the 16 sets left over. The 16 sets of this step contain 8×8^2 or 8^3 units. Since none were left over we need no 8^3 and therefore place 0 in that position. Since there are fewer than 8, namely 2, of the last obtained sets we cannot form them into sets 8 times as large. These last two sets are indicated in the result by a 2 in the 8^4 position.

The foregoing method enables us to find the digits in the new notation from smallest to largest position, ones, eights, sixty-fours, and so on. We can approach the problem in still another way, finding the highest ordered digit first and working down. Our problem is to express 8437 in terms of powers of 8. We first find the powers of 8 until we reach one which exceeds 8437. $8^0 = 1$, $8^1 = 8$, $8^2 = 64$, $8^3 = 512$, $8^4 = 4096$, $8^5 = 32,768$. We do not need 8^5 because 32,768 is greater than 8437. But $8^4 = 4096$ is not. We wish to use 8^4 as many times as we can. We find the number of times by division, $8437 \div 4096$. This gives 2 as quotient and remainder 245. If we place 2 in the 8^4, or fifth, position we have then expressed all but 245 of the original 8437.

We repeat the process with 245. Since it is less than 512 we can use no 8^3 and therefore place 0 in that position. Next we find how many 8^2 or 64's there are in 245 by division, $245 \div 64$. This gives 3 for quotient with 53 for remainder. Then we place 3 in the 8^2 position. Now 53 consists of six 8's plus 5, so we place 6 in 8^1 position and 5 in ones position.

Using this approach the digits are found as *quotients* rather than remainders, the *remainders* rather than quotients are used in finding succeeding steps, and we find the digits from *highest* to *lowest* rather than lowest to highest.

Each of these methods is perfectly general. Generalizing the first approach, we may find the digits, from right to left, of a number in any base by dividing the number and succeeding quotients by the desired base. The remainders are the required digits.

For example, if we wish to express $83_{(ten)}$ in base two we divide as follows:

$$\begin{array}{r} 41 \\ 2\overline{|83} \end{array} \qquad \text{remainder 1}$$

$$\begin{array}{r} 20 \\ 2\overline{|41} \end{array} \qquad \text{remainder 1}$$

$$\begin{array}{r} 10 \\ 2\overline{|20} \end{array} \qquad \text{remainder 0}$$

$$\begin{array}{r} 5 \\ 2\overline{|10} \end{array} \qquad \text{remainder 0}$$

$$\begin{array}{r} 2 \\ 2\overline{|5} \end{array} \qquad \text{remainder 1}$$

$$\begin{array}{r} 1 \\ 2\overline{|2} \end{array} \qquad \text{remainder 0}$$

$$\begin{array}{r} 0 \\ 2\overline{|1} \end{array} \qquad \text{remainder 1}$$

and obtain

$$83_{(ten)} = 1010011_{(two)}$$

which may be verified by evaluating

$$1010011_{(two)} = 1 \times 2^6 + 0 \times 2^5 + 1 \times 2^4 + 0 \times 2^3 + 0 \times 2^2$$
$$+ 1 \times 2^1 + 1 \times 2^0 = 64 + 16 + 2 + 1 = 83$$

The following table shows the base ten, eight, and two representation of the named numbers:

| | Decimal | Octonal | Binary |
Number name	(base ten)	(base eight)	(base two)
one	1	1	1
two	2	2	10
seven	7	7	111
eight	8	10	1000
twenty-four	24	30	11000
sixty-five	65	101	1000001
one hundred eighty-three	183	267	10110111
five hundred twelve	512	1000	1000000000

Some electronic computers employ octonal numbers in conjunction with their use of binary numbers, due to the ease with which one may convert from one base to the other. A number in binary notation can be converted to octonal notation as follows. In binary notation the analogy to digits is "bigits." Electronic engineers have shortened this to "bits." Group the "bits" in threes, starting from the right. For example, one hundred eighty-three in binary notation is

$$10 \quad 110 \quad 111$$

Convert each of the three "bigit" numbers thus formed to octonal notation

$$10 = 2, \quad 110 = 6, \quad 111 = 7$$

The result gives the octonal representation

$$10110111_{(two)} = 267_{(eight)}$$

We can move from octonal to binary in the same fashion. Merely write each octonal symbol in binary notation

$$437_{(eight)} = 100 \ 011 \ 111_{(two)}$$

because $4_{(eight)} = 100_{(two)}$; $3_{(eight)} = 11_{(two)}$ and $7_{(eight)} = 111_{(two)}$. We can make this same conversion by expressing $437_{(eight)}$ as

$$4 \times 8^2 + 3 \times 8^1 + 7 \times 8^0 = 4 \times 2^6 + 3 \times 2^3 + 7 \times 2^0$$

since $8 = 2^3$. Then expressing the digits in powers of 2 we have

$$437_{(eight)} = 2^2 \times 2^6 + (2^1 + 2^0)2^3 + (2^2 + 2^1 + 2^0)2^0$$
$$= 2^8 + 2^4 + 2^3 + 2^2 + 2^1 + 2^0$$

But this, written in base two, is

100011111

Exercises

1 Convert $937_{(ten)}$ to base eight.

2 Convert $110011111_{(two)}$ to base eight; to base ten.

3 Convert $732_{(eight)}$ to base ten.

4 Convert $173_{(eight)}$ to base two.

5 Convert $173_{(ten)}$ to base two.

6 Convert $374_{(twelve)}$ to base ten.

7 Convert $374_{(eight)}$ to base ten.

8 Convert $374_{(twelve)}$ to base eight.

9 Convert $21022_{(three)}$ to base four.

10 Convert $21022_{(four)}$ to base three.

11 How many digit symbols are needed for base twelve notation? Why?

2.9 CALCULATIONS WITH OCTONAL NUMERALS

An algorithm is a schematic device for performing a mathematical operation. When we refer to the division algorithm we refer to the systematic scheme used to carry out the division. The assertion that the Hindu–Arabic system derives its superiority from its utilization of place value, making the algorithms possible, is forcefully illustrated by considering calculation with positional numerals with a base other than ten. The only source of difficulty is unfamiliarity with the symbolism. The mechanics of the algorithms is identical.

If we compute with base eight notation we need new addition and multiplication tables. This is not to say the sums and products will be changed; the only thing that changes is the way they are written.

Addition facts, base eight

0+0=0	1+0=1	2+0=2	3+0=3	4+0=4	5+0=5	6+0=6	7+0=7
0+1=1	1+1=2	2+1=3	3+1=4	4+1=5	5+1=6	6+1=7	7+1=10
0+2=2	1+2=3	2+2=4	3+2=5	4+2=6	5+2=7	6+2=10	7+2=11
0+3=3	1+3=4	2+3=5	3+3=6	4+3=7	5+3=10	6+3=11	7+3=12
0+4=4	1+4=5	2+4=6	3+4=7	4+4=10	5+4=11	6+4=12	7+4=13
0+5=5	1+5=6	2+5=7	3+5=10	4+5=11	5+5=12	6+5=13	7+5=14
0+6=6	1+6=7	2+6=10	3+6=11	4+6=12	5+6=13	6+6=14	7+6=15
0+7=7	1+7=10	2+7=11	3+7=12	4+7=13	5+7=14	6+7=15	7+7=16

Seven plus six still equals thirteen. Recall, page 25, that we have agreed to use conventional number names when referring to numbers by name. We merely indicate thirteen as 1 eight plus 5 ones.

EXAMPLE 1.   Calculate: $437_{(eight)} + 253_{(eight)} + 176_{(eight)}$

SOLUTION.
$$
\begin{array}{r}
437 \\
253 \\
176 \\
\hline
1110
\end{array}
$$

We add columnwise precisely as we do when ten is base. In the right-hand column we add $7 + 3 + 6$ ones. In the middle column we add $3 + 5 + 7$ eights. In the left column $4 + 2 + 1$ sixty-fours. From the addition table $7 + 3 = 12$. We proceed with the ones column $12 + 6$ by obtaining $2 + 6 = 10$ from the table, giving $12 + 6 = 20$. Thus 0 is in the ones column and 2 is carried to the eights column. From the table $3 + 5 = 10$; and $10 + 7 = 17$ since $0 + 7 = 7$. Thus $17 + 2$ (carried) $= 21$ because $7 + 2 = 11$. This gives the 1 in the eights column with 2 carried to the left-hand, or sixty-fours, column. In the left column $4 + 2 = 6$ and $6 + 1 = 7$; but $7 + 2$ (carried) $= 11$. Therefore we have 1 in the third column from the right and 1 in the fourth.

CHECK.   If we write the addition we have performed in base ten we get

$$7 + 3 + 6 = 16 \text{ ones in the right column}$$
$$3 + 5 + 7 = 15 \text{ eights in the middle column}$$
$$4 + 2 + 1 = 7 \text{ sixty-fours in the left column}$$

If we total these three subtotals we get

$$16 + 120 + 448 = 584.$$

The base eight answer 1110 expressed in base ten is

$$1 \times 8^3 + 1 \times 8^2 + 1 \times 8^1 + 0 \times 8^0 = 512 + 64 + 8 + 0 = 584.$$

As a further check:

$$
\begin{array}{llr}
437_{(eight)} = 4 \times 64 + 3 \times 8 + 7 & & = 287 \\
253_{(eight)} = 2 \times 64 + 5 \times 8 + 3 & & = 171 \\
176_{(eight)} = 1 \times 64 + 7 \times 8 + 6 & & = 126 \\
\hline
1110_{(eight)} = 1 \times 512 + 1 \times 64 + 1 \times 8 + 0 & = & \overline{584}
\end{array}
$$

Multiplication facts, base eight

$0\times0=0$	$1\times0=0$	$2\times0=0$	$3\times0=0$	$4\times0=0$	$5\times0=0$	$6\times0=0$	$7\times0=0$
$0\times1=0$	$1\times1=1$	$2\times1=2$	$3\times1=3$	$4\times1=4$	$5\times1=5$	$6\times1=6$	$7\times1=7$
$0\times2=0$	$1\times2=2$	$2\times2=4$	$3\times2=6$	$4\times2=10$	$5\times2=12$	$6\times2=14$	$7\times2=16$
$0\times3=0$	$1\times3=3$	$2\times3=6$	$3\times3=11$	$4\times3=14$	$5\times3=17$	$6\times3=22$	$7\times3=25$
$0\times4=0$	$1\times4=4$	$2\times4=10$	$3\times4=14$	$4\times4=20$	$5\times4=24$	$6\times4=30$	$7\times4=34$
$0\times5=0$	$1\times5=5$	$2\times5=12$	$3\times5=17$	$4\times5=24$	$5\times5=31$	$6\times5=36$	$7\times5=43$
$0\times6=0$	$1\times6=6$	$2\times6=14$	$3\times6=22$	$4\times6=30$	$5\times6=36$	$6\times6=44$	$7\times6=52$
$0\times7=0$	$1\times7=7$	$2\times7=16$	$3\times7=25$	$4\times7=34$	$5\times7=43$	$6\times7=52$	$7\times7=61$

As with addition, no products have been changed. Five times seven is still thirty-five. But we express thirty-five as 4 eights and 3 ones. Hence $5 \times 7 = 43$.

EXAMPLE 2. Calculate: $263_{(eight)} \times 57_{(eight)}$

SOLUTION.

$$
\begin{array}{r}
263 \\
57 \\
\hline
2345 \\
1577 \\
\hline
20335
\end{array}
$$

With the aid of the multiplication table we find $3 \times 7 = 25$; we write 5 and carry 2. Then $6 \times 7 = 52, 52 + 2$ (carried) $= 54$; we write 4 and carry 5. Next, $7 \times 2 = 16, 16 + 5$ (carried) $= 23$; we write 23, completing the first line of partial products. Similarly $5 \times 3 = 17$; we write 7 and carry 1. Then $5 \times 6 = 36, 36 + 1$ (carried) $= 37$; we write 7 and carry 3. Finally, $5 \times 2 = 12$, $12 + 3 = 15$, we write 15.

Adding the partial products, we bring down 5. Then $4 + 7 = 13$; we write 3 and carry 1. Then $3 + 7 + 1 = 13$; we write 3 and carry 1. Next $2 + 5 + 1 = 10$, we write 0 and carry 1. Finally, $1 + 1 = 2$, we write 2.

CHECK. $263_{(eight)} = 2 \times 64 + 6 \times 8 + 3 = 179$

$57_{(eight)} = 5 \times 8 + 7 = 47$

$20335_{(eight)} = 2 \times 4096 + 3 \times 64 + 3 \times 8 + 5 = 8413$

and

$$
\begin{array}{r}
179 \\
47 \\
\hline
1253 \\
716 \\
\hline
8413
\end{array}
$$

In similar fashion the inverse operations of subtraction and division may be performed. We illustrate with division.

EXAMPLE 3. Calculate: $472_{(eight)} \div 13_{(eight)}$

$$
\begin{array}{r}
34 \\
13\overline{)472} \\
41 \\
\hline
62 \\
54 \\
\hline
6
\end{array}
$$

CHECK. $472_{(eight)} = 4 \times 64 + 7 \times 8 + 2 = 314$
$13_{(eight)} = 1 \times 8 + 3 = 11$

$$
\begin{array}{r}
28 \\
11\overline{)314} \\
22 \\
\hline
94 \\
88 \\
\hline
6
\end{array}
$$

The quotient $34_{(eight)} = 3 \times 8 + 4 = 28$ and the remainder $6_{(eight)} = 6$.

We would proceed in precisely the same manner as above if the new base were other than eight. If we use two as base the only addition facts we need are $0 + 0 = 0$, $1 + 0 = 1$ and $1 + 1 = 10$. The multiplication facts are $0 \times 0 = 0$, $1 \times 0 = 0$ and $1 \times 1 = 1$. The advantage of such a system which is derived from the number and simplicity of addition and multiplication facts is offset by the increased number of digits required.

EXAMPLE 4.   Use binary notation to find 125 times 89.

SOLUTION.   Divide 125 and 89 successively by 2 to convert to binary notation.

$$
\begin{array}{ccccc}
62 & 31 & 15 & 7 & 3 \\
2\overline{)125} & 2\overline{)62} & 2\overline{)31} & 2\overline{)15} & 2\overline{)7} \\
124 & 62 & 30 & 14 & 6 \\
\hline
1 \text{ rem.} & 0 \text{ rem.} & 1 \text{ rem.} & 1 \text{ rem.} & 1 \text{ rem.}
\end{array}
$$

$$
\begin{array}{cc}
1 & 0 \\
2\overline{)3} & 2\overline{)1} \\
2 & 0 \\
\hline
1 \text{ rem.} & 1 \text{ rem.}
\end{array}
$$

Therefore, $125_{(ten)} = 1111101_{(two)}$.

$$
\begin{array}{ccccc}
44 & 22 & 11 & 5 & 2 \\
2\overline{)89} & 2\overline{)44} & 2\overline{)22} & 2\overline{)11} & 2\overline{)5} \\
88 & 44 & 22 & 10 & 4 \\
\hline
1 \text{ rem.} & 0 \text{ rem.} & 0 \text{ rem.} & 1 \text{ rem.} & 1 \text{ rem.}
\end{array}
$$

$$
\begin{array}{cc}
1 & 0 \\
2\overline{)2} & 2\overline{)1} \\
2 & 0 \\
\hline
0 \text{ rem.} & 1 \text{ rem.}
\end{array}
$$

Therefore $89_{(ten)} = 1011001_{(two)}$

$$
\begin{array}{r}
1111101 \\
1011001 \\
\hline
1111101 \\
1111101 \\
1111101 \\
1111101 \\
\hline
10101101110101
\end{array}
$$

CHECK. $125 \times 89 = 11125$ but $10101101110101_{(two)} = 1 + 4 +$
$16 + 32 + 64 + 256 + 512 + 2048 + 8192 = 11{,}125.$

Finding the partial products causes no problem here. The addition of the partial products is more complicated. In the fourth column we have $1 + 1 = 10$; we write 0 and carry 1. In the fifth column we have 1 (carried) $+ 1 = 10$, $10 + 0 = 10$, $10 + 1 = 11$; we write 1 and carry 1. In the sixth column we have 1 (carried) $+ 0 = 1$, $1 + 1 = 10$, $10 + 1 = 11$; we write 1 and carry 1. In the seventh column we have 1 (carried) $+ 1 = 10$, $10 + 1 = 11$, $11 + 1 = 100$, $100 + 1 = 101$; we write 1 and carry 10. In the eighth column we have 10 (carried) $+ 0 = 10$, $10 + 1 = 11$, $11 + 1 = 100$; we write 0 and carry 10. In the ninth column we have 10 (carried) $+ 1 = 11$, $11 + 1 = 100$, $100 + 1 = 101$; we write 1 and carry 10. In the tenth column we have 10 (carried) $+ 1 = 11$, $11 + 1 = 100$, $100 + 1 = 101$; we write 1 and carry 10. In the eleventh column we have 10 (carried) $+ 1 = 11$, $11 + 1 = 100$; we write 0 and carry 10. In the twelfth column we have 10 (carried) $+ 1 = 11$, we write 1 and carry 1. In the last column we have 1 (carried) $+ 1 = 10$; we write 10.

Exercises

1 If we let 1, 5, 25, 125 be represented by $\#$, $\oplus$, $\times$, $\square$ respectively, we may use these symbols for a simple additive number system with base five. Express the numbers 27, 131, 33, 252 in this system.

2 If we let 0, 1, 2, 3 be represented by $\#$, $\oplus$, $\times$, $\square$ respectively, we may use these symbols for a positional number system with four as base. Express the numbers 112, 65, 15, 300 in this system.

3 Construct tables showing the needed addition and multiplication facts if five is used as base.

4 Add: $143_{(five)} + 22_{(five)} + 313_{(five)}$.

5 Multiply: $321_{(five)} \times 42_{(five)}$.

6 Add: $10010_{(two)} + 11001_{(two)} + 10011_{(two)}$

7 Multiply: $1011_{(two)} \times 1101_{(two)}$

8 Add: $635_{(eight)} + 272_{(eight)} + 134_{(eight)}$.

9 Multiply: $436_{(eight)} \times 36_{(eight)}$.

10 Are there values of b for which 43_b is an even number? For which 53_b is even? Why?

11 What base is used if $4 \times 4 = 24$?

12 Are there values of b for which 32_b is an odd number? For which 42_b is odd? Why?

13 Determine the base of notation and the missing digits such that the following addition will be correct.

$$
\begin{array}{r}
123 \\
- \, - \, - \\
111 \\
323 \\
\hline
2131
\end{array}
$$

14 Find $a + b$ in base eight if $a =$ ten and $b =$ thirteen.

15 Determine the base in which the following multiplication is written, assuming the computation is correct.

$$
\begin{array}{r}
432 \\
54 \\
\hline
3012 \\
3444 \\
\hline
41452
\end{array}
$$

16 (a) In what base or bases would 53 be an even number?
(b) In what base or bases would 75 be an odd number?
(c) In what base or bases would 42 be an odd number?
(d) In what base or bases would 43 be an even number?

17 Fill the blank so that the answer will be correct.

$$134_{(five)} + 323_{(five)} + \text{———} = 1130_{(five)}$$

18 Convert $667_{(eight)}$ to base five without going through base ten.

19 Add the following base eight numbers $276 + 312 + 765$.

20 Are each of the following numbers even or odd? Why?
(a) $353_{(seven)}$ (b) $432_{(five)}$ (c) $388_{(nine)}$ (d)$425_{(six)}$
(e) $4301_{(seven)}$

21 Is a "base one" scale of notation possible? Why?

22 Find $321_{(four)} \times 856_{(nine)}$.

23 Correct the following base four subtraction.

$$
\begin{array}{r}
432 \\
313 \\
\hline
129
\end{array}
$$

24 In the following additions determine the base and find the missing digits.

$$(a) \quad \begin{array}{r} 13- \\ 11- \\ 310 \\ \hline 1220 \end{array} \qquad (b) \quad \begin{array}{r} 1-4 \\ 315 \\ 4-2 \\ \hline 1163 \end{array}$$

25 If forty is written as follows what base is used in each case?

$$(a)\ 34 \quad (b)\ 50 \quad (c)\ 130 \quad (d)\ 101000$$

26 Can 321 represent the number forty in any base? If so what base? If not why not?

27 Answer Question 26 relative to the number one hundred.

2.10 OCTONAL FRACTIONS

Much of the utility of a positional number system is lost unless the concept of place value is extended to quantities less than one. The utility and the simplicity of decimal fractions is so great it is difficult to appreciate the fact that approximately a thousand years were required to make the extension. With decimal fractions our number system enables us not only to write a number arbitrarily large but arbitrarily small as well.

We call the fractions decimal, but it is far more important that they are *positional*. A decimal fraction is a fraction whose implied denominator is some power of ten. This is important only because ten is the base of our notation. For example, $.231 = \frac{231}{1000}$ but more significantly $.231 = \frac{2}{10} + \frac{3}{100} + \frac{1}{1000}$.

The idea of a positional fraction (we might call it a basimal fraction) is just as adaptable to a base other than ten as it is to ten.

Just as $73_{(eight)}$ means $7 \times 8 + 3$, so $.73_{(eight)}$ means $\frac{7}{8} + \frac{3}{64}$.

We have said the *position* of a symbol in an integer determines its value. In 1537, the 5 has the value five hundred because it stands in the third or hundreds position. As we move to the left from the decimal point successive digits imply multiplication by $1, 10, 10 \times 10$, and so forth. In precisely the same fashion successive digits to the right of the decimal imply multiplication by $\frac{1}{10}, \frac{1}{10} \times \frac{1}{10}, \frac{1}{10} \times \frac{1}{10} \times \frac{1}{10}$, and so forth. Then if we shift the decimal point one place to the right we have multiplied the number by ten because the value of each digit is increased tenfold.

Notice that if we multiply .231 by ten we get 2.31 and the integral part of the answer is the first digit of the fraction. If we multiply the new fraction .31 by ten we get 3.1, and the integral part of this result is the second digit of the original fraction. Finally, if we multiply .1 by ten we get 1, an integer, which is the third digit of the original fraction.

In a similar manner, shifting the octonal point one place to the right in a base eight number multiples the number by eight. For example, $.314_{(eight)}$ means $3 \times \frac{1}{8} + 1 \times \frac{1}{8} \times \frac{1}{8} + 4 \times \frac{1}{8} \times \frac{1}{8} \times \frac{1}{8}$, but $3.14_{(eight)}$ means $3 \times 1 + 1 \times \frac{1}{8} + 4 \times \frac{1}{8} \times \frac{1}{8}$. Now if we multiply $.314_{(eight)}$ by 8 we get the integer 3, which is the first digit of the original number and the fraction $.14_{(eight)}$. If $.14_{(eight)}$ is multiplied by 8 we get $1.4_{(eight)}$, giving the integer 1, which is the next digit of the original number, and the fraction $.4_{(eight)}$. If .4 is multiplied by 8 we get the integer 4, or the last digit of the original $.314_{(eight)}$. But regardless of the base in which $.314_{(eight)}$ might be written, both its value and 8 times its value are unchanged. In other words, 8 times the number will yield the integer 3 plus a fraction which equals $.14_{(eight)}$ regardless of our base of notation.

The foregoing suggests a means of converting a fraction less than one to a new base. We multiply the fraction by the desired base. The integer we obtain is the highest digit in the desired notation. We then multiply the fraction which remains by the desired base and proceed as before, the integer being the next digit of the answer and the fraction being used to obtain the next digit.

EXAMPLE 1.   Write $.15625_{(ten)}$ in base eight.

SOLUTION. $\begin{array}{r} .15625 \\ 8 \\ \hline 1.25000 \end{array}$ $\begin{array}{r} .25 \\ 8 \\ \hline 2.00 \end{array}$ therefore $.15625 = .12_{(eight)}$

CHECK. $.15625_{(ten)} = \dfrac{15625}{100000} = \dfrac{5}{32}$

$.12_{(eight)} = \dfrac{1}{8} + \dfrac{2}{64} = \dfrac{5}{32}$

Some fractions when written decimally will terminate, as $\frac{1}{4} = .25$. Others form a repeating cycle, as $\frac{4}{33} = .12\overline{12} \ldots$ The bar over 12 indicates that it repeats endlessly. Whether a given number will terminate or repeat when expressed as a positional fraction depends upon the base. A number might well terminate in one base and repeat in another, repeat in each of two bases, or terminate in each.

EXAMPLE 2. Write $.3_{(ten)}$ in base eight.

SOLUTION.

$.3 \times 8 = 2.4$	$.4 \times 8 = 3.2$	$.4 \times 8 = 3.2$
$.4 \times 8 = 3.2$	$.2 \times 8 = 1.6$	$.2 \times 8 = 1.6$
$.2 \times 8 = 1.6$	$.6 \times 8 = 4.8$	$\ldots$
$.6 \times 8 = 4.8$	$.8 \times 8 = 6.4$	$\ldots$
$.8 \times 8 = 6.4$		

$$\therefore \quad .3_{(ten)} = (.231\overline{463146}\ldots)_{(eight)}$$

CHECK.

Base ten notation left of equality sign.

$$\text{Let } n = .231\overline{463146}\ldots$$
$$\text{then } 8n = 2.31\overline{463146}\ldots$$
$$\text{and } 8^4 \times 8n = 8^5 n = 23146.\overline{3146}\ldots$$
$$\text{Subtracting: } 8^5 n - 8n = 23146.\overline{3146}\ldots - 2.\overline{3146}\ldots$$
$$32768n - 8n = 23144$$
$$32760n = 23144$$

Base eight notation right of equality sign.

Hence we see that $n = \dfrac{23144_{(eight)}}{32760_{(ten)}}$

and changing the numerator to base ten

$$n = \frac{9828}{32760} = \frac{3}{10} = .3$$

The same relationship that we observed between octonal and binary representation of a whole number also holds for a fraction. We may change from base two to base eight by grouping the "bigits" in threes, starting at the binary point. These three "bigit" numbers are the octonal digits.

EXAMPLE 3. Write $.101110111_{(two)}$ in base eight.

SOLUTION.
$$101_{(two)} = 5_{(eight)}, \quad 110_{(two)} = 6_{(eight)}, \quad 111_{(two)} = 7_{(eight)}$$
$$\therefore \quad .101110111_{(two)} = .567_{(eight)}$$

CHECK. As check we may multiply $.567_{(eight)}$ and succeeding fractions by 2 to convert to base two. Remember, we are using the octonal multiplication table.

.567	.356	.734	.670	.560	.340	.700	.600	.400
2	2	2	2	2	2	2	2	2
1.356	0.734	1.670	1.560	1.340	0.700	1.600	1.400	1.000

$$\therefore \quad .567_{(eight)} = .101110111_{(two)}$$

We have not stated why the above relationship works. This will be discussed in Chapter Ten. But granting it for the present, it follows that the fraction will either terminate in both base eight and base two notation or will repeat in both.

As a further check we can convert both the base eight representation and the base two representation to base ten.

$$.567_{(eight)} = 5/8 + 6/8^2 + 7/8^3 = 5/8 + 6/64 + 7/512 = 375/512$$
$$.101110111_{(two)} = 1/2 + 1/2^3 + 1/2^4 + 1/2^5 + 1/2^7 + 1/2^8 + 1/2^9$$
$$= 1/2 + 1/8 + 1/16 + 1/32 + 1/128 + 1/256 + 1/512$$
$$= 375/512$$

Does the number terminate as a positional fraction in base ten?

Finally, if we wish to change the base of notation of a mixed number we can divide the integral part and its successive quotients by the desired base, and we can multiply the fractional part and succeeding fractions by the desired base.

EXAMPLE 4.   Write $376.24_{(eight)}$ in base ten.

SOLUTION.   We change $376_{(eight)}$ to base ten. The computation, in base eight, is

$$
\begin{array}{ccc}
31 & 2 & 0 \\
12\overline{)376} & 12\overline{)31} & 12\overline{)2} \\
36 & 24 & 0 \\
\overline{16} & \overline{5} & \overline{2} \\
12 & & \\
\overline{4} & & \\
\end{array}
$$

$$\therefore \quad 376_{(eight)} = 254_{(ten)}$$

We change $.24_{(eight)}$ to base ten

$$
\begin{array}{cccc}
.24 & .10 & .20 & .40 \\
12 & 12 & 12 & 12 \\
\overline{50} & \overline{20} & \overline{40} & \overline{100} \\
24 & 10 & 20 & 40 \\
\overline{3.10} & \overline{1.20} & \overline{2.40} & \overline{5.00} \\
\end{array}
$$

$$\therefore \quad .24_{(eight)} = .3125_{(ten)}$$

$$\therefore \quad 376.24_{(eight)} = 254.3125_{(ten)}$$

CHECK.

$$376.24_{(eight)} = 3 \times 8 \times 8 + 7 \times 8 + 6 + 2 \times \tfrac{1}{8} + 4 \times \tfrac{1}{8} \times \tfrac{1}{8}$$
$$= 192 + 56 + 6 + \tfrac{1}{4} + \tfrac{1}{16}$$
$$= 254\tfrac{5}{16} = 254.3125$$

Exercises

1 Convert the following to common fractions in base ten:
(a) $.4_{(twelve)}$ (b) $.3_{(six)}$ (c) $.24_{(five)}$ (d) $.21_{(seven)}$.

2 Convert the following to positional fractions in base eight:
(a) $.32_{(four)}$ (b) $.625_{(ten)}$ (c) $.1101_{(two)}$ (d) $.1101_{(four)}$
(e) $.209_{(twelve)}$.

3 Convert the following to base five:
(a) $.336_{(ten)}$ (b) $.688_{(ten)}$ (c) $.96_{(ten)}$.

4 Will a fraction which repeats in base ten also repeat in base eight? Why?

5 Convert $.5625_{(ten)}$ to base eight, and without multiplying, from base eight to base two.

6 Devise a method for converting from base four to base two analogous to the scheme from eight to two.

7 How can one most easily change from base nine to base three?

8 Is it possible for a fraction to terminate in base five but repeat in base ten? If so, find one. If not, explain why.

2.11 THE GAME OF NIM

Binary notation has many applications, some useful, some amusing. Unless you have ambitions as a gambler or confidence man the following falls in the second category.

Nim is a game for two players. The game begins by placing matches or any convenient counters in several piles. The number of piles is immaterial. Each pile may have any number of counters. The players alternate moves. On each move the player removes from any one pile as many counters as he wishes, anything from one counter to the entire pile. The player removing the last counter wins the game.

There is a system of play, based on binary notation, whereby one is almost certain to win if his opponent does not know the system. In fact, machines for playing the game have been constructed which, given the initial advantage, cannot be beaten.

Obviously, the player who first plays to a single pile wins. The simplest situation which the winner can force on the loser is a single counter in each of two piles; the loser takes one, leaving one for the winner. The player who forces his opponent to play to two counters in each of two piles will win. If the opponent takes one counter, the player takes one counter from the other pile. If the opponent removes one pile the player removes the other. Forcing the opponent to play to three piles containing one, two, and three counters respectively constitutes a winning situation. If the opponent takes the pile consisting of one counter, the player takes one from the pile of three.

Start	/	//	///
Opponent's play		//	///
Counter play		//	//

If the opponent takes one from the pile of two, the player takes all of the pile of three.

Start	/	//	///
Opponent's play	/	/	///
Counter play	/	/	

If the opponent takes all of the pile of two, the player takes two of the pile of three.

Start	/	//	///
Opponent's play	/		///
Counter play	/		/

An interchange of the foregoing moves will yield all other possible moves by the opponent and correct countermoves. In other words, regardless of what move the opponent makes, there is a countermove which will leave two identical piles, each having either two counters or one counter.

The system of play can best be described through an example. Suppose we have four piles containing 15, 13, 7, and 5 counters. We write these numbers in binary notation, add the columns, and write the column sums in ordinary base ten notation.

$$15_{(ten)} = 1111_{(two)}$$
$$13_{(ten)} = 1101_{(two)}$$
$$7_{(ten)} = 111_{(two)}$$
$$5_{(ten)} = 101_{(two)}$$
$$\overline{2424}$$

Each column contains an even number of 1's. This is called an *even* combination. The player who can first force his opponent to play to an even combination will be the ultimate winner—if he makes no mistakes. Notice that two piles of one each is an even combination

$$\begin{array}{r} 1 \\ 1 \\ \hline 2 \end{array}$$

also two piles of two each is even

$$\begin{array}{r} 10 \\ 10 \\ \hline 20 \end{array}$$

as is three piles of one, two, and three

$$\begin{array}{r} 1 \\ 10 \\ 11 \\ \hline 22 \end{array}$$

If one or more column sums is an odd number, we have an *odd* combination. The player who plays to an even combination *must* leave an odd combination. In the above situation something must be taken from one and only one pile. This means that a 1 must be removed from at least one column, but nothing else in that column can be disturbed. Since we must remove counters from only one pile at each play only one of the numbers 15, 13, 7, and 5 can be changed. For instance, if one counter is taken from the pile of 13, the right hand column will have only three 1's and a 1 cannot be taken from any other pile. If two are taken from the seven pile a single counter remains in the second column from the right and neither of the zeros in this column can be changed to ones because we can change the count in only one pile. When playing to an even combination the player must leave an odd combination. But when playing to an odd combination the player *can*, if he knows how, leave an even combination. The winning system consists of forcing the opponent to play to an even combination every time.

The following example shows how one can play to an odd combination and leave it even. Suppose we have 15, 13, 5, and 1 counters. We write these numbers in the binary scale:

$$\begin{array}{r} 15 - 1111 \\ 13 - 1101 \\ 5 - 101 \\ 1 - 1 \\ \hline 2314 \end{array}$$

The two middle columns are odd. If we make an even combination we must make all odd columns even. There are three 1's in the third column from the right. Since a 1 in this position stands for four counters, we must take four counters from either the 15, the 13, or the 5 pile. If subsequent columns are already even we leave them intact. This is true of the right-hand column. If subsequent columns are odd, we replace counters in case our pile has a zero in that column. If our pile has a 1 in the column being considered, we remove it. There are three possible ways to make the above combination even. We can take six from the pile of 15. We would then have the even combination:

$$9 - 1001$$
$$13 - 1101$$
$$5 - 101$$
$$1 - 1$$
$$\overline{2204}$$

We can also remove two from the pile of 13. This amounts to removing four and replacing two. We would then have the even combination:

$$15 - 1111$$
$$11 - 1011$$
$$5 - 101$$
$$1 - 1$$
$$\overline{2224}$$

Or, finally, we can remove two from the pile of five. Again, this amounts to taking four and giving two back. This move gives the even combination:

$$15 - 1111$$
$$13 - 1101$$
$$3 - 11$$
$$1 - 1$$
$$\overline{2224}$$

The player who is forced always to play to an even combination can never pick up the last counter.

2.12 RUSSIAN PEASANT MULTIPLICATION

Another application of the notion of binary notation is involved in Russian peasant multiplication. If you happen to know a Russian who never heard of this kind of multiplication it could be because he is not a peasant. In any event the method probably had its origin with the ancient Egyptians; who used a method that is very close to this one. We can best describe the method through an example.

EXAMPLE 1.   Use the Russian peasant method to multiply 375 by 48.

SOLUTION: In parallel columns we double one of the factors and halve the other, ignoring remainders. Continue until one is reached in the halved column.

$$\begin{array}{cc}
\cancel{375} & 48 \\
\cancel{750} & 24 \\
\cancel{1500} & 12 \\
\cancel{3000} & 6 \\
6000 & 3 \\
12000 & 1 \\
\hline
18000 &
\end{array}$$

Then, in the doubled column we strike out all numbers which lie opposite even numbers in the halved column. Add the remaining numbers in the doubled column. This sum is the required product.

If we write 48 in base two it becomes apparent why the above method works.

EXAMPLE 2.   Convert $48_{(ten)}$ to base two.

SOLUTION:

$$\begin{array}{llll}
2\underline{|48} & 2\underline{|24} & 2\underline{|12} & 2\underline{|6} \\
\quad 24 \text{ rem. } 0 & \quad 12 \text{ rem. } 0 & \quad 6 \text{ rem. } 0 & \quad 3 \text{ rem. } 0 \\
\end{array}$$

$$\begin{array}{ll}
2\underline{|3} & 2\underline{|1} \\
\quad 1 \text{ rem. } 1 & \quad 0 \text{ rem. } 1
\end{array}$$

$$\therefore \quad 48_{(ten)} = 110000_{(two)}$$

The numbers in the doubled column are actually 375×1, 375×2, 375×4, 375×8, 375×16, and 375×32.

Comparison of Example 2 with the halved column in Example 1 shows that we have used 375 multiplied by those powers of two that we must add to get 48, $48 = 16 + 32 = 2^4 + 2^5$.

$$6000 = 375 \times 16$$
$$12000 = 375 \times 32$$
$$18000 = 375 \times 16 + 375 \times 32 = 375(16 + 32) = 375 \times 48$$

Obviously, it makes no difference which factor is doubled.

EXAMPLE 3.   Find 375×48 by doubling 48 and halving 375.

SOLUTION:

375	48
187	96
93	192
46	~~384~~
23	768
11	1536
5	3072
2	~~6144~~
1	12288
	18000

Here we have

$$48 \times 1 + 48 \times 2 + 48 \times 4 + 48 \times 16 + 48 \times 32 + 48$$
$$\times 64 + 48 \times 256 = 48(1 + 2 + 4 + 16 + 32 + 64 + 256)$$
$$= 48 \times 375.$$

Exercises

1 If $.13 + .56 = 1.02$, what base of notation is used?

2 What is wrong with the following?

$$\begin{array}{r} 3.42_{(five)} \\ \underline{1.34_{(five)}} \\ 10.26_{(five)} \end{array}$$

3 Convert the following to base ten by evaluating each symbol and adding:
(a) $1011.11_{(two)}$ (b) $63.15_{(eight)}$ (c) $.75_{(eight)}$ (d) $.1111_{(two)}$

4 Change to base eight by dividing the integer and multiplying the fraction by eight, as illustrated in Section 2.9:
(a) $176.8_{(ten)}$ (b) $1101.11101_{(two)}$

5 Will a fraction which terminates in base two also terminate in base eight? Base ten? Why?

6 Will a fraction which terminates in base ten also terminate in base eight? Will one which terminates in base eight terminate in base ten?

7 Is the first play an advantage or disadvantage in a game of Nim in which there are piles of 19, 21, and 6 counters?

8 State three correct plays if faced with 16, 25, and 23 counters in a game of Nim.

9 State the system of play if the objective of the game of Nim is changed so that the *loser* picks up the last counter.

10 Will the Russian peasant method work with decimal fractions? Try the method on 23.46×12.5.

11 Will the Russian peasant method work with octal numbers? Try it with $137_{(eight)} \times 23_{(eight)}$. Remember the computation is in base eight.

12 Use the Russian peasant method to find 975×96. Convert the entire problem to base two. In the new notation what determines when we get remainders in the halved column?

13 Multiply $345_{(seven)}$ by $53_{(seven)}$ by the Russian peasant method.

14 In a game of Nim there are six piles of counters containing 12, 8, 2, 5, 7, and 18 counters. Who has the advantage, and what is the most appropriate move?

15 Distribute 20 counters into three piles so as to make an even combination in a game of Nim.

Suggested Supplementary Readings

Andrews, F. E., *New Numbers*. New York: Essential Books, 1944.

———, "Revolving Numbers," *The Atlantic Monthly*, Vol. 155, February 1935, pp. 208–211.

Banks, J. Houston, *Elements of Mathematics*, Second Edition. Boston: Allyn and Bacon, Inc., 1961. Pp. 49–77.

Dantzig, Tobias, *Number, The Language of Science*. New York: The Macmillan Company, 1945. Pp. 1–56.

Eves, Howard, *An Introduction to the History of Mathematics*. New York: Rinehart and Company, Inc., 1953. Pp. 7–22.

Guttman, Solomon, "Cyclic Numbers," *The American Mathematical Monthly*, Vol. 41, March 1934. Pp. 159–166.

Mueller, Francis J., *Arithmetic, Its Structure and Concepts*. Englewood Cliffs, N.J.: Prentice-Hall, Inc., 1956. Pp. 1–47.

Smith, D. E., and Jekuthiel Ginsburg, *Numbers and Numerals*. New York: Teachers College, Columbia University, 1937.

Developing Concepts Fundamental to Positional Notation

CHAPTER THREE

O NE DOES NOT HAVE TO UNDERSTAND the principles of the internal combustion engine to be able to drive today's automobiles. Nor is one necessarily a better driver by virtue of being an expert mechanic. We can remain ignorant of electronics and still enjoy television spectaculars to the fullest—until a tube goes out. But such impunity does not apply to ignorance of the number system. Understanding of its structure is a prerequisite to its most efficient use. Grant that one may learn to multiply 432 by 98 as a completely rote process. It remains for the pupil who understands the number system to discover for himself that the product may be obtained by subtracting 864 from 43,200.

Mathematical concepts are not gained full blown as flashes of insight. They unfold and grow to maturity slowly and pass through many stages of revision and refinement. The three-year-old possesses a rudimentary concept of number which is a far cry from that of a research mathematician. We do not decide to study the notation system on the second week of the third month of the fourth grade, from which point it becomes something we have "had." In fact, regardless of what organizational approach to arithmetic we use, we need never study the notation system as an instructional unit. Yet we are studying the notation system throughout the study of arithmetic.

This fact in itself makes it all the more imperative for the teacher of arithmetic to be alert to the need for developing certain concepts essential to the full understanding and mastery of our system of notation.

3.1 THE HINDU-ARABIC SYSTEM

The decimal character of our notation system is not obvious to the child who is learning to count, regardless of whether he is counting rationally or by rote. The "troublesome teens" is not solely an allusion to adolescence. The second decade number names constitute an unfortunate stumbling block, the magnitude of which we sometimes fail to appreciate. If thirteen means three and ten why not oneteen and twoteen for eleven and twelve? It is scant comfort to the seven-year-old that eleven originally meant literally "one left," implying ten and one left over or that twelve means "two left." Further to complicate matters, when we reach the third decade we say twenty-three for two tens and three. Why not onety-three rather than thirteen? The inconsistent numeration of the teens can only serve to confuse the beginner and hide the essential decimal nature of both numeration and notation.

Although the positional characteristic and the decimal aspect of our notation system are two separate and independent attributes, an attempt to develop one of the concepts in isolation from the other is both difficult and undesirable. This does not imply that the two should be interchangeable in the pupil's mind. When he studies the Roman system of notation he should be aware not only of the fact that the system has a base but that its base is ten. The use of ten as base does not imply the concept of place value. The X in XII represents ten because it is X, and not because of its position in the Roman numeral for twelve. Nor does the use of place value require the base ten. The Mayan Indians of Central America had a notation system which was positional and had twenty as its base. The ancient Babylonians used a positional system with sixty as base.[1] The independence of the two concepts is clearly shown by our numeration system. In spite of the inconsistencies in the naming of the teen numbers, the base of the numeration system is ten, and we use exactly the same numeration system with Roman as with Hindu-Arabic notation. For example, regardless of whether we use the symbol 24 or the symbol XXIV to indicate the number, we give the number the *name* "twenty-four."

In learning the number names to one hundred the child should be made to realize that there are essentially only eleven number names involved, provided we are willing to consider eleven as "ten and one left" and twelve as "ten and two left." These two exceptional number names should be presented to the pupil in this way. Eleven should not be learned as just another name for a number as is seven or eight. The child should be taught to think "ten and one" synonymously with eleven, and "ten and two" synonymously with twelve. In fact, the structure of the system should be emphasized until it is thoroughly mastered. The child should develop an awareness that "one hundred fifty-six" is not just a number name, it is a number name but it also reveals the makeup of the number—1 hundred, 5 tens, and 6 ones.

The counting frame is an excellent device for teaching the decimal aspect of the number system. The frame consists of ten lines, ten counters to the line. A very satisfactory frame can be constructed at little cost. Welding rods may serve as wires for a frame as in Figure 1. Wooden beads can be obtained from a hobby shop. The beads on consecutive lines should be of different colors. This will give added emphasis to the grouping of the decades. The counting frame should not be confused with the bead abacus, Section 3.2, p. 70. The purpose of the abacus is to teach place value, but the counting frame shows the decimal aspect of the system. The counting frame does not have a ones line, tens line, hundreds line, and so on. The third bead on the third line is bead number twenty-three. Each bead represents a different number from one to one hundred. In Figure 2, the number for which each bead stands is shown. They are arranged from right to left. A left to right arrangement would do just as well. But the right to left form is recommended

[1] For a short description of these systems see J. Houston Banks, *Elements of Mathematics* (2nd ed.; Boston: Allyn and Bacon, Inc., 1961), pp. 56–59.

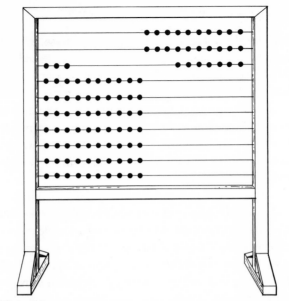

Figure 1 TWENTY-SEVEN ON THE COUNTING FRAME.

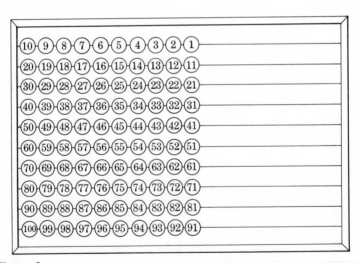

Figure 2 EACH COUNTER ON THE COUNTING FRAME REPRESENTS
A NUMBER IN THE COUNTING SERIES.

because it seems more natural, in moving the beads while counting, to move them from left to right.

One should not infer from Figure 2 that the counters should be numbered. This would be an advantage in the development of the ordinal concept, see Section 3.7. But it would be a disadvantage in the discovery of addition facts and such grouping equivalencies as a set of six and a set of seven are equivalent to a set of ten and a set of three.

If the counting frame illustrated the place value principle each of the counters numbered 11 through 20 would represent one set of ten. This is not the case, each counter represents *one* no matter where it is. The decimal character of the notation system is illustrated by virtue of the fact that there are ten counters on each line. If the first line were the ones line it would contain only nine beads. Bead number ten would be the first bead on the second line, and it would represent one set of ten. In this connection an important distinction should be noted between our system of numeration and that of notation. In numeration we go all the way to ten before any combining of names occurs, but the combining of symbols in the notation system begins with ten—one ten and no units.

Six- and seven-year-olds are just beginning to develop small muscle control, but they are interested in gadgets and like to manipulate them. This makes the counting frame ideal for work with counting and simple addition. Best results are obtained if the room is equipped with a large demonstration frame, large enough to be seen all over the room, and each child has his individual smaller frame.

When children have learned to count rationally through ten the next step should be counting by tens through one hundred. On the counting frame this means counting by lines. The child is then ready to represent on the frame quantities from his experience. When asked to indicate on the frame the number of children in the room he must find how many sets of ten (full lines) and how many more. He should visualize two tens and four ones in a class of twenty-four:

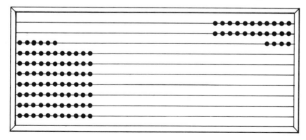

Figure 3 THE "100 CHART."

The "100 chart" is another useful device in the development of the decimal concept. This consists of a ten-by-ten array numbered as in Figure 3. The chart is easily made from cardboard. The numbers should be large enough to be seen from the rear of the room. A more useful chart can be made by using plywood. Small finishing nails are driven into the wood in the ten-by-ten array. Removable numbers— cardboard squares will serve—can then be hung on the nails. This form of chart adapts itself to a number of useful variations. Some of the numbers can be placed face in and the children asked to identify them. They can be placed on the chart out of order and the children allowed to arrange them correctly. Objects such as bottle caps can be used rather than numbers in teaching addition facts. The child may be asked to show on the chart that his 7¢ bottle of milk and 8¢ soup is the same as one ten and five more. The child should be taught to think of a full line as a single set of ten, not as ten ones.

The significance of the *tenness* of the number system is apparent in teaching addition and subtraction. When we combine a set of six and a set of seven the child is as correct in thinking this is equivalent to 2 sixes and a one or 2 fives and 3 ones as 1 ten and 3 ones. The result thirteen should be thought of as a set of ten and a set of three. Thus addition is here thought of as regrouping rather than combining into a single set:

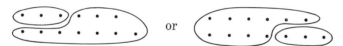

It is as important that the child's concept of *eight* include the idea *two less than ten* as it does *seven and one*.

3.2 PLACE VALUE

Closely allied with the decimal nature of the system of notation is its *positional* character. The value of an individual symbol depends upon its position in the ordered sequence, zero through nine. This value is constant; 5 always means one more than 4 and one less than 6. Its value also depends on its *position in the digits of the numeral*. The symbol 5 has the value 5 tens only when it is the tens position, the second digit from the right if the number is a whole number.

We cannot begin too early in helping the child develop this

concept. As soon as two-digit numbers are encountered this characteristic should be emphasized: verbally, forty-seven (four tens and seven ones); symbolically, 47 = 4 tens + 7 ones; on the counting frame, four full lines and seven on another line.

When properly used, an abacus can be an invaluable aid in establishing this concept. For this purpose a variation of the Oriental bead abacus is recommended. One may be constructed exactly as a counting frame except that each line should contain *only nine* beads, and the number of lines is arbitrary. On the abacus, the lines should be in a vertical position. The extreme right line represents ones, the next line to the left represents tens, the next line hundreds, and so on.

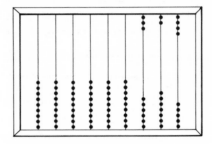

Figure 4   ABACUS SHOWING 324

Three beads raised on the third line from the left indicates three sets of 100. If the abacus is placed flat on the desk, moving a bead to the top of the frame presents no problem. For a large demonstration model, some means of holding the moved beads in place is necessary. If the beads fit the rods tightly enough friction will hold them in place. Otherwise, a clothespin or spring clip placed under the beads at the top of each rod will do nicely.

The teacher should not attempt to use the abacus and the counting frame simultaneously. The use of the abacus may well be delayed until higher decade addition and subtraction are encountered. Figure 5 contrasts the representation of 53 on the counting frame and on the abacus. The child who has used the counting frame in an earlier grade will not fail to appreciate the greater simplicity and utility of the abacus. The abacus utilizes place value in precisely the same manner as does the system of notation. The value of each bead depends on its place, what line it is on. Thirty is represented by three counters on the tens line rather than by three full lines of ten. No line

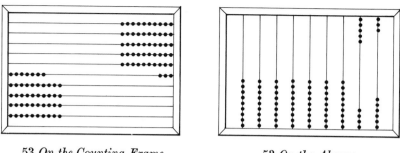

53 *On the Counting Frame*   53 *On the Abacus*

Figure 5 COUNTING FRAME AND ABACUS CONTRASTED.

can contain more than nine counters just as we can represent no more than nine in any digit.

Unlike the counting frame, the abacus does not lend itself to the ordinal conception of number. There is no eleventh counter. But the cardinal use of number is well illustrated. The arrangement of

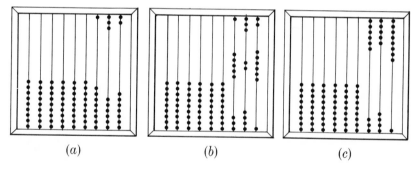

(a)   (b)   (c)

Figure 6 ADDITION ON THE ABACUS: $132 + 526 = 658$.

the counters in the representation of eleven indicates a set which is composed of *one* set of ten and one set of one.

Addition or subtraction on the abacus is quite simple if no re-grouping ("carrying" or "borrowing") is involved. In Figure 6 the sum $132 + 526$ is indicated. In Figure 6*a* the first addend 132 has been recorded. Figure 6*b* shows the second addend 526 being added. The final sum 658 is recorded in Figure 6*c*.

Subtraction without "borrowing" is performed by reversing the addition process.

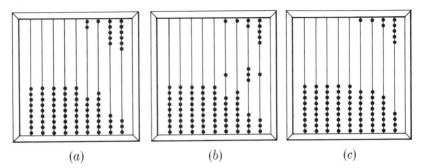

Figure 7 SUBTRACTION ON THE ABACUS: 2156 − 1031 = 1125.

"Carrying" in addition and "borrowing" in subtraction can be seen quite concretely with the aid of the abacus. In Figure 8 the "carrying" process is illustrated. In Figure 8a we have registered 163 on the abacus. We wish to add 278 to this. The ones line has only six counters available to add to the three. When we add the six, the ones

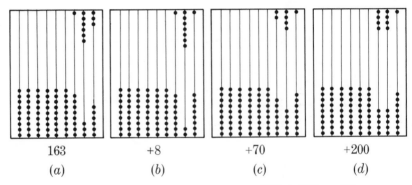

163	+8	+70	+200
(a)	(b)	(c)	(d)

Figure 8 CARRYING IN ADDITION: 163 + 278 = 441.

line (digit) is full. In order to add one more one we must "carry" the ten ones (more than the line can hold) to the tens line where it is represented by a single counter. Now all nine counters are available on the ones line and we can add one of them to fill out the eight ones to be added, Figure 8b. This is more easily visualized as adding ten and subtracting two.

Other number properties may also be made meaningful. The "carry" idea may be illustrated as follows: Having added the 8 ones, the tens line has only two counters not in use. We wish to add 7 more tens. But 7 being 3 less than 10 we add 10 tens by adding a single hundred and taking off 3 tens. We add 2 more counters on the hundreds line to complete the addition.

"Borrowing" is illustrated in Figure 9. We wish to subtract 17 from 32. Figure 9 shows 32 on the abacus. We have only 2 ones available on the ones line. But by using one from the tens line we have 12 ones available, thus leaving 5 ones when we take 7 from 12. Then, removing one of the two remaining counters on the tens line completes the subtraction. Here again the complementary idea can be

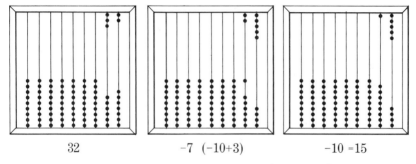

32   −7 (−10+3)   −10 =15

Figure 9 BORROWING IN SUBTRACTION: 32 − 17 = 15.

illustrated; rather than subtract 7 ones we can subtract one ten and add 3 ones.

Thus, the abacus can be of real help in showing what "carrying" and "borrowing" really are. They are really regrouping or *renaming* the number.

Place value enables us to think of any whole number as the sum of *sets*, sets of one, sets of ten, sets of one hundred, and so on. We never have to visualize more than nine of a given kind of set. It is in a very real sense that our numeration system is constructed from the symbols 0 through 9. It is one thing to try to visualize 218 distinct objects and quite another to visualize 2 sets of 100 objects, 1 set of ten objects, and 8 sets of one object.

The place value box is another useful teaching aid in developing the decimal and the positional aspects of the notation system. A series of cans attached to a board makes a very good place value box. Tongue depressors, paper spoons, or any convenient sticks may be used for counters. The place value box is quite similar to the abacus. Each counter in the ones can represents one, each counter in the tens can represents ten, and so on. Two counters in the tens can and three in the ones can indicate the number 23. A variety of exercises can be devised to develop the concept of place value. One type of exercise is determination of the number represented, as in the figure below. Such thought questions as: How many counters are needed to show 1023? What is the smallest number that can be shown with these same counters? The largest? How can you show 16 tens and 12 ones?

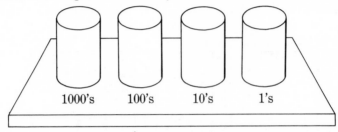

A device of this sort is sometimes used wherein a package of ten counters represents ten and a package of ten packages of ten counters represents one hundred. This practice does emphasize the decimal characteristic of notation but it misses the point relative to place value. If two packages of ten are placed in tens position the place value principle requires that 200, not 20, is represented. In using devices of this sort it should be emphasized that a given number of counters, say three, represents three ones when in ones position, three tens when in tens position, and so on.

The concept of a base other than ten is increasingly finding its way into the elementary school arithmetic program. The theory for this is the belief that such activities will help to clarify the concept of place value. The place value box is useful for this purpose. Suppose we use the base seven. We merely change the position value of the containers to ones, sevens, forty-nines (7×7), three hundred forty

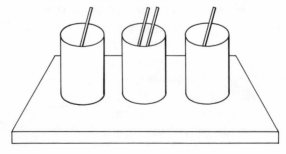

threes ($7 \times 7 \times 7$), and so on. What number is represented by one counter in the first and third cans from the right and two counters in the second can? We have 1 one, 2 sevens, and 1 forty-nine equals sixty-four. Notation in base seven follows immediately, sixty-four is written in base seven as $121_{(seven)}$.

It is also an instructive to write the counting sequence in various bases:

1,	2,	3,	4,	5,	6,	7,	8,	9,	10,	11,	12,	13,	14,	15,	16 (ten)
1,	2,	3,	4,	5,	6,	10,	11,	12,	13,	14,	15,	16,	20,	21,	22 (seven)
1,	2,	3,	4,	10,	11,	12,	13,	14,	20,	21,	22,	23,	24,	30,	31 (five)
1,	10,	11,	100,	101,	110,	111,	1000,	1001,	1010,	1011,	1100,	1101,	1110,	1111,	10,000 (two)

We should not call $20_{(five)}$ "twenty" or "twenty, base five." Unless we wish to invent a new system of numeration to coincide with the notation, we must call it "ten" or "two-zero, base five."

Exercises

1 Distinguish between a notation system and a numeration system. Why is it important that the distinction be made in early elementary school arithmetic instruction?

2 List all of the inconsistencies you can think of which exist between our system of numeration and our system of notation.

3 Upon what two things does the value of an individual symbol in a numeral depend in the Hindu-Arabic system?

4 Distinguish between a number and a numeral. Between a number and a number name.

5 What is the role of the nine in each of the following numerals? (a) 5829 (b) 5982 (c) 9528 (d) 2895

6 Explain why the counting frame is better suited for teaching the decimal aspect of our notation system, whereas the abacus is helpful in teaching its positional aspect.

7 What is the largest number that can be represented using the abacus pictured in Figure 5?

8 Describe what a counting frame would be like if we used a positional notation system with seven as base. How would thirty-four be represented on such?

9 Describe what an abacus would be like if we used a positional notation system with seven as base. How would thirty-four be represented on such?

10 Describe some classroom activities utilizing the one hundred chart which will aid in learning rational counting.

11 If the child is to discover the sum $18 + 7$ on the counting frame describe several possible ways it might be done.

12 How is 1437 represented on the abacus? How would you add 3684 to this?

13 How many distinct symbols are needed for a positional notation system if five is used as base?

14 How many counters per line are needed for an abacus designed for base five notation?

15 What is the largest number that can be represented with three digits in base five notation? How would one hundred be written?

3.3 ZERO

The history of zero is a fascinating story. It entered the household of number through the back door, so to speak. Presumably it was originally invented as a symbol to indicate that a position on the abacus was empty. It was not a number, it was rather a means of indicating that no number was there. This absence of number, the *place holder* role, is one concept of zero which is most important to the child in developing his conception of the number system. From this point of view, zero is superfluous in the Roman system of notation. If we wish to write one hundred seven we write CVII. It is unnecessary to emphasize the absence of tens. This would be the case in any system not employing place value. We do not place the zero between the one and the seven in 107 to emphasize the fact that we have no tens. It is necessary in order that the 1 may indicate hundreds; that is, receive its proper place value. We have observed that the usual system of numeration is decimal. It is not positional; we do not say "one hundred no tens seven." There is a growing, and useful, tendency to call the number "one zero seven" which does employ the positional characteristic. But this is oral notation rather than numeration. We may ultimately dispense with our set of number names. For example, it is rather common practice to read 206.025 as "two zero six point zero two five" rather than "two hundred six *and* twenty-five thousandths." But so long as the child is apt to hear both forms he should be aware of the distinction between the written symbols where the zeros are mandatory and the number names which omit them. Specifically, when the child sees 500 he should think "five hundreds and that is all because of the zeros."

However, the child should not be led to think of zero merely as a place holder. It is a number on an equal footing with the counting numbers. Just as five designates the "how many" of the fingers on a normal human hand, so zero designates the "how many" of an *empty set*. This is a concept not foreign to young children. If Jane has a candy sucker for each of her playmates except Susie, Susie is acutely aware of the "not any" aspect of the situation. Zero is the number which answered the "how many" question for Susie. We may say that zero is the number which designates the count of all empty sets in precisely the same manner that three is the count of all sets which can be placed into one-to-one correspondence with the set of names one, two, three. It is true that the place holder role of zero embodies the "not any" idea, but this is incidental. Consider 506. The zero does indicate there are no tens, but our concern with the presence or absence of tens stems from the presence of hundreds. We have no thousands present either, but are not obliged to place a zero to the left of the five.

Zero has yet another important role. It is an arbitrarily chosen point of reference on a directed scale. When it is used as a reference point zero may and may not imply "not any." Children have experience with this concept long before positive and negative numbers are developed in algebra. Games where points may be scored for or against are a case in point. We start even with the world and can score points or "go in the hole" in a number of card games. Temperature scales offer a very good example of the use of zero where "not any" is not implied. They also serve to emphasize the arbitrariness of the choice of point of reference. Zero Centigrade and zero Fahrenheit are certainly not the same and in neither case is the absence of heat implied. To recapitulate—there are three distinct concepts of zero which the child must know and differentiate: (1) zero is a place holder, (2) zero is a number which identifies empty sets, (3) zero is an arbitrary point of reference on a directed scale.

3.4 THE DECIMAL POINT

Much of the difficulty children have with decimal fractions can be alleviated if they have prior understanding of the positional character of the system. The child should be fully cognizant of the fact that the value of a digit is ten times as great as the same digit one place to the right and consequently $\frac{1}{10}$ as great as the same digit one place to the left. Up to this point all digits of a number are oriented to the extreme right digit, the ones or units digit.

Many students apparently do not understand why an integer may be multiplied by 100 by merely affixing two zeros on the right. They frequently insist on

$$\begin{array}{r} 156 \\ 100 \\ \hline 15{,}600 \end{array}$$

This form is apparently a concession that it is shorter than

$$\begin{array}{r} 156 \\ 100 \\ \hline 000 \\ 000 \\ 156 \\ \hline 15{,}600 \end{array}$$

The fact seems to be missed that when we affix a zero to the right of a whole number it is multiplied by ten because the digit position of each symbol has been moved one place to the left, or what is the same thing, the ones digit position is moved one place to the right. The idea can be approached as follows: "What would happen to the value of 75 if the 5 became the hundreds digit and the 7 became the thousands digit?" Since the value of each digit is 100 times as great the resulting number is 100 times as great. "How can we make the 5 occupy the hundreds place and the 7 the thousands place?" By filling in the tens and ones places. "But how can this be done without further increasing the number?" By filling in blanks, zeros. In introducing the idea it is well to emphasize the fact that the original digits are actually moved:

thousands	hundreds	tens		
		7	5	original position
7	5	0	0	new position

The extension of positional notation to quantities less than one requires a means of fixing the position of the ones digit other than by virtue of its being fixed as the extreme right-hand digit. The decimal point is a separator; it separates the whole number part of the number from the fractional part. But more significantly, its role is that of fixing the ones digit, enabling us to extend the number to the right of the ones position. It is unfortunate that out of the welter of proposed notations one could not have been chosen which more clearly points up this fact. For instance if 517.15 were indicated 51715 it *better*

would be more obvious that we orient all other digits to the ones place, not to the decimal point. One place to the left and right of the ones place indicates *tens* and *tenths* respectively, two places to the left and right *hundreds* and *hundredths*, and so forth.

If the child has grasped the fact that the decimal point merely fixes the ones position it is not difficult for him to realize that moving the decimal point merely changes the ones position and all other positions similarly, since they are determined from it. Similarly, dropping a terminal zero from an integer or adding an initial zero to a fraction simply shifts the ones position one place to the left and thus divides the number by ten.

3.5 NUMBER NAMES

Learning the number names in their serial order is the essence of rote counting. However, few adults have ever counted by rote as high as one million. A knowledge of large number names is useful in reading such numbers. Relatively few adults find a need to compute with very large numbers, at least insofar as their bank accounts are concerned. But a knowledge of the pattern of names is not one of the questionable "fringe" items of the arithmetic curriculum. It easily passes the test of utility if utility is to include the ability to read and interpret current issues. National debts and annual budgets in the billions have become commonplace.

Although the number names follow a systematic pattern it should be observed that the pattern is not wholly in keeping with our system of notation. After the individual names for numbers 0 through 9 we invent a name for the base—10. Subsequent names are compounded until we reach the base squared—100—for which we invent a new name. We then compound the names, hundreds, tens, and ones, up to but not including the base cubed—1000—which requires a new name. The compounding continues, but we do not invent a name for 10^4 or 10^5; the next new name *million* is applied to 10^6. No new inventions after million are required until we reach 10^9, then 10^{12}, 10^{15}, and so on for each increase of three in the exponent.

We do not have an independent name for each power of ten but it should be noted that neither do we use a minimum of new names. Or, what amounts to the same thing, we do not fully utilize the compounding idea. We could call one thousand *ten hundred* and reserve the next new name, thousand, for one hundred hundred or 10^4. Following this plan, one million would be applied to 10^8

We point out this apparent lack of system for two reasons, first to emphasize what system *is* used, and second to point out the fact that we do not use exactly the system in the United States as that used in Europe.

Numbers which have more than four digits are customarily set off by commas in groups of three starting from the ones digit and moving to the left. Each of the groups of three digits is called a period. The right-hand digit in the group names the period. Thus the periods are ones, thousands, millions, billions, trillions, and subsequent names compounded from the Latin number names, as quadrillions, quintillions, and so on.

A diagram similar to the following will be found helpful in teaching the reading of large numbers. To read the number we must first determine the highest period.

The digits in the highest period are read as a three (or fewer) digit number, then the period is identified. This is repeated for each period in order from high to low. If a period consists of three zeros that period is omitted in reading the number. The ones period is not identified by name. For example, 17,336 is read "seventeen *thousand,* three hundred thirty-six" rather than "seventeen *thousand,* three hundred thirty-six *one.*"

Period:	trillions			billions			millions			thousands			ones		
	9	3,		8	0	7,		4	0	0,	0	0	0,	8	6	5
	ten trillions	trillions		hundred billions	ten billions	billions		hundred millions	ten millions	millions		hundred thousands	tens thousands	thousands	hundreds	tens	units

The number is correctly read "ninety three trillion, eight hundred seven billion, four hundred million, eight hundred sixty-five."

The British divide their numbers into periods of six digits rather than three. Their number names through one million are the same as ours. The periods are named ones, millions, billions, trillions, and so on. One billion is to the British 1,000000,000000, which is our 1,000,000,000,000—or one trillion. Our billion 1,000,000,000 is their one thousand million.

A convenient shortened notation, known as *scientific notation,* will be discussed in Section 12.7 in connection with approximate numbers. This notation is being used increasingly in the place of the number names for very large numbers.

3.6 READING DECIMAL FRACTIONS AND MIXED NUMBERS

We do not customarily find decimal fractions separated into periods in the manner that integers are. Reading fractions presents a different problem. In this case we must indicate *two* numbers, the numerator and the denominator (implied by the position of the decimal point). The fraction is correctly read by reading the numerator as if it were a whole number, then the denominator. The numerator is simply the number represented by the digits to the right of the decimal point, initial zeros if any being ignored. The denominator is obtained by counting from the ones digit (decimal point) to the right. As we move to the right successive digits are named precisely as those to the left except that the suffix *-th* is added.

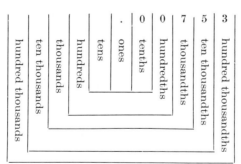

The number diagramed above is read "seven hundred fifty-three [the numerator] hundred thousandths [the denominator]."

A mixed number is a number not a whole number but greater than one; thus it has a whole number part and a fractional part. A mixed number is correctly read by reading the whole number part as one reads a whole number, reading the fractional part as one reads a fraction, but separating the two with the word *and*. The number 16,706.00405 is read "sixteen thousand seven hundred six *and* four hundred five hundred thousandths." Technically, this is the only permissible use of the word *and* in reading a number. However, this rule of mathematical grammar is probably as frequently disregarded as is any grammatical usage. We are more apt to hear 707 read as "seven hundred and seven" than "seven hundred seven." Another deviation from what is considered correct reading is "seven oh seven." We also frequently hear mixed numbers read "seven hundred fifteen *point* one six" for 715.16. This usage is gaining in popularity and is a satisfactory form. In fact, the excuse for any rule is the avoidance of ambiguity. If *and* is not used exclusively as the separator of the whole number from the fraction we might interpret "seven hundred and seven thousandths" as either 700.007 or .707. Even so, the accepted form is not completely void of ambiguity. "Six and five hundred thousandths" may mean 6.00005, but it could be interpreted 6.500. Using the newer form we would say "six point zero zero zero zero five" in the first case and "six point five zero zero" in the latter.

Exercises

1 Give the name for each of the following numerals:
(a) .4386274   (b) .100002   (c) .333
(d) 1.0027   (e) 100.27   (f) .127

2 Write the numeral in decimal form for each of the following:
(a) one and seven tenths   (b) one hundred and seven tenths
(c) one hundred seven tenths   (d) one hundred thirty-two thousandths   (e) one hundred and thirty-two thousandths
(f) one and thirty-two hundred thousandths   (g) one thousand two millionths   (h) one thousand and two millionths.

3 Give two acceptable ways to read each of the following:
(a) 700.002   (b) .702

4 Tell how the symbol zero is used in each of the following:
(a) The Yankees won 5 to 0.
(b) Forecast for tonight 0°.
(c) It is 106 miles from here to Junction City.

5 Use a diagram similar to that on page 81 to show the meaning of each digit in the number 372.72.

6 What name do the British use for the number we call one billion three hundred thousand six hundred two?

7 How would the British write the numeral to represent the number named in Exercise 6?

8 Describe a class exercise designed to develop the concept of the decimal point as a means of indicating ones position in a numeral.

9 Describe a class exercise designed to develop the idea that a whole number can be multiplied by ten by affixing a zero on the right.

3.7 ORDINAL VERSUS CARDINAL

One is apt to gain the impression from a reading of the literature that we have two sets of counting numbers, ordinal numbers and cardinal numbers. We have only one system of positive integers which may be used for either ordinal counting or cardinal counting. Cardinal counting answers the question "How many?" Ordinal counting answers the question "Which one?"

Most writers on the subject seem to believe the cardinal concept of numbers is the more primitive. This is open to question. One of man's earlier mathematical achievements consists of the development of the calendar. By far the more frequent use of the calendar is ordinal. We use the calendar to help keep track of "What day is it?" far more frequently than to determine "How many days is this?" Primitive man was at least as much concerned with "Is this fast day?" or "Is this the day to plant?" as with being reminded "There are just x shopping days till Christmas."

Early concern with the calendar and its effect upon the number system is forcefully illustrated by the number system of the Mayan Indians. They used a positional system with 20 as base in all but the second position, where 18 was used. This peculiarity was due to the fact that they considered the year 360 days long. The year was divided into 18 intervals of 20 days each. Thus in ones position as many as 19 days were recorded—a one in the next position stood for 20 days or one "month." This position was used to record up to 17 "months." A one in the next, the years, position represented 18 "months."

On the other hand, man's decided preference for ten as a number base seems to imply greater concern for the cardinal aspect of number. The fingers served as a reference set for purposes of comparison. "How many tents are there in the village?" "As many as the fingers on the hand" or "three less than the fingers of both hands." There is hardly room for doubt that man invented names to describe sets containing different numbers of objects. This could well have occurred before there was any notion of comparing the size of two sets by means of the names which described them. In fact, our language indicates that the business of naming the size of a set even antedates the notion of sameness of two sets which have the same count. We refer to a *flock* of geese, a *bevy* of beauties, a *herd* of cattle, and a *bunch* of carrots. And more specifically to indicate two we refer to a *pair* of dice, a *couple* of dollars, *twin* primes, and a *brace* of hounds.

Of one thing we may be sure. In early times the two ideas of ordinal and cardinal were quite distinct. This is carried over today in the number names: we have the cardinal one, two, three, and the ordinal first, second, third. However, it is a grave mistake to assume that we always use the different word form for ordinal use. It is quite as correct to refer to "line five" as to "the fifth line."

Regardless of which concept emerged first in man's thinking, we use both quite extensively. For those who think our major use of number is cardinal it would be enlightening to catalogue all their uses of number for a 24-hour period and compare the cardinal with the ordinal applications.

As the child's conception of number begins to mature the distinction between these two kinds of use should be made clear to him. The one hundred chart, where the removable numerals are used, can be used to emphasize the ordinal notion of number. The symbol 76 is associated with a particular counter. The number gives it an identity. The child must learn where it belongs in the sequence. It is the sixth counter on the eighth line. It is just before 77 and just after 75. On the other hand, when the child is working with the counting frame, he should associate 76 with 7 groups of ten and six more—the important thing here is the collection of counters.

An essential component of the counting process is the notion of *one-to-one correspondence*. Two sets of things are placed in one-to-one correspondence when we associate one and only one member of each set with one and only one member of the other. That is, the elements are paired off, one with one, no member of either set is unused and no member is used more than once. We count a set of objects by placing the members of the set into one-to-one correspondence with an *ordered* set of natural number names. The set of names must be ordered; we cannot use ten before any of the names that precede it in the ordered sequence because we may not get to ten. The last number name used is called the *cardinal number* of the *set* counted.

In a very real sense when we count a set of objects we are doing both ordinal and cardinal counting. The distinction lies in *why* we count. If we count to find how many objects are in the set we are not concerned with the order in which the objects are used. This does not alter the fact that the individual objects are enumerated in *some* order. If the objects of the set are arranged in order relative to the trait that concerns us—size, value, pulchritude, or what have you—then our concern is with the position of each element relative to the remainder of the set. We have nonetheless found the ordinal number of the last element and therefore the cardinal number of the set.

Without regard to counting, when a number is used to identify an object, to set it apart from all other objects of the set to which it belongs, it is an ordinal number. An automobile license plate is one of a series, it has a position in the series. But the significant thing is that no other car has that number. The number is a means of identifying that particular object.

When first-grader Johnny learns that he rides school bus number 7 and he can identify his bus by that symbol he is using ordinal numbers intelligently. This does not require him to have the concept of a set of seven, or even that he can count by rote to seven. As we help a child develop his concept of number we should be sure that both the cardinal and the ordinal concepts are gained. Counting the number of children present, counting the lunch money, counting overcoats, the chairs in a row, the books on a library table—there are endless opportunities for cardinal counting. But there are also readily available opportunities for ordinal counting. "What day is next Friday?" counting on the calendar. "Who is third tallest in the room?" "Who is next to lightest?" "Who is fifth heaviest?" "What is the third word on line seven?" "Find page 26."

3.8 EXACT VERSUS APPROXIMATE

Numbers may be classified according to the use to which they are put in still another way. We refer to numbers as exact or approximate. This is not something inherent in the number but rather the use to which it is put. If we replace $\frac{2}{3}$ by .66 the latter is approximate, but if we decide, as we sometimes do, to use $\frac{2}{3}$ in place of the .66 then $\frac{2}{3}$ is approximate.

The nature of approximate numbers will be discussed more

thoroughly in connection with measurement. The concepts of measurement and approximate numbers should receive attention quite early in the child's school experience—right along with ordinal and cardinal counting. Just as there are numerous opportunities for counting so there are for measuring, an activity which young children enjoy. The weights and heights of the children are a part of their health records. This affords an excellent opportunity to teach some of the fundamental concepts of measurement. Let the children measure one another's height, several children measuring the same person. Varying results will be reported. There will doubtless be mistakes, but when these are eliminated there will still be error in evidence. If the activity is in the first grade the measurements will be made only to the nearest inch. The children can discover the meaning of approximate numbers by observing that children whose heights are recorded the same actually differ in height.

3.9 OTHER NUMBER CONCEPTS

The cardinal concept of number—the "how many" of a set—should include the notion of subgrouping, separating a set into other smaller sets. When the child has developed the set concept of 7 he should

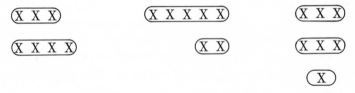

Figure 10 SUBGROUPINGS OF SEVEN.

associate the number not only with the total set but with subgroupings of 3 and 4, of 5 and 2, of 6 and 1. This concept of number is extremely important, particularly as it relates to ten. The ten concept should include the notion of sets of 9 and 1, 8 and 2, and so on. The meaning of a set of 13 should include such subgroupings as 10 and 3, 6 and 7, and 5 and 8. The subgrouping should not be limited to two; 13 should also mean to the child 2 sets of 6 and a third set of 1.

A refinement of the foregoing idea consists of subgrouping into equal sets. The concept of 12 should include the concepts of 3 sets of 4, 4 sets of 3, 2 sets of 6, and 6 sets of 2, as well as 12 sets of 1.

From the adult viewpoint there is no such thing as a concrete number. All numbers are pure abstractions, as is all of mathematics. We apply the abstractions to concrete things. When we find the cost of 3 apples at 5 cents each we do not multiply 3 apples by 5 cents, we just multiply numbers. We speak of 3 apples in recognition of the fact that the collection of apples under discussion bears a one-to-one relationship with the set of words *one, two, three.*

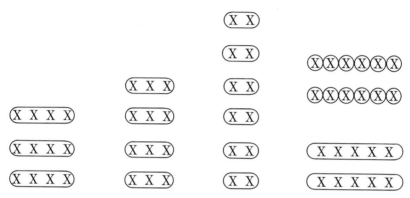

Figure 11 TWELVE AS EQUAL SETS.

It would of course be foolhardy to use the above approach with young children. Their early contacts with number should be concrete: 12 children, 6 marbles, 13 pennies, 4 ducks. The first abstraction should be an awareness of the property which is common to sets with the same number of objects, as "twelveness," that which is common to all sets of 12 whether it be ducks, pennies, marbles, children, lollipops, or ones. A further abstraction of the number concept is necessary to the mastery of elementary arithmetic. Even with the child we would not multiply apples by pennies. He must visualize 3 × 5 cents as 5¢ + 5¢ + 5¢. Granted that this is properly interpreted as the combining of three *sets* of 5 cents each, the three must be abstracted in that it originally concerned *apples*, not sets of pennies.

The idea that the multiplier indicates *how many* must be altered when we multiply fractions. The child must be led from the concrete to the abstract. He first learns that there are 4 sets of 3 marbles in

12 marbles. But he must ultimately come to the realization that 4 × 3 is equivalent to 12.

In the main, the numbers of elementary arithmetic consist of the positive whole numbers and rational fractions, ratios of whole numbers. When the child has enlarged his concept of number to include fractions *as numbers* he should be made aware of the basic difference between the original whole numbers and the enlarged set of numbers. First, he should be made aware that the original set of whole numbers are included as special kinds of fractions. For example, the new $\frac{5}{1}$ is just another symbol for five. This special kind of fraction, a whole number for numerator and 1 for denominator, gives results when added or multiplied which are consistent with the sum or product of the corresponding whole numbers. Since $5 + 2 = 7$ the sum $\frac{5}{1} + \frac{2}{1}$ must equal $\frac{7}{1}$. If this were emphasized such common mistakes as $\frac{5}{1} + \frac{2}{1} = \frac{7}{2}$ would be less frequent. Also, since $5 \times 3 = 15$, the product $\frac{5}{1} \times \frac{3}{1}$ must equal $\frac{15}{1}$.

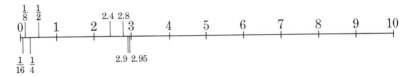

Figure 12   THERE IS A FRACTION BETWEEN ANY TWO FRACTIONS.

The fundamental difference between the enlarged set of fractions and the original set of whole numbers is characterized by the *density* property for fractions. The fact that there is no next fraction to zero, nor any other fraction for that matter, is a startling revelation when the full import of it is realized for the first time. The number line is quite useful in developing this concept. Its development is essential to a full understanding of much that is involved in measurement.

Exercises

1 Compare the 100 chart in the text with that given by Buckingham, p. 90 (see Suggested Supplementary Readings). List advantages of each.

2 List ways in which the 100 chart can be used in the primary grades.

3 Distinguish between the fact that the number system is decimal and the fact that it is positional. Which of these characteristics is essential in learning to count?

4 Contrast the counting frame with the abacus. Describe how the sum 23 + 34 is obtained on each.

5 Devise illustrations appropriate for use in the third grade of the roles which zero plays.

6 Contrast British and American custom relative to the decimal point and relative to dividing a number into periods. One billion is the larger number in which system?

7 Why is it helpful in reading a number to divide it into periods by means of commas?

8 List inconsistencies between our system of numeration and our system of notation.

9 Record for a typical day the uses to which you put numbers. List them as ordinal or cardinal.

10 Distinguish between ordinal counting and cardinal counting.

11 From the daily newspaper make a list of uses of number. Classify them as approximate or exact.

12 Are there more points on a one-inch line or a 100-mile line? Explain.

13 Identify the following number uses as cardinal or ordinal:
(a) He was born in the year 1854. ∂
(b) We work a 7-day week. ⊂
(c) UNion 3-8375 is my phone number. ○
(d) August 29 is the date. ○
(e) A class of 76 pupils is too large. ⊂
(f) You will find it on page 12. ◌
(g) What are the dates of the reign of Charles III? ○
(h) His license number is AD-173-29. ○
(i) This is a 137-page book. ∂
(j) Do you like Beethoven's Fifth Symphony? ◌

14 List six examples of numbers used as approximations and six exact uses.

15 How many unit fractions are there between zero and one? Why is there no nearest unit fraction to zero?

Suggested Supplementary Readings

Bell, Clifford, Clela D. Hammond, Robert B. Herrera, *Fundamentals of Arithmetic for Teachers.* New York: John Wiley and Sons, Inc., 1962. Pp. 16–37.

Buckingham, B. R., *Elementary Arithmetic: Its Meaning and Practice.* Boston: Ginn and Company, 1947. Pp. 3–47.

Bruckener, Leo J., and Foster E. Grossnickle, *How to Make Arithmetic Meaningful.* Philadelphia: The John C. Winston Company, 1947.

Dantzig, Tobias, *Number, the Language of Science*. New York: The Macmillan Company, 1945. Pp. 57–98.

Kasner, Edward, and James Newman, *Mathematics and the Imagination*. New York: Simon and Schuster, 1940. Pp. 27–64.

Morton, Robert L., *Teaching Children Arithmetic*. New York: Silver Burdett Company, 1953. Pp. 69–80.

Osborn, Roger, M. Vere De Vault, Claude C. Boyd, W. Robert Houston. *Extending Mathematics Understanding*. Columbus, Ohio: Charles E. Merrill Books, Inc., 1961. Pp. 12–24.

Spencer, Peter L., and Marguerite Brydegaard, *Building Mathematical Concepts in the Elementary School*. New York: Henry Holt and Company, 1952. Pp. 82–113.

Spitzer, Herbert F., *The Teaching of Arithmetic*. Third Edition, Boston: Houghton Mifflin Company, 1961. Pp. 14–54.

Stern, Catherine, *Children Discover Arithmetic*. New York: Appleton-Century-Crofts, Inc., 1951. Pp. 23–37.

Wheat, Harry G., *How to Teach Arithmetic*. Evanston: Row, Peterson and Company, 1951. Pp. 17–27.

Counting, Adding, Subtracting

CHAPTER FOUR

H ow many counting numbers are there? Why does $4 + 3 = 3 + 4$? If we count these marks $////$ and continue the count through these marks $///$ we get the same total as if we started with the set of three first and continued the count through the set of four. This can be verified by actually carrying out the count. Is this true of any two counting numbers a and b? Just what is a counting number anyway?

These are some of the questions we shall investigate in this chapter. We shall formalize the behavior of the counting numbers when they are combined by addition and the related operation subtraction. The system of numbers will be enlarged so that subtraction will always be possible. We shall approach the subject from the standpoint of sets. We say that a set *has* the number five if it contains five objects. But what *is* the number five?

4.1 ONE-TO-ONE CORRESPONDENCE

Consider the two sets of objects A = {bee, wagon, car, ship, plane} and B = {apple, banana, pear, peach, polecat}. In set A each object, also called *element*, of the set is a transportation vehicle, except the bee. Set B might be thought of as a set of fruit, but for the polecat. The elements of a set may have many properties in common which might characterize the set. For example, C = {ball, moon, ring, coin, marble} could be characterized as a set of round objects. Or D = {fire, pepper, steam, coffee, stove} might be considered a set of hot objects. But we would hardly claim that C is a round set or D a hot set. There is a difference in kind between the objects of a set and the set itself. The members of a basketball team are Tom, John, Bill, Cliff, and Algernon. The team is a set T = {Tom, John, Bill, Cliff, Algernon}, but Tom is not a basketball team. Perhaps you have known a player who thought he was the whole team. Even in the case where a set has only one element, the element and the set are not the same. Quite often the elements of a set are themselves sets. The National League is a set of baseball teams. Each team is a set of players. Suppose the teams in an independent league withdraw until only one team remains a member. The league and the one member team in the league are not the same. The league can vote itself out of existence without affecting the team. There is the story of the man who organized an exclusive club for the sole purpose of blackballing his enemies. He was the only member of the club. The club met weekly to vote on prospective members. When all of his enemies had been blackballed he killed the club, but he did not commit suicide.

All of the sets A, B, C, and T have a property in common which is independent of the nature of the individual elements. Any two of them can be placed in one-to-one correspondence. The matching

bee	wagon	plane	car	ship
↕	↕	↕	↕	↕
polecat	pear	peach	apple	banana

establishes the correspondence between set A and set B. There are of course, other pairings that could have been used. All that is necessary is a matching which corresponds each element of each set with exactly one element of the other.

We have seen that one-to-one correspondence is basic to the

counting process. This is not to say that they are synonymous. The notion of one-to-one correspondence is a more primitive concept; it is in no way dependent on the notion of counting.

If upon boarding a bus I find exactly one vacant seat and no one but me standing I know there are the same number of persons on the bus as there are seats. As passengers are picked up and discharged it is possible to determine at any time whether the number of passengers is less than, equal to, or greater than the number of seats merely by observing whether there are empty seats, all seats taken and no one standing, or all seats taken and passengers standing. The set of seats serves as a reference set. The set of passengers can be compared to it without benefit of counting or even the existence of number names.

If two sets of things can be placed into one-to-one correspondence the sets are said to have the same *cardinal number,* they are *equivalent sets.* The correspondence does not have to be done in a physical sense, nor do the members of either set necessarily have to have a physical existence. One set might be the adjectives (not the words but the ideas which they symbolize) *round, rough, black,* and *loud* while the other could be the nonsense syllables *dru, aug, tol,* and *sner.* The essential element of one-to-one correspondence is the *existence* of exactly one member of each set to pair with each member of the other. The actual pairing may be done mentally.

In case the one-to-one correspondence cannot be established, the cardinal number of that set which has members unmatched in the other set is said to be greater than the cardinal number of the other.

The sets A, B, C, and T above each *have* the cardinal number five. But what *is* the cardinal number five? It is the set of all sets that can be placed in one-to-one correspondence with set A, or B, or any other set equivalent to them. More particularly, it is the set of all sets that can be placed in one-to-one correspondence with the set {one, two, three, four, five}. Hence, it is a set of equivalent sets. It may seem a bit surprising to define the cardinal number five in this way. But we must keep in mind the fact that there is a difference in kind between the elements of a set and the set itself. Thus, sets A, B, C, and T are elements of the cardinal number five, which is itself a set of equivalent sets. Any other set that can be placed in one-to-one correspondence with the set {one, two, three, four, five} is an element of the set five. Any set which cannot be so placed in this correspondence is not an element of the set five, it does not have five as its cardinal number.

Exercises

1 How can one use a 6-foot rope to devise a one-to-one correspondence with ten sheep without cutting the rope?

2 Without resorting to any form of counting, determine which has the more letters, *California* or *Colorado*.

3 Which of the following pairs of sets has a one-to-one correspondence relationship?

(a) Husbands—wives

(b) Mothers—daughters

(c) States of the United States—United States Senators

(d) One-digit integers—two-digit integers

(e) Even integers—odd integers

(f) Months of the year—days of the week

(g) Brothers—sisters

4 In how many ways can the sets A = {chair, desk, table, lamp} and B = {shoe, tie, shirt, hat} be placed in one-to-one correspondence?

5 In Exercise 3(c) we see an example of two sets that can be placed in a one-to-two correspondence. Name another pair of sets which has this property.

4.2 COUNTING THE INFINITE

The set of numbers 1, 2, 3, 4, . . . we have called the counting numbers. They are also called the set of *natural numbers*. For all practical purposes this set is the same as the set of *positive integers* or the set of *finite cardinal numbers.*

The great Greek mathematician Archimedes, using the Greeks' cumbersome number system, succeeded in writing a number greater than the number of grains of sand which would be required to fill the universe. He was a piker, his number is puny compared to the number expressed by means of four 9s—$9^{9^{9^9}}$. The immensity of this number defies the imagination, but there are larger numbers. No matter how large a number we consider, there is always a larger one. Every counting number has a successor. This cannot be proved. The fact that we can add one to any specified number is not sufficient, for this assertion is justified only on the assumption that there is an endless succession of numbers. The fact that we cannot reach an end to counting proves nothing. Maybe we just cannot count long enough, or live long enough, to get to the end. The endlessness of the counting numbers is an *assumption* which is basic to the entire number system and to all of arithmetic. We express the idea by saying the positive whole numbers are *infinite*.

The positive even integers are also infinite. Any even integer, being an integer, must have a successor, but its successor also has a successor which is an even integer. Thus any even integer has an even integer successor.

Since only every other whole number is even can we say the infinite set of positive even integers is only half as large as the infinite set of positive integers? We have agreed that two sets have the same cardinal number if they can be placed into one-to-one correspondence. Consider the array

$$
\begin{array}{ccccccc}
1 & 2 & 3 & 4 & 5 & \ldots & n & \ldots \\
\updownarrow & \updownarrow & \updownarrow & \updownarrow & \updownarrow & & \updownarrow & \\
2 & 4 & 6 & 8 & 10 & \ldots & 2n & \ldots
\end{array}
$$

The top line consists of all positive integers and the bottom line all positive even integers. We say *all* because the three dots following the 5 mean "and so on" out to any number n, and the three dots following the n mean "and so on" endlessly. The double-pointed arrows indicate the means of pairing the elements of the two sets. Corresponding to any positive integer n of the set of positive integers we pair the positive even integer $2n$ of the set of positive even integers. Remember, we do not have to write down all the pairs. The essential thing is to show how we can match each element of each set with exactly one element of the other. Each member of the set of positive integers is paired with the even integer which is twice as large and each positive even integer is paired with the integer half as large. But how can this be, since all of the positive even integers are found among the positive integers? Can half of the positive integers be just as numerous as all the positive integers? This seeming paradox stems from the fact that we are dealing with infinite sets rather than finite. This is precisely what we need to make the distinction between finite and infinite sets. An infinite set is one which can be placed in one-to-one correspondence with a part of itself. Not just any part; we could hardly set up the correspondence between the first ten integers and all the integers. But if there exists a part such that the correspondence can be set up, we have an infinite set.

Defn ˙   If each element of set A is an element of set B, but at least one element of B is not an element of A, then A is called a *proper subset* of B. This is written $A \subset B$. The set of positive even integers is a proper subset of the set of positive integers.

Defn   *An infinite set is a set that can be placed in one-to-one correspondence with some proper subset of itself.*

Just as all finite sets that can be placed in one-to-one correspondence have the same cardinal number, so also do all infinite sets. All sets that can be placed in one-to-one correspondence with the counting numbers have the same cardinal number. Obviously, such

Defn ˙ numbers are not finite, they are called *transfinite* numbers.

4.3 DENUMERABLE INFINITY

Any infinite set which can be placed in one-to-one correspondence with the set of positive integers is said to be *denumerably* or *countably* infinite. Such sets have the transfinite cardinal number $\aleph_0$ (*aleph-null*). We can easily show the set of positive odd integers have the same cardinal number as the set of positive integers. Since the positive integers consist of the even positive integers plus the odd positive integers we must conclude

$$\aleph_0 + \aleph_0 = \aleph_0$$

The set of unit fractions, that is, fractions whose numerator is one, is countably infinite.

$$
\begin{array}{ccccccc}
1 & 2 & 3 & 4 & 5 & \cdots & n & \cdots \\
\updownarrow & \updownarrow & \updownarrow & \updownarrow & \updownarrow & & \updownarrow & \\
\frac{1}{1} & \frac{1}{2} & \frac{1}{3} & \frac{1}{4} & \frac{1}{5} & \cdots & \frac{1}{n} & \cdots
\end{array}
$$

Even if these were all the fractions between zero and one; for instance, if there were no fractions between $\frac{1}{2}$ and $\frac{1}{3}$, we would have shown there are as many fractions between the consecutive integers zero and one as there are integers. There are, however, a countably infinite number of such intervals created by the integers. Then the fractions consist of a countably infinite number of countably infinite sets. Surely there are more fractions than integers! The arithmetic of the infinite behaves rather strangely. We can show there are just as many positive integers as there are positive fractions. Consider the array:

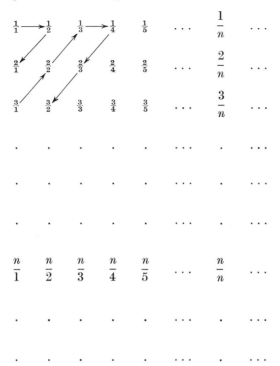

The first row contains all unit fractions, the second all possible fractions with numerator 2, and so on. In each row we use every possible denominator and in each column we use every possible numerator. If we follow the arrows we see the scheme for counting the array—for placing its elements in one-to-one correspondence with the positive integers. As we move along the arrows we drop out any fraction previously appearing as $\frac{2}{2}$, $\frac{4}{2}$, $\frac{3}{3}$, $\frac{2}{4}$. The pairing begins

1	2	3	4	5	6	7	8	9	10	11
$\updownarrow$	$\updownarrow$	$\updownarrow$	$\updownarrow$	$\updownarrow$	$\updownarrow$	$\updownarrow$	$\updownarrow$	$\updownarrow$	$\updownarrow$	$\updownarrow$
$\frac{1}{1}$	$\frac{1}{2}$	$\frac{2}{1}$	$\frac{3}{1}$	$\frac{1}{3}$	$\frac{1}{4}$	$\frac{2}{3}$	$\frac{3}{2}$	$\frac{4}{1}$	$\frac{5}{1}$	$\frac{1}{5}$

Note that the fractions do not have to be counted in order of magnitude. This would be impossible because we can show that between any two fractions there is a countable infinity of others. We merely have to display a scheme for setting up the pairs such that each member of each set is paired with one and only one member of the other.

The set of elements in each row is countably infinite, the denominators being the set of counting numbers. The set of rows is countably infinite, each counting number being used as the numerator throughout a row. Hence we must conclude that

$$\aleph_0 \cdot \aleph_0 = \aleph_0$$

Perhaps the thought has presented itself that all infinite sets have the same cardinal number. This is not the case. As we shall see, there are more real numbers between zero and one than all of the rational numbers.

Exercises

1 Show a one-to-one correspondence between the set of positive odd integers and the set of positive integers.

2 If there is a one-to-one correspondence between set A and set C and a one-to-one correspondence between set B and set C, show that there must be a one-to-one correspondence between set A and set B.

3 Prove that there are as many multiples of five as there are unit fractions.

4 Show, by means of one-to-one correspondence, which of the two sets is the greater,

$$A = \{1, 2, 3, 4, 5, 6, 7, 8, 9, 10\} \quad B = \{\tfrac{1}{1}, \tfrac{1}{3}, \tfrac{1}{5}, \tfrac{1}{7}, \tfrac{1}{11}, \tfrac{1}{13}, \tfrac{1}{17}, \tfrac{1}{19}\}.$$

5 How can one show that two infinite sets do not have the same transfinite cardinal number?

6 Show that $\aleph_0 - 10 = \aleph_0$.
Show that $\aleph_0 + 100 = \aleph_0$.

7 What does $10\aleph_0$ equal?

8 Can one say what $\aleph_0 - \aleph_0$ is equal? Why?

9 Complete the following one-to-one correspondence

$$
\begin{array}{ccccccc}
1 & \tfrac{1}{2} & \tfrac{1}{3} & \tfrac{1}{4} & \cdots & \dfrac{1}{n} & \cdots \\
\updownarrow & \updownarrow & \updownarrow & \updownarrow & & \updownarrow & \\
10 & 20 & 30 & 40 & \cdots & & \cdots
\end{array}
$$

This shows what two infinite sets have the same cardinal number?

4.4 SOME PROPERTIES OF SETS

The child's first contacts with addition consist of combining sets of concrete objects into a single set. He combines sets of pennies, sets of marbles, sets of children. This putting together of sets into a single set is a kind of abridged counting. He learns that a set of three chairs put with a set of five chairs forms a new set of eight chairs. This

result could be obtained by counting the first set and continuing to count uninterrupted through the second.

The next step is the realization that a set of five of anything combined with a set of three of the same thing yields a set of eight of the same thing. Finally, he adds numbers, $3 + 5 = 8$, without the necessity of relating the numbers to any particular object or set of objects.

One of the most difficult, yet indispensable, attributes of a skillful teacher is the ability to see the learning situation from the learner's point of view. In elementary instruction we frequently take for granted many difficult concepts underlying elementary arithmetic. When the child is made to memorize "three plus five equals eight" it is small wonder that he is merely parroting sound patterns. What does "plus" mean? What does "equals" mean? For that matter what do three, five, and eight mean?

There is the story of little Bobby, who could not learn to add problems involving "carrying." The teacher had exhausted her resources and was ready to give up when Bill volunteered "Let me try to show him." The teacher left Bobby and Bill to their own devices in a corner by themselves. In short order Bobby was all smiles—he had caught on. The teacher in amazement asked Bill what he did. Bill's reply: "Well, you know where you told us to carry, I just told him to tote it." There is a valuable lesson in this feeble joke. We should never assume that as a matter of course our words convey the intended adult meaning to the child. We are prone to think the words "numerator" and "denominator" could hardly be more descriptive of their correct mathematical interpretation. Quite true, from the adult standpoint. But what about the child? "Numeration" and "denomination" may not be in his vocabulary, and if they are their meanings are probably quite hazy.

It is well that we inquire into some of the most obvious, and therefore most obscure, concepts which the child is expected to develop in arithmetic. We shall attack them from an adult abstract point of view, not that the approach is recommended for children, but so that you the teacher may have a fuller grasp and deeper appreciation of what is involved.

Two sets of objects sometimes have elements in common. We noted that each element of the proper subset $\{2, 4, 6, \ldots 2n, \ldots\}$ of the set of counting numbers $\{1, 2, 3, 4, \ldots n, \ldots\}$ is also an element of the latter. It is possible for two sets to have elements in common even though neither is a proper subset of the other. The Jones family is a set of persons $J = \{$Mr. Jones, Mrs. Jones, Tom Jones, Jim Jones, Mary Jones$\}$. The Jones boys play on a basketball team, another set of persons, $T = \{$Bill Smith, Tom Jones, John Brown, Jim Jones, Sidney Throgmorton$\}$. The two sets J and T have two elements in common, Tom Jones and Jim Jones. But $\{$Tom Jones, Jim Jones$\}$ is also a set. It is called the *intersection* of T and J.

The intersection of two sets A and B is the set whose elements are those elements that are common to sets A and B. This is written $A \cap B$, it is read "A intersection B" or "A cap B."

Another set which can be determined from two given sets is the set consisting of those elements which are members of either of the two original sets. This is called the *union* of two sets. The union of sets A and B is written $A \cup B$, and read "A union B" or "A cup B."

$T \cup J = \{$Bill Smith, Mr. Jones, Mrs. Jones, John Brown, Jim Jones, Tom Jones, Sidney Throgmorton, Mary Jones$\}$

It is not at all necessary that two sets have any elements in common. No positive integer can be both even and odd. The set of even positive integers $E = \{2, 4, 6, \ldots 2n, \ldots\}$ and the set of odd positive integers $O = \{1, 3, 5, \ldots 2n - 1, \ldots\}$ have no elements in common. Must we say the intersection $E \cap O$ does not exist? The concept of a set that has no elements has proven to be useful. Such a set is called the *empty set* or the *null* set; the symbol for the null set is ϕ. In set symbols, we have $\phi = \{\ \}$. Two sets that have no elements in common are called *disjoint sets*. Their intersection is the null set.

$$E \cap O = \phi$$

Venn diagrams are frequently helpful in visualizing relationships between sets. If we let the points within a circle represent the elements of a set, the points lying in either or both of two circles represent the union of the corresponding sets. The overlap, the points common to the two circles, represents their intersection. In figures (*b*) and (*e*)

$B \subset A$. In figures (c) and (f) A and B are disjoint, and in figure (f) we have $A \cap B = \phi$.

We have said that every set, finite or infinite, *has* a cardinal number, and each cardinal number *is* a set of equivalent sets. What about the null set ϕ? We did not include zero in the set of natural numbers, but it is a cardinal number. It is the cardinal number of the null set. Here we must be careful to observe the distinction between a set with one element $\{a\}$ and that one element a. The cardinal number 0 is the set of sets equivalent to the null set. But there is just one null set. The set of women Presidents of the United States is the

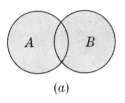 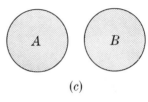

$\quad\quad$ (a) $\quad\quad\quad\quad\quad\quad$ (b) $\quad\quad\quad\quad\quad\quad$ (c)

Shaded Area is $A \cup B$

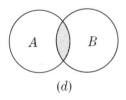 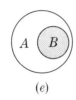 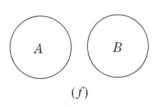

$\quad\quad$ (d) $\quad\quad\quad\quad\quad\quad$ (e) $\quad\quad\quad\quad\quad\quad$ (f)

Shaded Area is $A \cap B$

same as the set of men twenty-feet tall, that is, the null set. The set ϕ is zero. In this one case we define the cardinal number of the set as the set itself, $0 = \phi$. The set whose single element is the set ϕ has the cardinal number 1. But the cardinal number 1 *is* the set of equivalent sets of which $\{0\}$ may be considered a representative element. That is, $\{0\}$ is not the null set, $\{0\}$ is a set with one element. This one element happens to be the cardinal number 0.

$\quad\quad$ Since $\{1, 2, 3\}$ is an element of the set of equivalent sets which is the cardinal number 3, are we guilty of circular defining? Is the cardinal number 3 an element of an element of itself? Here again it is imperative that we keep before us the distinction in kind between a set and its elements. It is true that 1, 2, and 3 are cardinal numbers; but $\{1, 2, 3\}$ is a *set of* cardinal numbers, a different kind of object.

$\quad\quad$ It is possible to select, as representative element of a set of equivalent sets, a set constructed from ϕ as follows:

$0 = \phi$; zero is by definition the null set.
$1 = \{\phi\} = \{0\}$; a set with one element.
$2 = \{\phi, \{\phi\}\} = \{0, 1\}$; a set with two elements.
$3 = \{\phi, \{\phi\}, \{\phi, \{\phi\}\}\} = \{0, 1, 2\}$; a set with three elements.

$4 = \Big(\phi, \{\phi\}, \{\phi, \{\phi\}\}, \{\phi, \{\phi\}, \{\phi, \{\phi\}\}\}\Big) = \{0, 1, 2, 3\}$; a set with four elements.

Evidently this process may be continued indefinitely, each representative set having one more element then its predecessor, that element being the predecessor. Thus, it is possible to represent each cardinal number after zero as the *set* of cardinal numbers preceding it.

A word about symbols. You will note that we have used capital letters to name sets, set A, set B, set T, and so on. We have also indicated a set by enclosing its elements in braces { }. Thus the set whose elements are the numbers 1, 2, and 3 is $\{1, 2, 3\}$. The order in which the elements are listed is of no consequence whatever, $\{1, 2, 3\}$, $\{3, 1, 2\}$, $\{2, 1, 3\}$ are merely three ways to indicate the same set.

Exercises

1 If $A = \{1, 2, 3, 4, 5, 6, 7, 8, 9, 10\}$ and $B = \{2, 4, 6, 8, 10, 12, 14\}$ find $A \cap B$ and $A \cup B$.

2 If $C = \{\text{cat, dog, bird, rabbit}\}$ list as many proper subsets of C as you can. (There are 15.)

3 Is the null set a proper subset of any other set? Is it a proper subset of itself?

4 Name three elements of the cardinal number three.

5 Is the cardinal number 1 an element of itself? Explain.

6 Distinguish between $A = \{1, 2, 3, 4, 5\}$ and $B = \Big(\{1, 2, 3\}, \{4, 5\}\Big)$.

7 Distinguish between $C = \{1, 2, 3, 4\}$ and $D = \{\frac{1}{2}, \frac{3}{4}\}$.

8 If $A = \{\text{apple, orange, egg}\}$ and $B = \{\text{fire, skillet, egg}\}$ what is the cardinal number of A? of B? of $A \cap B$? of $A \cup B$?

9 If $A = \{1, 2, 3, 4, 5\}$ and $B = \{1, 2, 3, 4\}$ what is the cardinal number of A? of B? of $A \cap B$? of $A \cup B$?

10 If $A = \{\text{Tom, Dick, Harry}\}$ and $B = \{\text{Bill, George, Sam, Mike}\}$ what is the cardinal number of A? of B? of $A \cap B$? of $A \cup B$?

11 If $A = \{13, 2, 7, 11\}$ and $B = \{5, 3, 17\}$ what is $A \cup B$? What is $B \cap A$?

12 If $A = \{16, 5, 19, 23\}$ and $B = \{22, 16, 8, 5\}$ what is $A \cup B$? What is $B \cup A$?

4.5 RELATIONS

We have said that two sets are equivalent if they can be placed in one-to-one correspondence. However, two sets are called *equal sets* if they have exactly the same elements. The sets $A = \{2, 1, 3\}$ and $B = \{ball, bat, glove\}$ are equivalent. But set $C = \{all\ one\ digit\ finite\ cardinal\ numbers\}$ and $D = \{0, 1, 2, 3, 4, 5, 6, 7, 8, 9\}$ are equal sets.

Sets A and B are equal in the sense that they have the same number of elements; they have the same cardinal number. Evidently, we use "equal" in a variety of ways. How is it used when we say set $A = \{2, 1, 3\}$? We would express the same idea if we said set A *is* $\{2, 1, 3\}$.

The assertion that two things are equal is an assertion that a particular kind of relationship exists between them. Two things may be related in many different ways. Tom and Jim may have the "brother of" relation, the "father of" relation, or the "cousin of" relation. There are other relations beside that of blood kinship, such as "prettier than," "next to," "a part of," "in love with," *ad infinitum*. Some of the relations which may exist between mathematical objects are "is equal to," "is greater than," "implies," "is similar to." We adopt symbols to indicate each kind of relation. For instance, if a and b are two mathematical elements (not necessarily numbers) the above relations between the two are indicated respectively $a = b$, $a > b$, $a \to b$, $a \sim b$. In general, if we wish to show a relation existing between a and b without specifying what the relation is we write $a\ R\ b$.

If a relation has the following properties it is called an *equivalence relation:*

Reflexive, or $a\ R\ a$.
Symmetric, or if $a\ R\ b$, then $b\ R\ a$.
Transitive, or if $a\ R\ b$ and $b\ R\ c$, then $a\ R\ c$.

A relation is reflexive if an element bears the relationship to itself. For example, the relation "knows the name of," applied to most people, is reflexive. This merely means that most people know their own names.

A symmetric relation is one such that if one element is related to a second then the second is related to the first in the same way. The above relation is not symmetric. Tom may know Joe's name without

Joe knowing Tom's. But "kin to" is symmetric. If Tom is kin to Joe, then Joe is kin to Tom.

A transitive relation is one such that, if the first element is related to a second and the second bears the same relation to a third, then the first bears this relation to the third. "Kin to" is not transitive. Tom may be Joe's cousin because their fathers are brothers and Joe may be Jim's cousin because their mothers are sisters. But this does not make Tom kin to Jim. "Taller than" is transitive. If Tom is taller than Joe and Joe is taller than Jim, then Tom is taller than Jim.

Consider the relation among people "in love with." This is reflexive, or at least the Bible assumes so in stating the Golden Rule. Many a heartbroken swain knows it is not symmetric for all people. Nor is it transitive, although some people of the "love me, love my dog" persuasion seem to think so.

Relative to the set of male persons, "brother of" is symmetric and transitive but not reflexive. It is transitive because if Tom is Bill's brother and Bill is Jim's brother then Tom is Jim's brother. It is symmetric because if Tom is Bill's brother, then Bill is Tom's brother. It is not reflexive, Tom is not Tom's brother, even though he is Tom's brother's brother.

The mathematical relation "greater than" applied to integers is transitive but not symmetric or reflexive. $10 > 8$ and $8 > 3$, therefore $10 > 3$. But 10 is not greater than 10, nor does $10 > 7$ imply that $7 > 10$. "Is an integral factor of" is reflexive (any number is a factor of itself) and transitive (3 a factor of 12 and 12 a factor of 36 implies 3 a factor of 36). But it is not symmetric (5 a factor of 15 does not imply 15 a factor of 5).

The relation "implies" applied to propositions is reflexive. $a \to a$ simply means that the truth of proposition a implies the truth of proposition a. But it is not symmetric. If $a \to b$ it does not necessarily follow that $b \to a$. For example (a—a number ends in 5) $\to$ (b—the number is a multiple of 5) but (b—a number is a multiple of 5) $\not\to$ (a—the number ends in 5). Thirty is a multiple of 5 but it ends in zero. [The sign $\not\to$ means "does not imply."] The fact that "implies" is transitive is a basic principle of logic. If the truth of proposition a implies the truth of b and the truth of b implies the truth of c we accept without hesitation that the truth of a implies the truth of c. If we wish to indicate that a symmetric relation does exist between two *particular* propositions a, b we indicate this by $a \rightleftarrows b$. In this case the two propositions are *logically equivalent*.

"Equal to" applied to the set of cardinal numbers is an equivalence relation.

It is reflexive: any number is equal to itself.

It is symmetric: if $3 + 2 = 5$ then $5 = 3 + 2$.

We express this by saying the equality sign can be read in either direction.

It is transitive: if $4 + 3 = 7$ and $7 = 5 + 2$ then $4 + 3 = 5 + 2$.

We might take the position that a relation which is reflexive, symmetric, and transitive is by definition the relation "equal." But there are other equivalence relations. Similarity of geometric figures is reflexive, symmetric, and transitive. We could think of similarity as a kind of equality—"equal" shape. Congruency used in the geometric sense (the word is also used in other mathematical contexts) is also an equivalence relation. As its symbol $\cong$ indicates, we have "equal" shape and area. *Equivalence* is the more general term which includes *equal* as equivalence in the numerical sense. Two numerical expressions are equal if they are two ways of saying the same thing: $2 + 3$, 5, $6 - 1$ are three ways of representing the same numerical quantity.

Equivalence of sets is reflexive—a set may be placed in one-to-one correspondence with itself.

Equivalence of sets is symmetric—when set A is in one-to-one correspondence with set B then set B is also in one-to-one correspondence with set A.

Equivalence of sets is also transitive.

Let set $A = \{a_1, a_2, a_3, \ldots a_n\}$
and set $B = \{b_1, b_2, b_3, \ldots b_n\}$
with the correspondence

$$
\begin{array}{ccccc}
a_1 & a_2 & a_3 & \cdots & a_n \\
\updownarrow & \updownarrow & \updownarrow & & \updownarrow \\
b_1 & b_2 & b_3 & \cdots & b_n
\end{array}
$$

Also set $B = \{b_1, b_2, b_3, \ldots b_n\}$
and set $C = \{c_1, c_2, c_3, \ldots c_n\}$
with the correspondence

$$
\begin{array}{cccc}
b_i & b_j & \cdots & b_x \\
\updownarrow & \updownarrow & & \updownarrow \\
c_1 & c_2 & \cdots & c_n
\end{array}
$$

where the subscripts $i, j, \ldots x$ indicate some order of the elements of the set B, not necessarily the order $b_1, b_2, \ldots b_n$. We can now obtain the correspondence between A and C as follows. Match a_1 with the

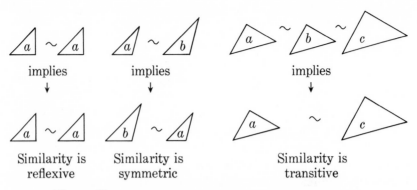

Figure 13 SIMILARITY IS AN EQUIVALENCE RELATION.

element of C that is matched with b_1, match a_2 with the element of C that is matched with b_2, and so on.

EXAMPLE. $\quad A = \{1, 3, 5, 7, 9\}$
$\qquad\qquad\quad B = \{8, 13, 12, 4, 6\}$

A one-to-one correspondence between A and B is

$$
\begin{array}{ccccc}
1 & 3 & 5 & 7 & 9 \quad \text{(elements of } A) \\
\updownarrow & \updownarrow & \updownarrow & \updownarrow & \updownarrow \\
8 & 13 & 12 & 4 & 6 \quad \text{(elements of } B)
\end{array}
$$

$$C = \{12, 3, 6, 2, 7\}$$

A one-to-one correspondence between B and C is

$$
\begin{array}{ccccc}
4 & 6 & 8 & 12 & 13 \quad \text{(elements of } B) \\
\updownarrow & \updownarrow & \updownarrow & \updownarrow & \updownarrow \\
12 & 3 & 6 & 2 & 7 \quad \text{(elements of } C)
\end{array}
$$

This gives the following one-to-one correspondence between A and C:

$$
\begin{array}{ccccc}
1 & 3 & 5 & 7 & 9 \quad \text{(elements of } A) \\
\updownarrow & \updownarrow & \updownarrow & \updownarrow & \updownarrow \\
6 & 7 & 2 & 12 & 3 \quad \text{(elements of } C)
\end{array}
$$

Hence equivalence of sets is an equivalence relation. Equality of sets is also an equivalence relation. Here equality is used to mean *identically the same*.

Exercises

1 State which of the properties, *reflexive, symmetric,* and *transitive,* the following relations possess:
(a) "Is the father of" applied to people
(b) "Is the brother of" applied to people

5 , T

(c) "Is the brother of" applied to male people

(d) "Is the cousin of" applied to people

(e) "Is stronger than" (on the basis of scores) applied to football teams

(f) "Is acquainted with" applied to people

(g) "Is north of" applied to locations on the earth

(h) "Is east of" applied to locations on the earth, North and South Poles excluded

(i) "Is one half of" applied to line segments

(j) "Is perpendicular to" applied to lines in space

(k) "Lives in the house with" applied to people

(l) "Is the ancestor of" applied to people

(m) "Is less than" applied to integers

(n) "Is not equal to" applied to integers

2 Use the sets $A = \{$corn, potatoes, wheat, hogs$\}$ and $B = \{$apples, oranges, prunes, people$\}$ and the sets $B = \{$oranges, people, prunes, apples$\}$ and $C = \{$Jones, Smith, Brown, Roberts$\}$ to show equivalence of sets is transitive. Use the elements in the given order to establish the one-to-one correspondence between A and B and between B and C.

3 Give an example of a relation which has the reflexive, but not the symmetric or transitive properties.

4 Give an example of a relation which has the reflexive and transitive, but not the symmetric properties.

5 Give an example of a transitive, but not symmetric or reflexive, relation.

6 What property or properties do each of the following illustrate?

(a) If $8 + 4 = 12$ then $12 = 8 + 4$.

(b) If $6 > 3$ and $3 > 1$ then $6 > 1$.

(c) "A rose is a rose is a rose ..."

(d) $x + y = x + y$.

(e) Jim is taller than Betty, Betty is prettier than Bob, so Jim is smarter than Bob. (Answer—none).

(f) Jim and Bob are brothers because Jim is Tom's brother and Tom is Bob's brother.

(g) $2 + 3 = 5$ and $105 - 100 = 5$, therefore $2 + 3 = 105 - 100$.

(h) Jim is the brother of Bob and Bob is the brother of Mary, therefore Mary is the brother of Jim. (What is wrong here? what property is present and what property is not?)

4.6 ADDITION OF CARDINAL NUMBERS

We are now able to state formally what the addition of two cardinal numbers means. Consider two disjoint sets A, with cardinal number

a, and B, with cardinal number b. By $a + b$ we mean the cardinal number of the set $A \cup B$. Notice carefully the requirement that A and B are disjoint. If $P = \{$Smith, Jones, Brown$\}$ and $R = \{$Johnson, Jones, Jensen$\}$, then $P \cup R = \{$Smith, Jones, Brown, Johnson, Jensen$\}$. P and R are not disjoint since $P \cap R = \{$Jones$\}$. The cardinal number of P is 3, the cardinal number of R is 3. But the cardinal number of $P \cup R$ is 5, not $3 + 3$.

It seems that the child who holds up three fingers on one hand and four on the other, then counts the fingers to find $3 + 4$ knows more about addition than does the teacher who censures him!

We have observed that the order in which the elements of a set are named is of no consequence, $\{2, 4, 6\} = \{6, 2, 4\}$. Evidently $A \cup B = B \cup A$, since in either case the identity of the elements is our only concern. If $A = \{3, 5, 7, 8\}$ and $B = \{9, 6, 12\}$ then $A \cup B = \{3, 5, 7, 8, 9, 6, 12\}$ and $B \cup A = \{9, 6, 12, 3, 5, 7, 8\}$ but in either case the elements are 3, 5, 6, 7, 8, 9, and 12, and the order in which they are arranged is immaterial. Since $A \cup B = B \cup A$ the cardinal number of $A \cup B$ must be the same as the cardinal number of $B \cup A$. We conclude that for any two cardinal numbers a and b,

$$a + b = b + a$$

This is known as the *commutative property*. The cardinal numbers are commutative with respect to addition. Under the usual interpretation of addition, $a + b$ and $b + a$ are not identical, $12 + 7$ means we start with 12 and add 7 to it, but $7 + 12$ means we start with 7 and add 12 to it. In 50 years a one year old will be 51, but in one year a 50 year old will be 51. Hardly the same situation. When we say that addition is a commutative operation we merely mean that the end result is the same whether we add b to a on the one hand or a to b on the other.

Union is a binary operation, that is, an operation involving two sets. However, we can find the union of more than two sets, $A \cup B \cup C$, by finding the union of A and B then finding the union of this result with C, $(A \cup B) \cup C$. Since $A \cup B$ is the set of all elements in A or B or both, the union of $A \cup B$ with C is the set of all elements in any one or more of the sets A, B, and C. We reach the same conclusion relative to $A \cup (B \cup C)$. Since $(A \cup B) \cup C = A \cup (B \cup C)$ we know the two sets have the same cardinal number. If A, B, and C are disjoint, that is, no element is common to any two of them, and the cardinal number of A is a, of B is b, and of C is c, we have

$$(a + b) + c = a + (b + c)$$

This is the *associative property*.

$$(3 + 6) + 8 = 3 + (6 + 8)$$

On the left we are required to find $3 + 6 = 9$ then $9 + 8 = 17$. On the right we must find $6 + 8 = 14$ then $3 + 14 = 17$. By the associative property, for any three (not necessarily different) cardinal numbers the end result is unaltered whether we add the first and second and to this sum add the third, or on the other hand, add the sum of the second and third to the first.

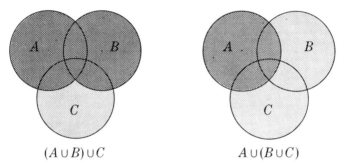

$(A \cup B) \cup C$ $A \cup (B \cup C)$

Since the null set ϕ has no elements, its union with any set A will consist of the elements of A.

$$A \cup \phi = A, \text{ for any set } A.$$

Furthermore, since ϕ has no elements it has no elements in common with any set. Hence ϕ and any set A are disjoint. Since the cardinal number of ϕ is 0, if the cardinal number of A is a we have

$$a + 0 = a, \text{ for any cardinal number } a.$$

Zero is the *addition identity element.* Adding 0 to any number a leaves a unchanged.

Is there any assurance that the sum of two counting numbers a and b is always a counting number? The assumption, stated on page 94, that every counting number has a successor establishes the existence of $a + 1$, the successor of a. But $a + 1$ has a successor $a + 1 + 1$, and $a + 1 + 1$ has a successor $a + 1 + 1 + 1$. Since b is finite, if we apply the successor principle b times we have the counting number $a + b$. This is equivalent to the proposition that if A and B are finite sets, $A \cup B$ is a finite set. This seems reasonable. If, to the contrary, $A \cup B$ is an infinite set it has an infinite proper subset C. But C includes at most a proper subset of at least one of the sets A and B. Now C, being infinite, has an infinite proper subset D. D includes at most a proper subset of at least one of the two disjoint subsets of C obtained from A and from B. If this process is continued, since both sets A and B are finite, one of them will ultimately be exhausted. We will then be in the awkward position of claiming an infinite set is a proper subset of some finite set.

The fact that, if a and b are counting numbers, $a + b$ is a counting number is the *closure* property. The counting numbers are closed with respect to addition. A set is closed with respect to an operation if and only if the operation on members of the set *always* produces a member of the set. The set of odd numbers is not closed with respect to addition because the sum of two odd numbers is not an odd number, $3 + 5 = 8$, an even number. However, the set of odd numbers is closed with respect to multiplication, the product of two odd numbers is invariably an odd number. For example, $3 \times 7 = 21$, 3 and 7 are odd numbers and so is the product 21.

To summarize, the cardinal numbers (natural numbers and zero) are governed by the following principles:

1. *Closure:* If a and b are cardinal numbers, $a + b$ is a cardinal number.
2. *Commutativity:* $a + b = b + a$
3. *Associativity:* $(a + b) + c = a + (b + c)$
4. *Identity:* $a + 0 = a$

Exercises

1 In which of the following is the set closed with respect to the operation? If not closed illustrate.
(a) The set of counting numbers with respect to division.
(b) The set of odd counting numbers with respect to subtraction.
(c) The set of counting numbers with respect to subtraction.
(d) The set of one digit counting numbers with respect to addition.
(e) The set of English words with respect to rearrangement of letters.

2 Which of the following is commutative?
(a) 12, 4—operation division.
(b) Read the morning paper, eat breakfast—operation "and then."
(c) 3, 5—operation multiplication.
(d) Put on shirt, put on shoes—operation "and then."

(e) 8, 6—operation subtraction.

(f) Put on coat, put on shirt—operation "and then."

3 Which of the following pairs of expressions are equal?

(a) $(12 - 5) - 1$ and $12 - (5 - 1)$

(b) $(5 + 3) - 2$ and $5 + (3 - 2)$

(c) $(3 \times 4) \times 5$ and $3 \times (4 \times 5)$

(d) $(12 \div 4) \div 2$ and $12 \div (4 \div 2)$

(e) $(9 - 6) + 3$ and $9 - (6 + 3)$

4 (a) If A is any non-empty set what is $A \cap A$? $A \cup A$?

(b) If A is any non-empty set and ϕ is the empty set what is $A \cap \phi$? $A \cup \phi$?

(c) Show that $\phi \cap \phi = \phi \cup \phi = \phi$.

(d) Justify the assertion that $\phi \cup \phi$ is the union of disjoint sets.

(e) Use (c) and (d) above to justify the equation $0 + 0 = 0$.

5 Does multiplication have an identity element? If so, what is it?

4.7 INVERSE OPERATIONS

The concept of *inverse* is an extremely important one in mathematics. Two operations are inverses if either one "undoes" the other. "What goes up must come down." Sometimes things like prices take quite a while. But something that has "gone down the drain" seldom comes back up. There is nothing inherent in the nature of things that requires the universal existence of an inverse. If operation A is the inverse of operation B, then B is also the inverse of A. This implies that either one may occur first and that the application of the other counteracts it.

The acts of starting and stopping an automobile are inverses. If the automobile is running, stopping it, then starting it, leaves it in its original state—running. If the motor is not running starting it, then stopping it, leaves it in its original state. On the other hand, in spite of the fact that it won't stay cut, cutting the grass does not have an inverse; one cannot "uncut" the grass. Going to sleep and waking up are inverses except that it would hardly be correct to assert that the person's condition is unchanged after a good night's sleep.

A really good analogy to inverse mathematical operations would involve two elements, that is, a binary operation. If we could unscramble our breakfast eggs this and scrambling the eggs would illustrate inverse operations nicely. Getting married illustrates the idea. The two "elements," single people, are "combined" into one married couple. As an aside we note that we do not have closure here, the resulting couple is not an element of the set of single people. The inverse, divorce, returns us to the original state at least to the extent that we then have two single people again. Yes, either operation may occur first. Married couples have been known to get divorced and then remarry. Even so, this is still not a perfect analogy to mathematical inverses. Two single persons do not have the choice of getting divorced, then getting married. Nor can we say that *any* two elements of the set of single people may be "combined" in marriage. If we go along with the numerologists this would be equivalent to combining an odd (male) number with an even (female) number. If marriage means plus the result is always odd (male), but if it means times the result is even (female). Let us let the numerologists worry about it!

4.8 THE INVERSE OF ADDITION

We have said in a vague sort of way that two operations are inverse if either "undoes" the other. By definition, subtraction is the inverse of addition. This means that if we add a number, then subtract the same number, the result is the original number:

$$12 + 3 = 15, \qquad 15 - 3 = 12$$

We define subtraction by means of the pair of equations

$$a - b = x \text{ if and only if } x + b = a$$

Hence $15 - 3 = 12$ because $12 + 3 = 15$. In words we are saying the difference, $a - b$, is whatever we must add to b to get a. If we substitute the value of x that is, $a - b$ from the first equation in the second we get

$$a - b + b = a \tag{4.1}$$

If we subtract b from a, then add b to the result, we obtain the original a.

Suppose we add b first, then subtract

$$a + b - b = x \tag{4.2}$$

We may think of this as subtracting the number b from the number $(a + b)$. Then by the definition of subtraction we have $(a + b) - b = x$ implies that $x + b = (a + b)$, now, subtract b from both sides and we get $x = a$. Substituting this in the first equation, we have $a + b - b = a$. Thus, whether we add b then subtract it, Equation (4.2), or subtract b and then add it, Equation (4.1), the end result is the original a.

In addition the two numbers added are called *addends* and the result the *sum*. When we subtract we are in a sense starting with a sum and taking away one of the addends. We call the original sum the *minuend*, the addend which we take away the *subtrahend*, and the remaining addend the *remainder* or the *difference*. Thus, in $a - b = x$ the minuend is a, the subtrahend is b, and the remainder is x.

4.9 NEGATIVE NUMBERS

We have defined subtraction *in terms of* addition. Regardless of how we define addition the definition of subtraction stands: It is the inverse of whatever addition means. Then obviously our *interpretation* of subtraction must depend upon what the basic operation addition means.

We have shown that it makes no difference which operation is performed first if we are to perform both addition and subtraction with the same element. However, it does not follow that we can combine any two elements by either or both operations. Suppose we are working with the set of positive whole numbers. We grant that we can always add any two of them. Having done so, we can subtract either addend from the sum. In this sense the inverse is always possible. We can undo what we have done. However, we know that we cannot always perform the undoing operation with any two elements. We have said that $a - b = x$ if and only if $x + b = a$. Now there may not be any number x which we can add to b and get a. We know from experience with positive whole numbers that there can be an x only if b is less than a. There is no positive whole number which we can add to 5 and get the sum 3. Hence $3 - 5$ is meaningless in the set of positive whole numbers.

We wish to enlarge the set of numbers so that subtraction will always be possible. To this end, we create the set of negative integers.

DEFINITION. If a is any positive integer, $-a$ is a negative integer such that
$$a + {-a} = 0$$

The set of integers is composed of the positive integers, zero, and the negative integers. By definition -5 is an integer which can be added to 5 to get the sum 0, the addition identity. Any two numbers whose sum is the addition identity are *additive inverse* numbers. Every integer has an additive inverse. The inverse of 3 is -3 because $3 + -3 = 0$. The inverse of -7 is 7 because $-7 + 7 = 0$. The inverse of 0 is 0 because $0 + 0 = 0$. In the above definition we used a to indicate a positive integer. If we let a be any integer, its additive inverse is $-a$. If $a = -5$ then $-a = -(-5)$. But the inverse of -5 is 5, hence $-(-5) = 5$.

The motive for creating negative numbers was to make subtraction always possible. This is accomplished because subtracting a number can be shown equivalent to adding its additive inverse. We wish to show

$$a - b = a + -b$$

If we add b to each side of the equation we have

$$a - b + b = a + -b + b$$
$$a = a + 0$$
$$a = a$$

The left side is equal a because we have both added and subtracted b, inverse operations. The right side is $a + 0$ because $-b + b = 0$, inverse elements.

This is all very well, but how much is $3 - 5$? If we add the inverse of 5 rather than subtract 5 we have $3 + -5$. Evidently, in order for this to be any help we must find out how to add integers when negative integers are involved. Since we have agreed that addition of positive integers means the combining of sets we can define the addition of negative numbers by stating what it means in terms of addition or subtraction (if subtraction is possible) of positive integers.

There are three cases to consider. If a and b are positive whole numbers then we have $a + (-b)$, $(-a) + b$, and $(-a) + (-b)$ as the three possibilities involving addition of negative numbers. When we select our definitions we must be sure the result satisfies the properties of the cardinal numbers. We can adopt a slightly different point of view. We shall *assume* that the set of integers has these properties and prove that addition of negative numbers means what it does as a consequence.

In either event, the definitions must be such that $a + (-b) = (-b) + a$ since the second of the three cases might just as well have been written $(-b) + a$ and since the commutative property must hold.

Consider the first case,

$a + (-b) = x$, if we add b to both sides we get
$a + (-b) + b = x + b$, but since $(-b) + b = 0$
$a = x + b$

This last equation is the condition on x which makes it equal to $a - b$. Then if $a - b$ exists $a + (-b) = a - b$. And $a - b$ does exist if a is greater than b. Hence, Rule

I. $a + (-b) = (-b) + a = a - b$ if a is greater than b.

EXAMPLE. $5 + -2 = 5 - 2 = 3$
$10 + -8 = 10 - 8 = 2$

Notice that this is merely what we have already shown, subtraction is equivalent to addition of the additive inverse. Suppose a is less than b. Then to

$a + -b = x$ we add $-a + b$
$a + -b + -a + b = x + -a + b$

and since addition is commutative

$a + -a + b + -b = x + -a + b$
$0 = x + -a + b$

Thus, x is the additive inverse or *negative* of $b + (-a)$. But by Rule I if b is greater than a, $b + (-a) = b - a$. Hence x is the negative of $(b - a)$, or $-(b - a)$ and we have Rule

II. $a + (-b) = (-b) + a = -(b - a)$ if b is greater than a.

EXAMPLE. $2 - 5 = -(5 - 2) = -3$
$9 - 10 = -(10 - 9) = -1$
$6 - 100 = -(100 - 6) = -94$

Now consider the third case $(-a) + (-b)$. If to

$(-a) + (-b) = x$ we add $a + b$ we get
$(-a) + (-b) + a + b = x + a + b$,

and since addition is commutative

$a + (-a) + b + (-b) = x + a + b$
$0 = x + a + b$.

Here x is the additive inverse or *negative* of $(a + b)$, it is $-(a + b)$. Hence, Rule

III. $(-a) + (-b) = -(a + b)$.

EXAMPLE. $(-5) + (-6) = -(5 + 6) = -11$
$(-8) + (-3) = -(8 + 3) = -11$

Now let us consider the question: Does this extension of the integers make it possible to subtract any two positive integers? Let a, b, be any two positive integers such that b is greater than a. (We know we can subtract if a is greater than or equal to b.)

$$a - b = x \text{ if and only if}$$
$$b + x = a$$

Add $(-b)$ to both sides and we get

$$b + (-b) + x = a + (-b)$$
$$x = a + (-b)$$

But by Rule II $a + (-b) = -(b - a)$. Substituting this in the original equation we get

$$a - b = -(b - a).$$

This shows that we can now subtract any two positive integers. But can we subtract any two integers? If the two integers are equal their difference is zero. We know that $a - a = 0$ because $a + 0 = a$. We may show that $(-a) - (-a) = 0$ as follows:

Let $(-a) - (-a) = x$
then if we apply the definition of subtraction, $(-a) + x = -a$
and adding a to both sides
$a + (-a) + x = a + (-a)$
$0 + x = 0$
$x = 0$

Then we have the following cases to consider, a and b different:

$a - b = a + (-b)$ because by the definition of subtraction we must have

$$b + [a + (-b)] = a, \text{ but}$$
$$b + [a + (-b)] = (b + a) + (-b)$$
$$= (a + b) + (-b)$$
$$= a + [b + (-b)]$$
$$= a + 0$$
$$= a$$

$a - (-b) = a + b$ because by the definition of subtraction we must have

$$-b + (a + b) = a. \quad \text{But}$$
$$-b + (a + b) = (-b + a) + b$$
$$= [a + (-b)] + b$$
$$= a + [(-b) + b]$$
$$= a + 0$$
$$= a$$

$(-a) - b = (-a) + (-b)$ because by the definition of subtraction we must have

$$b + [(-a) + (-b)] = (-a). \quad \text{But}$$
$$b + [(-a) + (-b)] = [b + (-a)] + -b$$
$$= [-a + b] + (-b)$$
$$= -a + [(-b) + b]$$
$$= -a + 0$$
$$= -a$$

$(-a) - (-b) = (-a) + b$ because by the definition of subtraction we must have

$$(-b) + [(-a) + b] = -a. \quad \text{But}$$
$$-b + [-a + b] = [(-b) + (-a)] + b$$
$$= [-a + (-b)] + b$$
$$= -a + [(-b) + b]$$
$$= -a + 0$$
$$= -a$$

We have applied the definition of subtraction and shown that we can always subtract any two integers because we can always add any two integers. We have not only shown that we can always subtract, we have also shown that *we never have to*. Two integers a and $-a$ are *inverse elements* under both *addition* and *subtraction*. The four equations above show us that we can add the inverse rather than subtract. We can also of course subtract the inverse rather than add. In other words, we can replace either operation, addition or subtraction, by the other if we also replace the number (to be added or subtracted) by its inverse.

We illustrate the addition and subtraction of negative numbers with the following examples:

Add $12 + (-7)$. Since 12 is greater than 7 we apply Rule I. $12 + (-7) = 12 - 7 = 5$.

Add $15 + (-23)$. Since 23 is greater than 15 we apply Rule II. $15 + (-23) = -(23 - 15) = -8$.

Add $(-8) + (-7)$. We apply Rule III. $(-8) + (-7) = -(8 + 7) = -15$.

(We note that in each case the sum is obtained by adding or subtracting two positive integers and making the result positive or negative.)

Subtract $7 - (-12)$. Using the inverse operation and inverse element this becomes $7 + 12 = 19$.

Subtract $(-7) - (-12)$. This is equivalent to $(-7) + 12 = 12 + (-7) = 12 - 7 = 5$.

Subtract $(-7) - 12$. This becomes $-7 + (-12) = -(7 + 12) =$ -19.

(Since $a + (-b) = a - (+b)$ the minus sign may be interpreted as either the sign of the operation subtraction or the sign of a negative number.)

Subtract $(7 - 12)$. We may think of this as either $7 - (+12)$ or $7 + (-12) = -5$.

Exercises

1 Evaluate each of the following expressions, giving the rule used for each.

(a) $(-9) + 13$ (b) $(-16) + (-29)$
(c) $(-27) + 19$ (d) $(-15) + 37$
(e) $(-8) + (-26)$ (f) $17 + (-63)$
(g) $63 + (-17)$ (h) $(-23) + (-42)$

2 Verify each of the following by evaluating each side of the equality independently.

(a) $(-7) + 9 + [(-9) + (-15)] = (-7) + [9 + (-9)]$
$$+ (-15)$$
(b) $[(-8) + (-6)] + (-9) = (-8) + [(-6) + (-9)]$
(c) $[15 + 9] + (-23) = 15 + [9 + (-23)]$
(d) $[16 + (-23)] + (-19) = 16 + [(-23) + (-19)]$

3 Evaluate each of the following

(a) $15 - (-7) - 6 - (-5)$
(b) $15 - [(-7) + 6 + (-5)]$
(c) $15 + 7 - (6 - 5)$
(d) $23 - 19 - 6 - 12$
(e) $23 - (19 + 6 + 12)$
(f) $76 - 8 - 17 - 40$
(g) $76 - (8 + 17 + 40)$

4.10 PROPERTIES OF SUBTRACTION

The integers are closed with respect to both addition and subtraction, each integer has an additive inverse. Zero is the addition identity. We could also call it the subtraction identity in that $a - 0 = a$ just as $a + 0 = a$. Addition obeys the commutative and associative laws. Since subtraction is the inverse of addition one might assume that it too obeys these laws, particularly since we can avoid subtraction by adding the inverse element.

That subtraction is not commutative it is sufficient to note that $10 - 7$ does not equal $7 - 10$. Although the latter expression is meaningless in the set of natural numbers, both expressions have meaning in the set of integers. But $10 - 7 = 3$ which is not equal to $7 - 10 = -3$.

Does $a - b$ ever equal $b - a$? If $a - b = b - a$, apply the definition of subtraction to the left side of the equation, $a - b$, and we have $b + (b - a) = a$ or

$$(b + b) - a + a = a + a$$
$$2b = 2a$$
$$b = a$$

We conclude that subtraction will obey the commutative law only when a number is subtracted from itself.

If we replace b with its additive inverse $-b$ and add, the commutative property does hold:

$$a + (-b) = (-b) + a$$

since both expressions are defined as $(a - b)$ if a is greater than b and as $-(b - a)$ if b is greater than a, Rules I and II.

Although it is not a commutative operation, *the order of successive applications of subtraction can be changed.* For example:

$$10 - 6 - 2 = 10 - 2 - 6$$

The things that have been commuted, reversed, are the operations, subtracting six and subtracting two, not minuend and subtrahend. The six and the two both remain subtrahends. We may justify the above property by replacing subtraction by addition of the additive inverse. We must show that $a - b - c = a - c - b$ and to establish this we note that $a - b - c = a + (-b) + (-c)$. But since addition is both associative and commutative:

$$[a + (-b)] + (-c) = a + [(-b) + (-c)] = a + [(-c) + (-b)]$$
$$= [a + (-c)] + (-b) = a + (-c) + (-b) = a - c - b.$$

Two facts should be noted. First, the corresponding statement applied to addition cannot be justified on the ground of commutativity alone. Consider the expression $10 + 5 + 2$. This means $(10 + 5) + 2$. It does not mean $10 + (5 + 2)$. However, the two expressions are equivalent because *addition is associative.* We may say $10 + 5 + 2 = 10 + 2 + 5$ only because we first regroup by the associative property

$$(10 + 5) + 2 = 10 + (5 + 2)$$

then commute the last two addends

$$10 + (5 + 2) = 10 + (2 + 5)$$

and apply the associative property again

$$10 + (2 + 5) = (10 + 2) + 5$$

We further note that the above property has only limited application if we restrict ourselves to positive numbers. In the expression $a - b - c$ we may be able to subtract neither b nor c from a, as $10 - 15 - 20$. We may be able to subtract either b or c but not both, as $10 - 8 - 7$. And we may be able to subtract one but not the other, as $10 - 8 - 12$.

If subtraction were associative this would mean $(a - b) - c = a - (b - c)$. To show that this is not correct consider

$$(10 - 5) - 3 = 5 - 3 = 2 \quad \text{but}$$
$$10 - (5 - 3) = 10 - 2 = 8$$

However, if we express the above in terms of addition we can apply the associative property and get

$$[10 + (-5)] + (-3) = 10 + [(-5) + (-3)]$$

Applying Rule III to the bracket on the right, we get

$$10 + [(-5) + (-3)] = 10 + [-(5 + 3)]$$

Here we are adding the negative number $-(5 + 3)$ to 10, which is equivalent to subtracting the positive number $(5 + 3)$. We conclude that we can add the subtrahends 5 and 3 and subtract the sum rather than subtract them individually:

$$10 - 5 - 3 = 10 - (5 + 3)$$

The principle applies to any number of successive subtrahends. In general $a - b - c - d - \ldots = a - (b + c + d + \ldots)$. *Successive subtractions may be performed by subtracting the sum of the subtrahends.*

Another property of subtraction is utilized in one of the subtraction algorithms. *The result is unaffected by adding the same amount to minuend and subtrahend:*

$$5 - 3 = (5 + 4) - (3 + 4) = 9 - 7 = 2$$
$$a - b = (a + c) - (b + c)$$

If we apply the definition of subtraction to the right side of the equation, $(a + c) - (b + c)$, we have

$$(b + c) + (a - b) = (a + c)$$
$$(b + c) + a + (-b) = (a + c)$$
$$(b + c + a) + (-b) = (a + c)$$
$$(a + c + b) + (-b) = (a + c)$$
$$(a + c) + b + (-b) = (a + c)$$
$$(a + c) + 0 = (a + c)$$
$$(a + c) = (a + c)$$

A justification for this lies essentially in the fact that we have added (add to minuend a) and subtracted (add to subtrahend b) the same quantity, which means we have added zero. Or, since subtraction is the inverse of addition, we may think of the minuend as a sum, the subtrahend as one addend, and the remainder as the other addend. If we increase one of the addends b, the sum a will be increased by the same amount:

Addition	*Subtraction*
If $a + b = c$	If $c - b = a$
then $a + (10 + b) = (10 + c)$	then $(10 + c) - (10 + b) = a$

Another property of subtraction stems from the fact that addition is commutative. If $a + b = c$, then $b + a = c$. But $a + b = c$ implies that $c - b = a$, and $b + a = c$ implies that $c - a = b$. *The minuend minus the remainder equals the subtrahend:*

$$12 - 5 = 7 \quad \text{and} \quad 12 - 7 = 5$$

A generalization of this is extremely useful to the child in learning the subtraction facts. Each subtraction fact implies another, obtained by interchanging subtrahend and remainder.

Summarizing: In subtracting integers the following rules hold. (They also hold with natural numbers and zero except for the fact that sometimes subtraction in this set is not possible.)

1. In continued subtraction, the order of subtrahends can be changed.

$$a - b - c = a - c - b$$

2. Continued subtraction may be performed by subtracting the sum of the subtrahends.

$$a - b - c = a - (b + c)$$

3. Increasing (or decreasing) both minuend and subtrahend by the same amount leaves the remainder unchanged.

$$a - b = (a + n) - (b + n) = (a - n) - (b - n)$$

4. Increasing (or decreasing) the minuend produces the same change in the remainder.

$$\text{If } a - b = c \text{ then } (a + n) - b = c + n$$
$$\text{and } (a - n) - b = c - n$$

5. Any subtraction fact implies another obtained by interchanging subtrahend and remainder.

$$\text{If } a - b = c \text{ then } a - c = b \text{ also.}$$

Exercises

1 Verify each of the following by evaluating each side of the equation separately:

(a) $17 - 9 - 6 = 17 - 6 - 9$
(b) $23 - (-50) - 70 = 23 - 70 - (-50)$
(c) $12 - 19 - 26 - 5 = 12 - 26 - 5 - 19$
(d) $37 - (-42) - 23 - 19 = 37 - 23 - 19 - (-42)$

2 Evaluate each of the following:

(a) $72 - (-13) - 15 - (-6)$
(b) $72 - [(-13) + 15 + (-6)]$
(c) $8 - 19 - 33 - 14$
(d) $8 - (19 + 33 + 14)$

3 Verify each of the following:

(a) $37 - 75 = (37 + 12) - (75 + 12)$
(b) $86 - 53 = (86 - 42) - (53 - 42)$
(c) $43 - 37 = (43 + 3) - (37 + 3)$

4 Evaluate the following:

(a) $17 - (-73)$
(b) $17 - 90$
(c) $(-23) - (-69)$
(d) $(-23) - 46$
(e) $(-19) - (-25)$
(f) $(-19) - 6$

5 Verify and state the principle upon which each of the following is based:

(a) $25 - 5 - 6 - 11 = 25 - 11 - 6 - 5$
(b) $100 - 9 - 3 - 27 - 15 = 100 - (9 + 3 + 27 + 15)$
(c) $50 - 17 = (12 + 50) - (12 + 17)$

6 Repeat Exercise 5 with each number interpreted as a base twelve number.

7 If $a - b = 10$, what does $a - 10$ equal?

4.11 INTERPRETATION OF NEGATIVE NUMBERS

We cannot give negative integers the same interpretation that we gave positive integers. We cannot say that -5 is the cardinal number of any set. If zero is the cardinal number of an empty set we need no cardinal numbers less than that; a set cannot have fewer than no elements in it.

One interpretation which we have given addition is that of counting on a number line. We visualize $3 + 2$ as starting at zero and

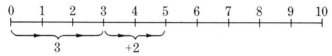

counting to 3, then counting on 2 more places. Here the number line is numbered from left to right. Then addition means "move to the right." The inverse, subtraction, should mean "move to the left." Then $3 - 2$ should mean: start at zero and move 3 places to the right, then move 2 places to the left. This same interpretation should serve

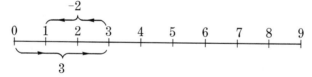

to illustrate the meaning of $3 + (-2)$, since we can use the inverse operation with the inverse element.

But suppose our problem is $3 - 4 = 3 + (-4)$. If we move 4 places to the left of 3 we run off the line. We have associated with each positive number a a distance to the right of the starting point. If we now extend the number line to the left we can associate the same distance to the *left* with the number $-a$. If we do this we won't run off the line when we move 4 places to the left of 3. In fact, we can

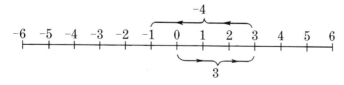

then move any number of places to the right or left regardless of where we start. This is the heart of the matter involving negative numbers. The natural numbers merely designate magnitude, size. Positive and negative numbers designate a magnitude *and a direction*. We think of 5 as the cardinal number of the set ⟨⟨⟨⟨⟨⟨ . But $+5$ is a directed number, 5 units in a direction, and -5 is a directed number, 5 units in the direction opposite that of $+5$. All of the rules for addition of integers can be verified on the number line. For example, to find $-5 + (-3)$ on the line, we can change this to $-5 - 3$. We start

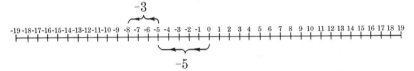

at 0 and move to the point -5 then move to the left 3 more places. We are then at -8. $-5 + (-3) = -(5 + 3)$ according to Rule III.

We may also interpret subtraction on the number line as finding the missing addend. To find $8 - 15$, letting subtraction mean "move to the left," we start at 8 and move to the left 15 places, ending at -7.

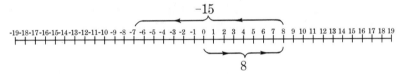

By the missing addend method the problem is to find what to "add" to 15 in order that we stop at 8. Since we must move 7 steps to the *left* the answer is -7.

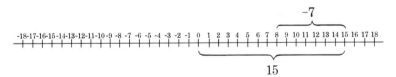

Exercises

1 If a positive number indicates each of the following, what does a negative number indicate?
(a) a profit
(b) a distance north
(c) population growth since the last census
(d) a distance south
(e) an acceleration

(f) feet above sea level

(g) a date A.D.

2 If the temperature is 12° below zero what will it be after it:

(a) drops 20°?

(b) rises 12°?

(c) rises 15° then drops 6°?

(d) drops 2° then rises 16°?

3 From Rules I and II, page 115, formulate a statement telling how to add integers with unlike signs.

4 Justify on the number line the statement obtained in Exercise 3 when:

(a) we have $a + (-b)$ with $a > b$

(b) we have $a + (-b)$ with $a < b$

(c) we have $(-a) + b$ with $a > b$

(d) we have $(-a) + b$ with $a < b$

5 From Rule III, page 115, and the addition of two positive integers formulate a statement for the addition of two integers with like signs.

6 Justify on the number line the statement obtained in Exercise 5.

7 Draw on the number line the illustration of each of the following:

(a) $3 + (-2) + (-6)$ (b) $16 - (-4)$

(c) $-7 + (-6) - 4$ (d) $12 - 15 + (-3)$

4.12 ADDITION ON A CIRCLE

We began our study of the integers by considering the positive integers as cardinal numbers of sets of objects. Addition, related as it is to the union of disjoint sets, means the putting together of two sets and finding the count of the new set thus created. Subtraction, although defined as the inverse of addition, can be interpreted as removing a subset of objects from a set and finding the count of the remaining subset.

With the creation of the complete set of integers we find that we need a new interpretation of number. Negative numbers cannot be interpreted as the cardinal numbers of sets. With the introduction of negative integers, an integer is interpreted as indicating a magnitude in one of two opposite directions.

Interpretation of the integers on the number line suggests another possibility, involving only a finite number of elements. A line can be considered a circle with an infinite radius. Let us construct a number circle. From an arbitrarily chosen point on the circle designated as 0 we indicate positive numbers to the right (clockwise) and negative numbers to the left (counterclockwise). In the figure we have used $\frac{1}{7}$ of the circumference as the unit distance. For convenience, the negative numbers are placed inside the circle. We designate addition

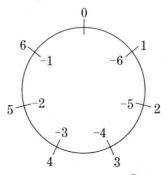

precisely as we did on the line. To find $a \oplus b$ start at 0, move clockwise to a, then move clockwise b more steps. To find $a \ominus b$, move to a, then move counterclockwise b steps. $2 + 3$ is found by moving to 2 then moving clockwise 3 steps, we stop at 5 hence $2 + 3 = 5$. $6 - 2$

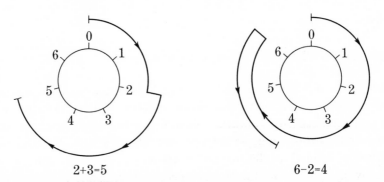

2+3=5   6-2=4

is found by starting at 0, moving to 6 and moving counterclockwise 2 steps, $6 - 2 = 4$.

We must be prepared for some unusual results. Let us find $5 + 6$. If we move to 5 then move 6 steps clockwise we stop at 4, hence $5 + 6 = 4$.

We certainly have closure with respect to addition. From any of the seven positions we can move clockwise from 0 to 6 steps and we will stop on one of the seven positions. The correctness of the

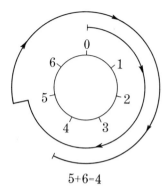

5+6=4

following addition table should be verified by actual addition on the circle.

	0	1	2	3	4	5	6
0	0	1	2	3	4	5	6
1	1	2	3	4	5	6	0
2	2	3	4	5	6	0	1
3	3	4	5	6	0	1	2
4	4	5	6	0	1	②	3
5	5	6	0	1	2	3	4
6	6	0	1	2	3	4	5

We agree to read the table as follows: To find $4 + 5$ we find 4 in the left margin and 5 in the top margin, the sum is in the row of the 4 and in the column of the 5. The sum, 2, is circled in the table. In general, to find $a + b$, locate a in the left column and b in the top row. The required sum is in the row with a and the column with b. If we wish to find $b + a$ this merely means that we interchange columns and rows, b is now found in the left column and a is found in the top row. Examination of the table reveals that entries symmetrically placed relative to the upper left to lower right diagonal are identical in every case. Hence an interchange of rows and columns will in no way change the table. This shows that the commutative property is satisfied.

It is easy to identify 0 as the addition identity element. From the standpoint of the definition of addition on the circle, $a + 0$ means move to a and take 0 steps clockwise, $0 + a$ means move to 0 and take a steps clockwise. In both cases we terminate at a. From the table, it is seen that the top row is repeated in the row opposite 0 in the left column, and the left column is repeated in the column headed with 0 in the top row.

Each element has an inverse. From the table:

$0 + 0 = 0$, hence 0 is its own inverse

$1 + 6 = 0$, hence 1 and 6 are inverses

$2 + 5 = 0$, hence 2 and 5 are inverses

$3 + 4 = 0$, hence 3 and 4 are inverses

The negative numbers on the inside of the circle in the first diagram are superfluous. However, it is of interest to notice that 6 and -1 are at the same point on the circle, similarly for 5 and -2, and for 4 and -3, and so on. Hence we are justified in saying $6 = -1$, $5 = -2$, $4 = -3$, $3 = -4$, $2 = -5$, and $1 = -6$; then as with ordinary integers, 1 and -1 are inverses, as are 2 and -2, and so on. We can now indicate inverses in the usual way, a and $-a$ are additive inverses.

The table can also be used as a subtraction table. Think of subtraction as the inverse of addition, $1 - 5$ equals whatever must be added to 5 to get the sum 1. If we look in the next to last row, the row with 5 in the left margin, we find a 1. Then the number at the head of the column in which the 1 is found, added to 5, will equal 1. Since this column is headed with 3 we know $1 - 5 = 3$ because $5 + 3 = 1$. Since the system is commutative we could also have found a 1 in the column headed with 5 and observed that it is in the row with 3 in the left margin.

Since all elements have additive inverses we can use the table in another way to find $1 - 5$. We can subtract by adding the additive inverse. From the table we know the inverse of 5 is 2 because opposite 5 and under 2 we find 0. We now add $1 + 2 = 3$, therefore $1 - 5 = 3$.

Does this system obey the associative law? Does $(2 + 5) + 6 = 2 + (5 + 6)$? Using the table, we have $(2 + 5) + 6 = 0 + 6 = 6$ and $2 + (5 + 6) = 2 + 4 = 6$. This does not prove that the associative law holds. It merely shows that it holds in this one case. Since there is only a finite number of cases to consider, we could settle the question by examining them all. This would become boring; there are only 343 cases to consider.

Consider again the definition of addition on the circle. We are to show that $(a + b) + c = a + (b + c)$. We have already shown that addition is commutative, hence $a + (b + c) = (b + c) + a$. Then it will be sufficient to show $(a + b) + c = (b + c) + a$. On the right hand side of the equation $(a + b) + c$ means move to a and move b steps clockwise then c more steps clockwise. In other words, we start at 0 and move clockwise $a + b + c$ steps. Here the $a + b + c$ is to be interpreted as ordinary addition of integers. Adding on the circle, $(b + c) + a$ means move to b and move clockwise c steps then clockwise a more steps. This amounts to starting at 0 and moving $b + c + a$ steps clockwise, with $b + c + a$ interpreted as ordinary addition. Hence we end at the same point whether we find $(a + b) + c$ or $a + (b + c)$.

EXAMPLE. $(5 + 6) + 4 = 5 + (6 + 4)$ because $(5 + 6) + 4$ means move from 0 clockwise 15 steps. But $5 + (6 + 4) = (6 + 4) + 5$ also means move from 0 clockwise 15 steps.

To summarize: We find the set of seven elements 0, 1, 2, 3, 4, 5, 6, with respect to addition on a circle of seven divisions has the properties:

1. Closure
2. Commutativity
3. Associativity
4. Identity element
5. Inverse elements

These are precisely the properties which were derived for the infinite set of integers with respect to ordinary addition.

Aside from the fact that we have seen a finite set which is structurally identical with the set of integers with respect to addition, of what value is this, other than chasing oneself around a circle?

We chose seven as the number of equal divisions of the circle because there are 7 days in a week. We could have used any number. The face of the clock uses 12. If the numeral 12 is replaced by 0 we have the same kind of system except for the number of divisions. On the face of the clock 8 plus 7 does not equal 15, it equals 3. Here of course, we mean start at 8 o'clock and move clockwise 7 hours.

Ordinary clocks do not tell you the day to the month. In fact if the clock shows 10 o'clock, you need something other than the clock to know whether it is 10 A.M. or 10 P.M. The clock adds hours for us but it throws out multiples of 12. It merely keeps track of the number of hours in excess of some multiple of 12.

We can interpret the table, page 127, as a table for the addition of days of the week. Let 0 represent Sunday, 1 represent Monday, and so on to 6 for Saturday. $5 + 6$ will stand for Friday plus 6 days, or 6 days after Friday. From the table $5 + 6 = 4$, but 4 stands for Thursday. Six days after Friday will be Thursday. Two minus four means Tuesday minus 4 days, or 4 days before Tuesday. Using the table for subtraction we find $2 - 4 = 5$. Since 5 stands for Friday, we conclude that 4 days before Tuesday is Friday.

There is another interpretation which is much more significant mathematically. If any integer is divided by 7 the remainder will be one of the numbers 0 through 6. This statement includes the negative integers. If we divide -15 by 7 the quotient is -2 and the remainder is -1, but remember that in our system $-1 = 6$. It is possible then to classify each element of the infinite set of integers into one of seven categories, the category being determined by the remainder when the integer is divided by 7. We find -96 and 9 in the same category because -96 has remainder $-5 = 2$ and 9 has remainder 2 when divided by 7. This relationship is stated "-96 is congruent to 9; modulo 7" and written

$$-96 \equiv 9, \text{mod } 7$$

Any two numbers are congruent, modulo 7, if they have the same remainder upon division by 7. The remainder is called the *residue* of the number.

Our table can be interpreted as an addition table for all integers, modulo 7. For example $6 + 5 = 4$ now means: any number whose residue is 6 added to any number whose residue is 5 will yield a number whose residue is 4.

76 has a residue 6
33 has a residue 5
$76 + 33 = 109$ has a residue $6 + 5 = 4$

Exercises

1 Use the table, page 127, to find the following:
(a) $3 + 6 + 4 + 5$
(b) $3 - 1 - 3 - 2$
(c) $3 - (1 + 3 + 2)$
(d) $3 + 4 = 3 - ? = ?$
(e) $2 + 3 - ? = 4$
(f) $4 - 2 = 4 + ? = ?$
(g) $4 - 5 = ?$

2 Draw a circle with six divisions and a circle addition table for the elements 0, 1, 2, 3, 4, 5.

3 From the table, Exercise 2, find the inverse of each element.

4 Use the Table from Exercise 2 to evaluate each of the following:
(a) $4 + 3 + 5 + 2$ (b) $4 - 3 - 1 - 4$
(c) $4 - (3 + 5 + 2)$ (d) $3 + 4 = 3 - ? = ?$
(e) $2 + 3 = 2 - ? = ?$ (f) $4 - 2 = 4 + ? = ?$
(g) $4 - 5 = ?$

5 In the table, Exercise 2, does $2 + 3 = 2 - 3$? Does $1 + 4 = 1 - 4$? Does $4 + 3 = 4 - 3$? If $a + b = a - b$ what do we know about b?

6 We have shown that with ordinary integers $a - b = b - a$ if and only if $a = b$. Is this true of addition on a circle with seven divisions? Is it true of addition on a circle with six divisions? Can you explain the difference?

Suggested Supplementary Readings

Banks, J. H., *Elements of Mathematics*, Second Edition. Boston: Allyn and Bacon, Inc., 1961. Pp. 79–116.

Cooley, Hollis R., David Guns, Morris Kline, and Howard E. Wahlert, *Introduction to Mathematics*. Boston: Houghton Mifflin Company, 1949. Pp. 17–65.

Dantzig, Tobias, *Number, the Language Science*. New York: The Macmillan Company, 1945. Pp. 206–229.

Harkin, Duncan, *Fundamental Mathematics*. Englewood Cliffs, N.J.: Prentice-Hall, Inc., 1941. Pp. 14–27.

Jones, Burton W., *Elementary Concepts of Mathematics*. New York: The Macmillan Company, 1947. Pp. 26–84.

Kasner, Edward, and James Newman, *Mathematics and the Imagination*. New York: Simon and Schuster, 1940. Pp. 27–64.

Mueller, Francis J., *Arithmetic, Its Structure and Concepts*. Englewood Cliffs, N.J.: Prentice-Hall, Inc., 1956. Pp. 48–95.

Richardson, Moses, *Fundamental Mathematics*. New York: The Macmillan Company, 1941. Pp. 42–87.

Developing Concepts Basic to Counting, Addition, and Subtraction

CHAPTER FIVE

THE OPERATIONS COUNTING, ADDITION, AND SUBTRACTION are considered together here because of their close association. Meaningful counting, rational counting, should be the psychological basis upon which one builds concepts of addition. The transition should be a natural and gradual one for the child. He should begin adding "before he knows it" as an extension of counting.

Subtraction should also be an outgrowth of counting activities, counting backward. Thus, it is also associated with addition in a way that is both psychologically meaningful and mathematically correct. It is the inverse of, the undoing of, addition.

5.1 COUNTING: THE ONE FUNDAMENTAL OPERATION

The present notion that there are four fundamental operations of arithmetic has not always been held. In times past duplation and mediation (doubling and halving), extraction of roots, and raising to powers were also considered fundamental. Actually, we can with propriety maintain that there are not four fundamental operations, there is but one—counting. The fundamental operations addition, subtraction, multiplication, and division can be interpreted as counting. A mastery and understanding of counting is basic to the study of the other four operations. Any problem that can be solved by means of the four fundamental operations with whole numbers, *can* be solved by counting, though it would take longer.

When the child first enters school his mathematical education is already under way. Some will have learned to count by rote to 100. Others will not be able to count to ten. *Rote counting* is the ability to recite the number names in their correct order. At first glance this seems to be a rather useless, pointless accomplishment. However, the child will never learn any more essential, more basic mathematical facts than the number names *one* through *ten* in their correct serial order. There is no logical reason why, no way to derive the fact that, *eight* comes before *nine* and after *seven* in the ordered sequence of names.

Many arithmetic facts, such as the one-digit multiplication facts, ultimately should be reduced to automatic responses simply as a matter of economy of time. The rote memorization of the sequence of number names is unavoidable.

In contrast with rote counting, *rational counting* is meaningful counting to determine the "how many" of a set or the "which one" of a member of a set. Closely associated with rational counting is the concept of *one-to-one correspondence*. Two sets of things are in one-to-one correspondence if it is possible to pair them, mentally or physically, so that each member of each set is paired with one and only one member of the other. The child who responds to the question "How many cookies?" by holding up three fingers when presented a plate containing three cookies is not counting, rote or rational. But he has in his mind established the one-to-one correspondence between his three raised fingers and the three cookies.

Some foundation programs lay great stress on matching activities to determine the presence or absence of one-to-one correspondence between sets of objects. To the extent that this is used as a foundation for counting it can easily be overdone. If in matching a set of toy soldiers with a set of boys there are unused toys, the only thing discovered is that there are *more* toys than boys. Without counting we do not know how many more toys, or how many toys, or how many boys there are. There is at best a remote connection with counting in such activities.

The real purpose of such activities is the development of the meaning of cardinal number. If two sets do have a one-to-one correspondence they have the same cardinal number. But the mere existence of the correspondence gives us no idea as to what the cardinal number is. Such activities would be more appropriate *after* the child has learned to count. Five pennies, five apples, and five children are sets with the same cardinal number because a one-to-one correspondence exists between any two of them. They have the cardinal number *five* because a one-to-one correspondence exists between any one of them and the set

{"one," "two," "three," "four," "five"}.

It is necessary for the child to place the number names into one-to-one correspondence with the objects in the set to be counted if he is to do rational counting. But this is not enough. The child who counts his fingers: "One, two, seven, three, five, four, six, eight, nine, ten" is not doing rational counting. He has placed the correct set of number names into one-to-one correspondence with his fingers. But the number names were not correctly ordered. The first rule in mathematics is *order*. Learning the correct order of the names is the essence of rote counting. It is true that one could always correctly identify a set of ten objects in the above manner but to count the set implies answering the question "How many?" not the question "Are there ten, less than ten, or more than ten?"

Rational counting correctly receives major attention in the professional literature. However, ignoring or discouraging rote counting is a mistake. The learning of rational counting is impossible without prior or concurrent mastery of the ordered sequence of number names. It is entirely possible that insistence upon the simultaneous learning of rote and rational counting may unnecessarily complicate the learning process for the child. There are three distinct aspects of learning to count. They are: (1) learning the ordered sequence of number names, (2) learning to place the number names, in their correct order, in one-to-one correspondence with the objects to be counted, and (3) learning to assess the significance of step 2. The child is not really counting until he can perform step 3. He must have an awareness of the fact that he has found out "how many." This implies an awareness of where the terminal number of his count is relative to the rest of the ordered sequence. Whether the teacher attempts to teach the three steps as distinct or three facets of one process, she should be sure the child is acquiring all three.

Rote counting is not analogous to memorizing the alphabet. Granted that the child should learn to recognize *man* as a single entity, a symbol for something, and not as a combination of the letters *m*, *a*, and *n*. It does not follow that he should learn to recognize 135 as a *single* symbol which describes a set containing 135 elements. The use to which the letter *m* is put, when used in a word, is in no way dependent upon the fact that it follows *l* and precedes *n* in the ordered alphabetical sequence. But the meaning of the numeral 5 when used in a number very much depends upon the fact that it follows 4 and precedes 6. The number 135 conveys no meaning in isolation from the number sequence. One can visualize a collection of three or four things, but it would be most difficult to visualize 135 separate things. The number has meaning first in that we know it is over 100 but under 200, we know further that it is between 130 and 140 and finally that it is between 134 and 136. Whether the parent who teaches his preschool child the alphabet has either wasted his time or actually done an injury we leave to the reading specialist. But the parent who has taught the child to count to 100 has done neither.

One school of thought in the teaching of arithmetic holds that the meaning of numbers should be developed independent of, and prior to, counting. According to this point of view the child will develop an understanding of the number seven through experience with sets whose cardinal number is seven. For the sake of argument, assume the child can learn the meaning of the number eight in the same way, without associating it with seven. The ability to recognize a set whose cardinal number is eight is an accomplishment of doubtful value unless eight has meaning in terms of the number sequence. Development of the meaning of numbers is inexorably related to rational counting.

5.2 THE FIRST DECADE

Thorough, unhurried mastery of the meanings attendant upon counting through ten will pay rich dividends later on. In developing meanings there should be a gradual transition from the concrete to abstract symbolism.

The first stages of counting should consist of counting the actual objects which the child can see and manipulate. Four pennies *and one more* penny makes five pennies.

The child should be encouraged to manipulate the group of five to see that it is 3 and 2, 2 and 3, two 2s and 1, 4 and 1, 1 and 4, and so on.

The first step toward abstraction consists of using pictures of concrete objects. Next, pictures of the actual object may be replaced by lines, circles, dots, crosses, or the like, to stand in the place of the pictures. Each mark stands for one of the objects. Then the final abstraction is made to the number symbols and written words. The child's conception of *five* must ultimately encompass the spoken word sound, the written word, the printed word, the numerical symbol, as well as the notion of a set of objects together with its possible subgroupings. Essential to counting is the idea of five as "four and one more" and "one less than six," or in the ordinal sense "the next one after four" and "the last one before six."

Songs, rhymes, and games involving counting are useful aids in establishing the correct serial order of the first decade numbers. Children enjoy rhythmic activities. Counting time in rhythm band, folk dances, and similar activities afford excellent means of establishing and reinforcing counting. Hopscotch, jacks, and dominoes aid in developing this and related skills. In hopscotch practice is provided in writing and reading the number symbols in their correct order. Jacks and dominoes are excellent means for establishing the concept of a number as the measure of a set, as well as for exploring possible subgroupings of a set. Parcheesi and similar games requiring the movement of markers a variable number of spaces are excellent free-time and enrichment activities.

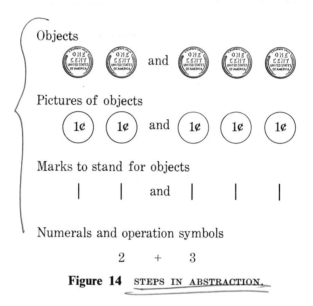

Figure 14 STEPS IN ABSTRACTION.

For more formal number activities each child can be provided a counting ring with a minimum of expense or effort. A very good ring may be made from a wire coat hanger on which are strung ten wooden beads. Spring type clothespins may serve instead of beads. This device is useful for learning the sums to ten and subtraction facts, as well as for counting. The counting frame, the one hundred chart, and loose objects such as marbles, bottle caps, applicators, spools, beans, and coins may be utilized in the concrete phase of number concept development.

Some children enter school quite advanced in their arithmetic development. Counting and simple addition and subtraction facts are well understood. Others have made little or no progress prior to school. For these early instruction in counting should consist of many opportunities for counting for which the child can see a use. The following are illustrative:

1. How many books do we need for the first reading group? Let's count to see how many are in the group. Bill and Bob will you count nine books for us?

2. Who wants to lead the line to the lunch room today? The teacher points to each child in succession as they count together "one, two, three, four, out, you, go." The child pointed to on "go" drops out. This is continued until one child remains.

3. "Today is November 10. How many days till Thanksgiving holidays?" The teacher points to the days on the calender beginning with 11, then 12, and so on. The pupils count 1, 2, . . . as each day is pointed to on the calender.

4. "We need three colors to color our pictures. Count to see how many crayons we need so each person will have three."

After the children have become interested and want to learn to count numerous other possibilities are appropriate.

1. "Use the 100 chart to count 13 numbers beyond 28"
2. "Jim, can you count backward from 21 without making a mistake."
3. "With practice, you can measure time by counting. Let's see how long it takes us to count to 60."

5.3 COUNTING BY GROUPS

Rote counting is prerequisite to the development of both cardinal and ordinal number concepts. Recognition of the relative size of small sets is essential to a thorough mastery of number concepts through ten. Children can usually differentiate between sets of one through four and possibly five objects without resorting to counting. They should be encouraged to see the larger sets up to ten as combinations of smaller sets. For example they may be asked "Without counting show me four" on the counting ring "now three more." "Now count to see how many that makes." "Without counting remove two and tell me how many you have." Smaller sets should also be recognizable in their relation to a set of ten. "Without counting show me three. Who can tell how many more are on the ring?" A set of four should come to be recognizable as a set of three and a set of one, two sets of two, as well as four sets of one. It should also mean a set of five with a set of one removed and thus a set of ten with five and one removed.

Cardinal counting, "how many" counting, should mean "adding on." "Four and one more makes five, and one more makes six, and one more makes seven . . ." should be the meaning he attaches to the counting process. Mastery of the first decade should include recognition, without counting, of small sets by name, counting by ones by means of one-to-one correspondence of the number names and objects, counting by combining sets of more than one, recognition of all possible subgroupings of each set, and recognition of each set in its relation to ten. The ordinal concept of "which one" further requires the concept of counting as the naming of each member of a set which implies knowledge of the relative position of all the number names in the sequence.

5.4 COUNTING BY TENS

Adults who are confronted with the necessity of counting a large number of objects, say a sackful of coins, will usually separate them, count like coins out in sets of ten, then count the sets. When children have mastered counting through ten the next step in learning to count should be counting by tens. The importance of this step derives from the fact that we are dealing with the *number base*. Otherwise there would be no more virtue in counting by tens than by eights or twelves.

As a preliminary to counting by tens the child should count out a supply of objects into groups of ten. Tongue depressors or other small sticks which can be bundled into tens are good counting materials for this type of exercise. The child should see the bundles of ten as a unit. He first counts one ten, two tens, three tens, . . . ten tens. Writing by tens should precede learning the number names. This involves the "not any" aspect of zero. On the one hundred chart the 1 in 10 stands for one *ten* and zero means not any extra. On the counting frame the idea of one ten is represented by one line full and no counters on the next line. Similar observations for the other decade numbers should be emphasized. Seven full lines on the counting frame means 7 *tens*. The 6 in 60 on the one hundred chart means 6 tens and the 0 means no extras.

When the ideas of counting tens and of the tens place are established there should be an easy transition to the number names for the decade numbers. We drop the "one" in "one ten" and call it "ten." Parenthetically this is an inconsistency in our system of numeration; we do not drop the "one" in one hundred or one thousand, nor do we invent a special name for two hundred or two thousand as we do for two tens. This makes it all the more imperative for the child to realize that "fifty" is just a special name for five tens.

The names "sixty" through "ninety" are consistently formed by adding "ty" to the word telling how many tens. Logic would dictate "onety," "twoty," "threety," "fourty," and "fivety" for the first five decades. Fortunately, the names "twenty" through "fifty" are phonetically close enough to the names which logic would dictate for the child, with some help, to see the relationship between "two tens," "twoty," and "twenty."

We have noted a number of inconsistencies in our set of number names. The inconsistent "teens," the inconsistencies mentioned in the paragraph above, the ones discussed in Section 3.5, as well as the inconsistent naming of the ordinals "first," "second," "third" rather than "oneth," "twoth," "threeth" all have one thing in common. They all occur at the *beginning* of the sequence. This is probably due to a later realization of the desirability of a consistent pattern. This observation casts some doubt upon the contention that the ordinal concept of number developed independent of, if not earlier than, the cardinal. The fact that these inconsistencies appear at the beginning of the sequence does not make the teacher's task any easier. However, the child should be made aware that they are inconsistencies.

When the integers through ten are thoroughly mastered, and the notion of counting by tens to one hundred understood and appreciated, a framework for the entire system of whole numbers is available. The child is ready for counting in general above ten.

5.5 TWO- AND THREE-DIGIT NUMBERS

Most of the difficulty with the second decade numbers stems from their names. Accordingly, the better sequence of learning activities should be: (1) experience with concrete materials that are one ten and some more in number, (2) representation of these quantities symbolically as a set of ten and a set of less than ten, (3) special names for the set consisting of a set of ten and a set of less than ten.

Let us say there are 17 boys in the room. The class wishes to find out how many that is. Since sets up to 10 are understood, the natural procedure is to arrange them in recognizable sets. Suppose one of the children arranges them in two sets of 7 and one set of 3. This is a correct solution; there are two sets of 7 and one set of 3 boys in the room. Furthermore, the child has succeeded in making a meaningful subgrouping of the larger inaccessible set. The child has shown ingenuity and insight. The development of mathematical competence is in no small measure the development of ability to see a more complex situation in its simpler components, reducing a problem that offers difficulty to simpler solvable problems—one might say, cutting the problem down to size.

Other suggestions are apt to follow, such as three sets of 5 and one set of 2, eight sets of 2 and one set of 1, or a set of 8 and a set of 9. This should be encouraged—first because they all contribute to really knowing what 17 is and secondly because it is of extreme importance to develop the habit of exploring many possibilities, resulting in the realization that there are many ways to solve a problem.

If the possibility of one set of 10 and one set of 7 has been suggested, the next step should be discovery of the advantage of this grouping. Otherwise, we consider the inconvenience or inadequacy of the other subgroupings when we represent the number on the counting frame or find it on the one hundred chart. The counting frame can be put to good use to show the equivalence of the various suggested subgroupings as well as the superiority of the ten–seven grouping.

At this point it is well to study the structure of the one hundred chart with the children. The first line gives the numbers to ten. The left-hand symbol 1 stands for *one whole set of ten*. The left-hand 1 in each of the numbers, except the last, in the second line also stands for a single set of ten. The right-hand symbols of each number are a repetition of the numbers in the top line. The 1, 2, 3, . . . of the top line become ten and 1, ten and 2, ten and 3, . . . of the second line. Although a number between one ten and two tens (the 17 boys) can be subgrouped many ways, the grouping employed on the number chart is always a set of ten and a smaller set.

Columnwise, the right-hand or ones number is fixed. By row, the left-hand or tens number is fixed. Every number in the fourth row contains 4 sets of tens. The following exercises suggest means for establishing the idea that numbers between 10 and 100 are expressed as a certain number of sets of ten and a set of less than ten. When we get to ten we start over on the second line with ten and 1, ten and

2, . . . until we get to 2 tens; then we start over again 2 tens and 1, 2 tens and 2, . . . to 3 tens. Questions similar to the following should be used to bring out the properties of the chart.

The "100 chart"

1	2	3	4	5	6	7	8	9	10
11	12	13	14	15	16	17	18	19	20
21	22	23	24	25	26	27	28	29	30
31	32	33	34	35	36	37	38	39	40
41	42	43	44	45	46	47	48	49	50
51	52	53	54	55	56	57	58	59	60
61	62	63	64	65	66	67	68	69	70
71	72	73	74	75	76	77	78	79	80
81	82	83	84	85	86	87	88	89	90
91	92	93	94	95	96	97	98	99	100

1. How much larger is any number than the number directly above it? *1*
2. What does a number end in if it is exact tens (none left over)? *0*
3. Where do you find the exact tens? *end*
4. Sally paid 3 dimes and 2 cents for her lunch; find on the chart the number of cents her lunch cost. *32*
5. How many numbers are in each row? *10*
6. How many rows are there? *10*   *10 — tens & ones*
7. What does the last number on the chart mean? (It should be pointed out that this is 10 tens, yet we cannot indicate *10* tens in the second digit from the right. The child should not visualize 100 as 10 (tens) and 0 (ones). We have the same difficulty here as we have when we reach 10 ones, and we resolve the difficulty in the same way. The 1 in 100 means not 10 sets of ten but *one* set of 10 tens, named one hundred. The middle zero indicates no additional tens and the right-hand zero no additional ones.)
8. Johnny had 28 cents and earned 5 cents more; find the number that tells how much he now has.
9. What number is five more than 48? 5 more than 78? Where will a number which is 5 more than a number ending in 8 be found?
10. Tom had 50 cents and spent 7 cents for ice cream. Find the numbers that tell how much Tom had before he bought the ice cream and after he bought it.

The two-digit number names offer no particular difficulty—2 tens and five (twenty-five), 7 tens and six (seventy-six), except in the case of the teens. In this case the child should be aware of the reversal of form, the ones followed by ten (teen) rather than the number of tens followed by the ones. Eleven and twelve are special cases and simply have to be treated as such.

Counting to three or more digit numbers is a rarely needed accomplishment. The ability to count with higher numbers nevertheless gives evidence of understanding, which is far more important. Ability to read, write, and interpret numbers of three or more digits should precede any attempt to compute with them. The child who counts "ninety-eight, ninety-nine, a hundred, two hundred, three hundred, . . ." or "ninety-eight, ninety-nine, one hundred, one hundred ten, one hundred twenty, . . ." has not grasped the significance of place value as exhibited in two-digit numbers. To say the least he has not generalized the notion that each numeral indicates that number of sets, sets of ones, sets of tens, sets of ten tens (hundreds), sets of ten hundreds (thousands), ...

The role of the place value aspect of the system of notation as it relates to counting is well illustrated by an odometer or similar counting device. The symbol in any position above "ones" will advance to the next position only after all positions below show "9," all of which move in unison to "0."

5.6 MULTIPLE COUNTING

Counting is the primary concern of the first- and second-grade teacher. Many problem situations arise involving addition and subtraction of whole numbers. These may be solved by counting forward or counting backward. Many such situations should precede formal instruction in addition and subtraction. The counting situations serve as a background of understanding for these operations, which should be learned as extensions of the counting process.

Counting experiences should not be confined to the first two grades, however. There are many worthwhile counting activities appropriate to higher grades.[1] Third-grade children can profit by counting on the abacus, a useful aid in establishing the place value concept. On the abacus ten is represented by a single counter just as in numerals it is represented by a 1. One hundred is similarly represented by one counter, not ten lines of ten counters. The abacus may

[1] Herbert F. Spitzer, *The Teaching of Arithmetic* (3rd ed.; Boston: Houghton-Mifflers Co., 1961), pp. 25–28.

also be used to advantage in introducing two and more digit addition and subtraction.

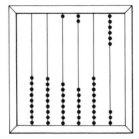

Figure 15 ONE THOUSAND TWO HUNDRED SIX ON THE ABACUS.

As a preliminary to multiplication, multiple counting is quite useful. A multiple counting chart is helpful for this kind of activity. Such a chart may be used to discover many useful number facts.

Multiple counting chart

1	2	3	4	5	6	7	8	9	10
2	4	6	8	10	12	14	16	18	20
3	6	9	12	15	18	21	24	27	30
4	8	12	16	20	24	28	32	36	40
5	10	15	20	25	30	35	40	45	50
6	12	18	24	30	36	42	48	54	60
7	14	21	28	35	42	49	56	63	70
8	16	24	32	40	48	56	64	72	80
9	18	27	36	45	54	63	72	81	90
10	20	30	40	50	60	70	80	90	100

First we note that we may count either across the line or down the column; some of the properties are more easily observed if the chart is viewed columnwise. The following are some of the useful number properties which may be extracted from the chart:

1. In counting by tens every number ends in zero.
2. In the nines column the ones digit decreases one each time and the tens digit increases one (we add nine by adding ten and subtracting one). The sum of the tens digit and the ones digit is always nine.

3. In the fives column the ones digits alternate 5–0–5–0. The tens digits fall in pairs, 1-1, 2-2, and so on.

4. In the sevens column every possible ones digit, 0 through 9, may be found. This is true only of columns 1, 3, 7, and 9.

5. All possible even ones digits are found in columns 2, 4, 6, and 8 but they appear in different orders. But in each column the same sequence appears twice, for example the sixes end in 6, 2, 8, 4, 0, 6, 2, 8, 4, 0.

6. The sum of the digits of each number in the threes column is in turn a number in this column. Also, the sum of the digits in the sixes column is a number in the threes column.

7. Double the first row and get the second, double the second and get the fourth, double the third and get the sixth.

8. Find all numbers that appear in just one column. They all appear on the 1–100 diagonal. Yet not all numbers on the diagonal are like this.

9. Compare the 1–100 diagonal with the 10–10 diagonal.

10. Combine the first and ninth columns, the second and eighth, and so on.

To as great an extent as possible the pupils should be led to discover these and similar relationships for themselves. The full significance of some of them must await further development but they are useful in learning multiplication.

Exercises

1 A child enters school able to count to 100. Suggest ways for the teacher to determine whether it is rote counting or rational counting.

2 Explain why one-to-one correspondence is an essential component of rational counting.

3 In playing hide-and-seek, the "seeker" counts to 100 while the others hide. What kind of counting is this?

4 Suggest reasons for the position that counting by tens to 100 should be mastered before counting by ones to 30.

5 List some ways to interest children in numbers.

6 Describe some learning situations which will lead children to want to learn more about counting.

7 What does "seven" mean?

8 Is it possible for a child to know the meaning of "seven" independent of the meaning of other number names? Is it desirable? Discuss.

9 Of what value is the learning of multiple counting?

10 Which concept should receive the greater emphasis, cardinal counting or ordinal counting? Why?

5.7 THE ADDITION FACTS

Rich and meaningful counting experiences should form the background for formal instruction with the basic addition facts. The meaning of addition and many of the basic addition facts should emerge from counting experiences. The child should be "adding before he knows it." "Three plus five" will come to mean "eight" as a result of counting five more beyond three, counting three more beyond five, and finding the "how many" of a set of three things combined with a set of five things. When the child recognizes the result as "eight" without recourse to counting he is adding whether or not he calls it that.

Introduction to formal work with the one-digit addition facts should be approached through problem situations. Learning is goal-seeking behavior but with young children the goal should not be too remote. There is scant motivation for the child if he is told he must master these facts in order to be an electronic engineer 25 years later. Nor is there much profit in the point of view which says in effect "We have been solving certain problems by counting, from now on we shall solve by addition." It does not help to point to the necessity of learning the addition facts if one wishes to multiply.

Suppose a problem situation arises (the teacher does not have to wait and hope for it to arise) requiring the addition of 8 and 5. The class is challenged to see who can get the answer first. After everyone is through the teacher may suggest that they see how many different ways the problem was solved. The different solutions will probably include counting five more on beyond eight, counting eight more beyond five, putting down a set of eight marks and another set of five marks then counting the entire set. There will probably be verbal solutions—"8 is 3 and 5 so the two 5s make 10, and 3 makes 13 in all" or "two 8s make 16, but 5 is 3 less than 8 so the answer is 3 less than 16, the answer is 13." If someone suggests "I just knew if you put 8 and 5 together you get 13," the superiority of this approach in terms of economy of time can be emphasized. Otherwise the teacher can suggest how much quicker it would be to "just know it is 13." Many experiences of this sort should form the basis of motivation for learning the addition facts as such.

In making the transition to addition we must help the child relate the process to counting. Addition becomes irregular counting but counting becomes a succession of steps of adding one. The sign + must be associated with the process of combining groups. In this connection we note that if John has 6 cents and Mary has 3 cents the symbol 6 + 3 is *a* correct representation of the number of cents they both have. 6 + 3 symbolizes *a* set with subgroups of 6 and 3 indicated. When we use the symbol 9 to represent the number of cents in the set we do so for convenience and economy of expression. Viewed thus, addition is a matter of *regrouping*. The equation 7 + 8 = 15 asserts that a set whose subgroups are 7 and 8 may be regrouped into subgroups of 10 and 5.

This is not in conflict with the idea that addition is finding the cardinal number of the union of disjoint sets, see page 108.

$$\{a,b,c,d,e,f,g\} \cup \{h,i,j,k,l,m,n,o\} = \{a,b,c,d,e,f,g,h,i,j,k,l,m,n,o\}$$
$$7 \quad + \quad 8 \quad = \quad 15$$

It merely goes a step beyond. The step being the application of the system of notation.

$$\{a,b,c,d,e,f,g\} \cup \{h,i,j,k,l,m,n,o\} = \{a,b,c,d,e,f,g,h,i,j,k,l,m,n,o\}$$
$$7 \quad + \quad 8 \quad = \quad \text{fifteen}$$
$$= \{a,b,c,d,e,f,g,h,i,j\} \cup \{k,l,m,n,o\}$$
$$= \quad 10 \quad + \quad 5$$

The basic facts that have a sum more than ten point up the crucial importance of knowing intimately the properties of numbers from one to ten, particularly the complements to ten. The child who knows these facts can "figure out for himself" what 7 + 8 is. "It takes 3 more to go with the 7 to make 10, and 8 is 3 and 5." Or, "it takes 2 more to go with the 8 to make 10, and 7 is 2 and 5."

The program of preparation for formal addition should include development of meanings for the terms plus, add, sum, total as well as the plus sign. Allied with, and as extensions of these meanings, many kinds of problem situations requiring addition should be experienced. Inability to determine which operation is appropriate to a problem is as apt to be due to inadequate vocabulary, to the fact that the problem situation is not meaningful, as it is to faulty or inadequate grasp of the meaning of the mathematical operation. The following are illustrative of the diversity of expressions implying addition.

1. John is 4 years old and Mary is 6 years *older*. How old is Mary?
2. What is the *total* cost of a 10-cent tablet and a 5-cent pencil?
3. *Add* the number of bottles of milk on the two tables.
4. We need 5 *more* bottles than we have. How many do we need?
5. The *difference* between their scores is 6. What is Bill's score if he is ahead and Jane's score is 17?
6. Yesterday the girls sold 12 boxes of cookies and today they sold 13 *more*. What is the *total* number of boxes sold?
7. Sue brought 6 cans from the store today. Since we had 19, these *additional* cans make how many?
8. School opens at 8 o'clock. What time is it two hours *later* when we go out to play?
9. Tom has 5 cents and Sue 3 cents; how much do they *both* have?
10. There are 6 crayons in this box and 7 in that box. How many are there *all together?*
11. Eight pennies *and* 3 pennies make how many pennies?

The teacher has the dual obligation to see that the problem is stated in the child's vocabulary and to provide opportunity for vocabulary growth. It is most undesirable for the child to associate the arithmetic operation with word cues. All of the italicized words in the above examples may be used to imply something other than addition. The important thing is to help the child recognize in the situation the requirement that the result of combining sets, putting together, or increasing by a fixed amount is to be found.

There are one hundred addition facts involving two one-digit addends. They should ultimately be learned to the point of immediate recall with 100 per cent accuracy. Some children will require years to reach this objective while others will do so in a matter of weeks. Any systematic instruction aimed at reducing the addition facts to immediate recall should be postponed until their meaning is established. It is a sheer waste of effort for a child to learn to parrot "Three—plus—three—ekals—six" or for that matter to write $3 + 3 = 6$ unless he understands the significance of the words and symbols.

Many authorities try to reduce the number of addition facts to 81 by eliminating those involving zero. The theory for this procedure is based upon the fact that when zero and some number are added the result is simply the other number (zero is the additive identity element). The children certainly should be aware of this generalization. But this seems hardly a justification for ignoring these facts. They are as basic as any of the others. Furthermore, children are apt to get the erroneous idea that adding zero is the same thing as not adding. The child should not think of $5 + 0$ as 5 and nothing added, in the sense that no addition has occurred. He should think of it as combining two sets, the first containing five things and the second containing no things, a sack of five marbles plus an empty marble sack.

The game isn't over until the last man is out. The score is 2 to 2 at the end of the eighth inning. The visiting team doesn't score in the ninth, visitor's score $2 + 0 = 2$; home team's score 2. Every baseball fan knows full well that there is a big difference between adding zero and not adding!

Why stop here? The addition facts involving 1 require nothing more than counting by ones. The idea of counting as the process of adding on one more will make these facts perfectly obvious. If these are eliminated we have only 64 facts to worry about. Of these, 8 are doubles, which the children already know if they can count by 2s. The remaining 56 facts consist of 28 different combinations and their reversals. Assuming the child is aware of the commutative property, though not by name, he sees $4 + 3$ and $3 + 4$ as the same combination. Then he has only 28 distinct facts to learn.

The above generalizations are useful. They should be utilized as aids in learning the 100 facts. But we cannot generalize 72 of them out of existence. The child should know all 100 of them as *separate* but *related* facts.

These observations should in no wise be interpreted as advocacy of rote memorization, which should be kept to a minimum. Those facts that are learned as the result of reasoning or of relating to other known facts are learned more easily and more permanently. For example, it is much better for the child to know that $8 + 9 = 17$ because 8 is 2 less than 10 and 9 is 1 less than 10, or better yet, since $8 + 10 = 18$ then $8 + 9$ is one less, than to have learned it in isolation and by rote. Many children will make such discoveries and generalizations unassisted. Others, with a little adroitness on the part of the teacher, may be led to make them. Those who cannot should be shown.

Knowledge of the following number properties will greatly facilitate learning the basic addition facts:

Commutative property. To the child this means that reversing the two numbers does not affect the sum, $12 + 15 = 15 + 12$. When applied to column addition it means the numbers in the column may be added in any order, not merely adding up or adding down.

100 Addition Facts

0	0	0	0	0	0	0	0	0	0
0	1	2	3	4	5	6	7	8	9
—	—	—	—	—	—	—	—	—	—
0	1	2	3	4	5	6	7	8	9
1	1	1	1	1	1	1	1	1	1
0	1	2	3	4	5	6	7	8	9
—	—	—	—	—	—	—	—	—	—
1	2	3	4	5	6	7	8	9	10
2	2	2	2	2	2	2	2	2	2
0	1	2	3	4	5	6	7	8	9
—	—	—	—	—	—	—	—	—	—
2	3	4	5	6	7	8	9	10	11
3	3	3	3	3	3	3	3	3	3
0	1	2	3	4	5	6	7	8	9
—	—	—	—	—	—	—	—	—	—
3	4	5	6	7	8	9	10	11	12
4	4	4	4	4	4	4	4	4	4
0	1	2	3	4	5	6	7	8	9
—	—	—	—	—	—	—	—	—	—
4	5	6	7	8	9	10	11	12	13
5	5	5	5	5	5	5	5	5	5
0	1	2	3	4	5	6	7	8	9
—	—	—	—	—	—	—	—	—	—
5	6	7	8	9	10	11	12	13	14
6	6	6	6	6	6	6	6	6	6
0	1	2	3	4	5	6	7	8	9
—	—	—	—	—	—	—	—	—	—
6	7	8	9	10	11	12	13	14	15
7	7	7	7	7	7	7	7	7	7
0	1	2	3	4	5	6	7	8	9
—	—	—	—	—	—	—	—	—	—
7	8	9	10	11	12	13	14	15	16
8	8	8	8	8	8	8	8	8	8
0	1	2	3	4	5	6	7	8	9
—	—	—	—	—	—	—	—	—	—
8	9	10	11	12	13	14	15	16	17
9	9	9	9	9	9	9	9	9	9
0	1	2	3	4	5	6	7	8	9
—	—	—	—	—	—	—	—	—	—
9	10	11	12	13	14	15	16	17	18

Associative property. To the child this is essentially regrouping. $5 + 6 = 5 + (5 + 1) = (5 + 5) + 1; 6 + 7 = (6 + 6) + 1 = (6 + 4) + 3$. Regrouping to obtain ten or a double enables the child to discover many of the facts.

Addition identity element. Zero added to any number equals the number.

Counting by ones is equivalent to adding ones.

Knowledge of doubles. This will aid in learning other facts particularly those whose sum is over 10. Since $8 + 8 = 16$, $8 + 9$ is one more and $8 + 7$ is one less.

Components of ten. Since $10 = 8 + 2$, $8 + 5 = 8 + 2 + 3 = 10 + 3 = 13$.

These properties should be stressed repeatedly, for their value does not end with mastery of the basic addition facts.

With a proper background of understanding, committing the addition facts to memory will consist largely of establishing immediate recall and identifying the more difficult combinations for intensive study. To this end, flash cards will prove most helpful.

Each child should make his own set of cards. They should be small enough for ease of handling. On one side the combination is given and on the other the combination and the sum. The teacher should also have a set of cards large enough to be seen easily by

$$\begin{array}{r} 7 \\ + 8 \\ \hline \end{array} \qquad \begin{array}{r} 7 \\ + 8 \\ \hline 15 \end{array}$$

all the children. Group flash card drill is not as effective as individual work. However, it can be used to stimulate interest and to discover those combinations on which the class as a whole should concentrate. In group drill the teacher holds up a card with the combination side showing. If the correct response is not given or is given too slowly the answer side is shown momentarily. A variety of activities can be devised. The class can compete with itself by keeping a record of the number of combinations missed and trying to lower its score, or teams such as boys against girls may compete. The individual cards hold much more learning value. The cards are shuffled with combination side up. The child goes through the cards, testing himself on each combination. He turns each card to the answer side to verify his answer. If he does not know the combination or if he misses the answer, that card is placed in a "missed" pile for special study. The pupils can work in pairs in an activity of this sort, each trying to have the fewer "missed" cards.

The above sample of flash cards shows the column form for addition. Many modern programs now lay great stress on the idea of mathematical sentences. This trend is eminently sound. The child should think of the expression "2 + 3" as merely another form for "two and three more," "two and three," or "two plus three." The expression "2 + 3 = 5" is a mathematical sentence, it is a mathematical way to write the perfectly good English sentence "Two plus three equals five." It happens to be a true statement, but "2 + 3 = 7" is also a statement, a *false* statement. The expression "2 + 3 = ?" is a question, a true answer to which is "5." The answer "7" is an answer all right, but it is a false one. The expressions "2 + 3 = □," "2 + 3 = ___," "2 + 3 = n," "2 + 3 = x" are different forms for the same open sentence. It is neither true nor false. The symbols □, ___, n, and x are place holders. Some people call them *pronumerals*, analogous to pronouns. Others call them *variables*. The open sentence is made true or false depending on the numeral used to fill in the place holder.

Since the idea of a mathematical sentence is an important one is there any justification for the column form? If we look ahead to the addition of addends with several digits it becomes quite evident that the column form is very useful. The addition algorithm would be quite awkward without it. In order that the child may become familiar with both forms it would be well for flash cards to show both.

$$7 + 8 = \underline{}$$

$$
\begin{array}{r}
7 \\
+8 \\
\hline
\underline{}
\end{array}
$$

$$7 + 8 = 15$$

$$
\begin{array}{r}
7 \\
+8 \\
\hline
15
\end{array}
$$

5.8 ADDING A ONE-DIGIT NUMBER TO A TWO-DIGIT NUMBER

Adding a one-digit number to a two-digit number is sometimes referred to as employing higher decade addition facts. However, it seems hardly practicable to attempt to reduce these to the status of the one-digit combinations. If the sum of the ones digits is less than ten no particular difficulty is encountered. Otherwise they deserve special treatment. They are essential to efficient addition of long columns of numbers and to multiplication.

The most commonly taught method is known as "adding by endings." For example, 74 + 8 ends with the same digit as 4 + 8 so we "bridge" to the next decade, the 80's, and end with 2. With 67 + 8 we bridge to the 70s and end with 5 since 7 + 8 ends with 5.

Another method which has much to recommend it is the method of completing tens. By this method with 74 + 8 we would think "6 of the 8 makes 80 and the remaining 2 makes 82." Or with 67 + 8, "we need 3 of the 8 to make 70 and the remaining 5 makes 75." This method is particularly useful in column addition. Frequently one addend can be split up to "make" more than one 10. For example, in adding a column 7 + 9 + 6 + 8 the thought process might be 7—16—20—30 by seeing the 6 as 4 + 2.

Adults probably use each of these methods on occasion. The wisdom of teaching either method exclusively is questionable. Children should be acquainted with both methods and encouraged to use whichever they prefer.

5.9 ADDITION OF 2 TWO-DIGIT NUMBERS

"There are thirteen girls and fifteen boys in the room. Who can find how many children are present today?" If the pupil is asked to find the answer on the counting frame the response is indicative of the degree of maturity of number concepts. The child may count each bead until 13 is reached then begin over and count on, a bead at a time, until 28 is reached. This is a perfectly good solution, but it does not exhibit imagination or maturing concepts. Another child may reach 13 by moving the entire first line all at once, then 3 of the second line. Adding 15 to this in the most efficient manner would require visualizing 15 as 7 + 8. After some experimentation and discussion there should emerge the idea of moving two full lines, one for the ten in 13 and one for the ten in 15, then adding on the 3 and the 5. However, the other procedure of adding 7 to 13 and then adding 8 is not an inferior method.

Most writers on the subject lay great stress on the idea that we can only add like things: we add groups of ones, we add groups of tens, and so on. This is an important idea, particularly when the numbers involved have more than two digits. But this is a consequence of the structure of the notation system rather than a limitation of the addition operation. We can and do add groups of one to groups of tens. An analogy is usually made employing denominate numbers with such assertions as "you cannot add 4 gallons and 3 quarts." Of course you can. You can even add 4 gallons of kerosene and 3 quarts of milk if you do not care what kind of mess the answer is. The youngster who claimed he "could too" add 5 apples and 3 peaches knew what he was talking about. When the teacher asked what he would get his answer was "fruit salad."

If the 2 two-digit numbers to be added do not require carrying, the best procedure is to add the ones and add the tens in the traditional manner. ("Regrouping" or "changing" are probably better words but "carrying" is too firmly entrenched in the vocabulary to do much about it.) This kind of addition problem will offer little difficulty for the pupil who has mastered the basic addition facts. Care should be exercised, however, to make sure the pupil realizes that he is combining ones with ones and tens with tens. For this purpose, since it employs place value, the abacus is superior to the counting frame. In the figure we show the addition of 52 and 23.

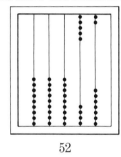 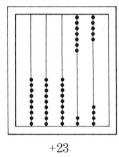

52   +23

The problem may then be written as

$$5 \text{ tens} + 2 \text{ ones}$$
$$\underline{2 \text{ tens} + 3 \text{ ones}}$$
$$7 \text{ tens} + 5 \text{ ones}$$

then as

$$50 + 2$$
$$\underline{20 + 3}$$
$$70 + 5$$

and finally in the usual fashion.

Money problems involving dimes and pennies are useful teaching aids here. This is better than bundles of ten ones. The single dime stands for ten of the pennies just as a single one in the tens place stands for 10 ones.

Carrying can be avoided when adding 2 two-digit numbers by extending the "bridging" idea of high-decade addition. For example, when we add $57 + 39$ we can add $9 + 57 = 66$ then $66 + 30 = 96$. This is a useful method and should be taught. But the usual carry method should be learned first and the method generalized to addends of any number of digits. In fact, higher-decade addition should be taught in close proximity to, if not in conjunction with, column addition.

5.10 CARRYING IN ADDITION

From the historical standpoint the addition algorithm has undergone less change than any of the others. The essential feature of any algorithm is simply the means whereby the place value aspect of the number is utilized. That is why the same algorithms can be used if we use a number base other than ten but cannot be used with a non-positional number system.

There are two early addition algorithms which are of interest in connection with the problem of carrying. The Hindus used a scratch method in which the addition was done from left to right:

$$
\begin{array}{r}
5863 \\
941 \\
2147 \\
\hline
7\cancel{8}41 \\
895
\end{array}
$$

Starting with the left hand column, we have $5 + 2 = 7$. In the next column $8 + 9 + 1 = 18$, we write the 8 in this column and scratch the left hand 7 replacing it with 8. Then $6 + 4 + 4 = 14$, we write the 4 and scratch the 8 replacing it with a 9. Finally, $3 + 1 + 7 = 11$, we write 1 and scratch the 4 making it a 5.

A method which was popular in the sixteenth century is occasionally seen today. It consists of writing down the sum of each column, then adding the column sums:

```
5492
 173
1861
 429
─────
  15 ← Sum of ones column
  24 ← Sum of tens column
17   ← Sum of hundreds column
6    ← Sum of thousands column
─────
7955 ← Sum of column sums
```

Of course, this does not completely eliminate carrying unless one wishes to re-apply the technique to adding the column sums:

```
136
872
 95
────
 13
 19
9
────
103
10
────
1103
```

Some writers advocate this as a method for permanent use, on the ground that it eliminates carrying. It would seem to have more merit as an introductory method, to be dropped after the child understands what he is doing when he carries.

When used as an introductory method it is well to give the column sums their correct place values by adjoining the necessary zeros.

```
5492
 173
1861
 429
─────
  15
 240
1700
6000
─────
7955
```

The one important idea in teaching carrying is the notion that we do not have room for more than 9 ones in the ones place, nor more than 9 tens in the tens place, and so on. Carrying then becomes discarding ten (or a multiple of ten) of a given size set and exchanging it for one set ten times as large. It is for this reason that we recommend an abacus containing only nine counters on each wire. It is possible on the Chinese abacus to have 15 units temporarily on the units line. The Japanese form permits 10. But with only nine counters to the line we have a better physical analogy to our notation system. The abacus can be very useful in developing the meaning underlying carrying. Figure 16 illustrates its use in adding 187 + 65. Figure 16a

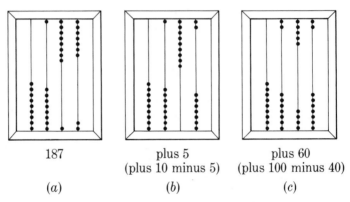

	187	plus 5	plus 60
		(plus 10 minus 5)	(plus 100 minus 40)
	(a)	(b)	(c)

Figure 16 ADDITION ON THE ABACUS, 187 + 65.

shows 187 entered. Our purpose is not merely to obtain the answer, but to show what happens when we carry. The child is asked to add 65. He can put only 2 of the 5 on the ones line. When he empties the ones line he has only discarded 9, so when he exchanges them for a 1 in the tens place he has added on one more of the five. He then enters the remaining 2 on the ones line. Figure 16b shows the abacus with the first step completed. He must now add 6 in the tens place, but it is already full. When he exchanges the 9 tens for a single hundred he has added one of the 6 tens, so 5 is then entered in the tens place.

Pupils can use the abacus with more finesse as they get the idea. After some practice the above problem will be worked something like the following. Step one: "I need 3 more to make a ten out of the 7 ones and I will still have 2 of the 5 ones. So I add one ten and leave 2 ones." Step two: "The tens line is full, so I will add 1 in the hundreds place. But that is 4 tens too much so I take off 4 tens." Practice with the abacus is highly recommended—not teacher-dicted, rule-of-thumb drill but experimentation. This is conducive to thinking about numbers and discovery of number relationships.

Those who see no value in the abacus as an instructional aid miss the point. Experience with a base of notation different from ten is believed to have value in giving meaning to the structure of positional notation. With the possible exception of members of the Duodecimal Society, no one seriously entertains the notion that computation in base twelve is going to replace base ten. So it is with the abacus. Its value in arithmetic instruction stems from the opportunity it affords for experimentation, discovery, and development of insight into the significance of positional notation. A high degree of technical facility with the abacus should hardly be our objective unless one plans to live in the Orient.

5.11 COLUMN ADDITION

Most pupil difficulties with column addition stem from two sources:

(1) *Keeping the columns straight.* The proper alignment of the digits is no easy task for young children, particularly so if all addends do not have the same number of digits. It is helpful for the child to know *why* this is so important. It is also an aid to have the pupil draw vertical lines to separate the columns.

(2) *Carrying.* Many teachers instruct the pupil to write down the number carried in the column to which it is carried. This may have some merit, and many adults consistently follow the practice, but it has its dangers. In checking the work, it may be mistaken for one of the original numbers. Apparently writing the carried digit down implies that it is to be added in last. A better procedure is to let the carried number be the first addend in the new column. This of course introduces the necessity of adding an unseen number to a seen one, which is the third major source of difficulty. This difficulty is unavoidable for we must always add a seen and an unseen number after the first sum in each column is found. For example, if we add $8 + 9 + 6 + 5 + 9$ we are adding $8 + 9$ (seen), then 17 (unseen) $+ 6$ (seen), then 23 (unseen) $+ 5$ (seen), and finally 28 (unseen) $+ 9$ (seen). Higher-decade addition will help alleviate this difficulty. In fact, without higher-decade addition column addition would be a hopeless task anyway.

Initial practice in column addition should consist of methodical addition of one symbol at a time in order from top to bottom or bottom to top. This will be the only way some pupils will ever add a column. However, after this has been mastered the capable pupils should be encouraged mentally to alter the order of the numbers in a column when it is advantageous to do so, to look for complements of ten, to recognize the sum of more than two addends at a glance, and to employ these and various other devices that a person usually competent in addition employs. These ideas should not be presented as different methods to be rigidly followed. They should be suggested as optional means of gaining greater proficiency. When a few such suggestions are pointed out the capable pupil will discover his own and use those that he finds helpful.

5.12 CHECKING ADDITION

The habit of checking his work is one of the most useful habits a child can form in his arithmetic work. It will markedly reduce the number of computational mistakes.

One valuable check consists of reworking the problem by a different method. The possibility of more than one method of solution of a problem should be stressed continuously. In the early stages of instruction in addition the sum can be found on the counting frame as a check. Groups of objects may be used to represent the addends and the combined group counted. With two or more addends the numbers may be reversed. In column addition, if we add up the column we can check the work by adding down the column. Bridging by endings and by completing tens may each be used as a check against the other. The problem may be solved on the abacus to check the solution.

The check of nines is an interesting check which does not consist of working the problem again by another method. The effectiveness of such a check depends upon bringing all digits into the computation. To check addition by the check of nines:

(1) Find the sum of the digits of each addend. If the sum has more than one digit repeat the process, that is, find the sum of its digits. Continue until a one digit result is obtained. If the one digit result is nine replace it with zero.

(2) Find the sum of the results obtained in step one. If this result has more than one digit proceed as in step (1).

(3) Find the sum of the digits in the sum of the original addends, that is, the sum of the digits of the answer. If the result has more than one digit repeat the process as in steps (1) and (2) until a one digit result is obtained. If steps (2) and (3) yield the same result the addition checks. Otherwise a mistake has been made.

We illustrate the method with the following:

ADD: CHECK:

786	$6 + 8 + 7 = 21 - 1 + 2 = \quad 3$
1543	$1 + 5 + 4 + 3 = 13 - 3 + 1 = \quad 4$
129	$1 + 2 + 9 = 12 - 2 + 1 = \quad 3$
2458	$\overline{10} - 1 + 0 = 1$

$$8 + 5 + 4 + 2 = 19 - 1 + 9 = 10 - 1 + 0 = 1$$

A justification for the check is developed in the next chapter, page 200. The following should be a satisfactory explanation for middle and upper grade pupils. Any whole number is a multiple of nine plus the sum of its digits. Thus:

$$786 = 7(99 + 1) + 8(9 + 1) + 6 = 7 \times 99 + 7 + 8 \times 9 + 8 + 6$$
$$= 9(7 \times 11 + 8) + 7 + 8 + 6$$
$$1543 = 1(999 + 1) + 5(99 + 1) + 4(9 + 1) + 3$$
$$= 1 \times 999 + 1 + 5 \times 99 + 5 + 4 \times 9 + 4 + 3$$
$$= 9(111 + 5 \times 11 + 4) + 1 + 5 + 4 + 3$$
$$129 = 1(99 + 1) + 2(9 + 1) + 9 = 1 \times 99 + 1 + 2 \times 9 + 2 + 9$$
$$= 9(11 + 2) + 1 + 2 + 9$$

Similarly, the sum 2458 is a multiple of 9 plus the sum of its digits. Hence the digit sum in step (3) should equal the sum of the digit sums in step (2).

Fourth or fifth graders will find the check of nines an interesting and useful check. Since the check of nines will not catch a mistake of transposition of digits the teacher may wish to employ the check of elevens as well. The check of elevens works exactly like the check of nines except that we alternately add and subtract digits rather than merely add them. To illustrate:

ADD: CHECK:

786		$6 - 8 + 7 = \quad 5$
1543		$3 - 4 + 5 - 1 = \quad 3$
129		$9 - 2 + 1 = \quad 8$
2458	$8 - 5 + 4 - 2 = 5$	$\overline{16} \quad 6 - 1 = 5$

The check of elevens may prove to be difficult because of the likelihood of the appearance of negative numbers. This can be avoided although it complicates the check. We can avoid negative numbers by agreeing that whenever we are required to subtract a larger number from a smaller one the smaller shall be increased by 11:

ADD:

CHECK:

$$3 - 8 \text{ is impossible, therefore}$$

483
924
9603

$$14 - 8 + 4 = 10$$
$$4 - 2 + 9 = 11$$
$$3 - 0 + 6 - 9 = 0$$

11,010

$$\overline{21}$$ 1 − 2 is im-

$$0 - 1 + 0 - 1 + 1$$
$$11 - 1 + 0 - 1 + 1 = 10$$

possible therefore

$$12 - 2 = 10$$

The justification of the check of elevens is essentially the same as that of the check of nines. The essential difference stems from the fact that whereas 10, 100, 1000 and so on are each one more than a multiple of 9 they are alternately one less and one more than a multiple of 11. Thus, $10 = 11 - 1$, $100 = 99 + 1$, $1000 = 1001 - 1$.

Perhaps the most useful of all checks consists of estimating the answer. It is extremely important for the child to develop the habit of estimating the answer, preferably before the solution is found. This is one place where instruction in arithmetic is in great need of improvement. Very few children develop this most valuable habit. All too frequently pupils are uncritically willing to accept answers that are ridiculously impossible. The pupil who realizes his answer cannot be correct though he cannot find his mistake is far better off than the one who is blissfully unaware that his solution is wrong.

The ability to estimate the answer requires some knowledge of rounding off. We illustrate by estimating the answer to the above example. Since 483 is about 5 hundreds, 924 is about 9 hundreds, 9603 is about 96 hundreds, the answer should be about $96 + 9 + 5 = 110$ hundreds or 11,000.

Exercises

1 Should a child be permitted to count on his fingers to find addition facts? The counting frame? Loose counters? Discuss the pros and cons.

2 Distinguish between "bridging" in higher decade addition by "endings" and by "completing tens." Which method is superior? Illustrate the two methods with $37 + 5$.

3 What are the "basic addition facts?"

4 Show how carrying can be made meaningful with each of the instructional aids: number line, abacus, pennies and dimes.

5 Should the child be taught $4 + 3$ and $3 + 4$ as the same addition fact?

6 What difference, if any, is there in the meaning of $4 + 3$ as opposed to $3 + 4$?

7 How should addition be introduced when formal work in addition is begun?

8 What is the difference in implication of the two expressions "3 and 4 more" and "3 with 4?"

9 Show how to use the number line to verify that $5 + 8 = 8 + 5$.

10 Add the following and check by the check of nines. Check by the check of elevens.

$$381 + 246 + 867$$

11 Describe other ways to check the addition in Exercise 10.

12 What generalizations should be used as aids in learning the basic addition facts?

5.13 PREPARING FOR SUBTRACTION

Development of the concepts of subtraction should proceed hand in hand with those of addition. Just as a sum may be obtained by counting, so a difference may be found by counting backward. This applies to the counting frame and the number line as well as to loose counters. Whereas addition is made to mean the combining of two sets into a single set, subtraction may be made to mean the removal of a subset from a set. When the child learns the addition facts he should associate with them the corresponding subtraction facts. When he discovers that a set of 3 added to a set of 5 yields a set of 8 he should learn to generalize this result to obtain the fact that if he takes a set of 3 from a set of 8 he will have left a set of 5. In other words, subtraction should be taught along with addition as its inverse, as the undoing of addition.

However, subtraction is inherently more difficult than addition. Addition is interpreted merely as one quantity increased by another quantity, two quantities put together. Subtraction, on the other hand, has three distinctly different interpretations. One is the *comparison* concept mentioned above. We may interpret $a - b$ to mean how many more a is than b. "John has 9 marbles, Tom has 4. *How many more* does John have?"

A second interpretation is the *take-away* concept. Here we interpret $a - b$ to mean how many are left when we take b from a. "There are 30 children in the room. If 16 dance at a time *how many are left?*"

The third meaning we may give subtraction may be called the *missing addend* concept. Here we are concerned with *how many more are needed.* "Billy is saving to buy a \$25 bike. He has saved \$18. How much more does he need?"

The child must learn to associate each of the three different kinds of problem situation with subtraction. Yet he should see each of them as the undoing of addition.

Since subtraction is the inverse of addition, we may think of it as finding one addend when we know the sum and the other addend. The sum is called the *minuend*. The known addend is called the *subtrahend*. The missing addend is called the *remainder* or the *difference*. We refer to it as the remainder, what is left, in take-away subtraction, and as the difference in comparison subtraction. The two words are quite descriptive of their respective interpretations of the operation. It is unfortunate that we use the word "remainder" with equal appropriateness in connection with division. Mathematics is guilty of occasional multiple use of technical terms. Care should be taken to show why the word "remainder" is used in both subtraction and division.

It is perhaps more obvious that take-away subtraction is the inverse of addition than is true of the other interpretations. Addition means putting together; subtraction means taking apart. However, much more important than the inverse nature of the operations is the relationship of the addition facts to the subtraction facts. It is from this point of view that we can most effectively show the child the appropriateness of the inverse concept applied to comparison subtraction. If $a - b$ is the number which tells us how many more a is than b it is certainly the amount we would have to increase b, that is, add to b, in order to make it the same size as a. Additive subtraction, in the sense that the problem situation calls for determination of how many more are needed, may be interpreted similarly.

It is helpful in developing the three interpretations of subtraction to interpret the same problem all three ways. For example: John and Betty are throwing darts. John's score is 45 and Betty's is

30. John's score is how many more than Betty's? (Comparison.) How many points will Betty have to make on her next throw to tie the score? (Missing addend.) If to win the game one person must get 50 points ahead of the other what would be the simplest way to record the score? (Take-away.)

Examples of this sort not only serve to develop the different *interpretations* of subtraction; they also point up the fact that there is really just *one* operation involved insofar as the quantitative relationships are concerned. From the standpoint of concrete manipulation, however, all three are different. In take-away subtraction we start with the minuend and remove the subtrahend. For example: Bill gave 3 of his 8 marbles to Tom. How many did he have left? Using loose counters the child will solve this by counting out 8 counters, then removing 3 from the total.

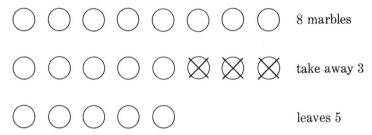

In comparison subtraction the minuend and subtrahend will both be counted out; then by pairing the subtrahend group with part of the minuend group the difference is obtained as the part of the minuend not used in the pairing. For example: If Jane brought 8 dolls and Mary brought 3, how many more did Jane bring?

In additive subtraction we begin with the subtrahend and add to it until the desired minuend is reached. For example: Jack needs 8 blocks to finish his house. If he has 3 how many more must he get?

In all three cases we are finding what must be added to 3 in order to get 8. In the first case this is because in a physical sense we "add backwards." We took 3 away from 8. If we put it back we will be adding 3 to the answer and the sum will certainly be 8. In the second example it is by implication that we have found the missing addend. We find out how many would have to be added to the subtrahend if we made it the same size as the minuend. In the last example we

Jack has 3 blocks

he must get 5 more

since he needs 8

actually add rather than subtract. This differs from ordinary addition in that one addend and the sum are known in advance, rather than the two addends.

5.14   THE SUBTRACTION FACTS

A variety of methods of subtraction are taught in today's schools. The subtraction facts which the child must learn will depend upon the method taught.

The take-away method is the more frequently taught in the United States while the additive method finds more favor in Europe. When the take-away method is employed the child learns the facts as "minuend take away subtrahend equals remainder." Seven pennies take away four pennies leaves three pennies. The fact may be stated in a number of ways: Seven take away three, three from seven, seven less three, seven minus three. The child should learn to recognize the situation from any of these expressions. The best initial phraseology is probably "three from seven" since it is more descriptive of the child's take-away concept of the operation. However, this expression is more apt to lead to confusion in view of the manner of writing the symbols 7 — 3. The child is apt to translate "three from seven" as

3 − 7. He must learn that the first number in the number symbols is what we start with. Given three counters, he can readily see that he cannot remove seven.

When the additive method is employed the child does not learn 7 − 3 = ? Instead he learns 3 + ? = 7. The argument that the additive method eliminates the necessity of learning any combinations other than the addition facts is a spurious one. Knowing the answer to 3 + 4 = ? is no more guarantee that the child will be able to generalize this to 3 + ? = 7 than that he can generalize to 7 − 3 = ? Success in making the generalization in either case depends upon the child's understanding of the inverse nature of the operation. Any advantage which either method possesses accrues from the ease with which the inverse concept is established.

There are 100 basic subtraction facts which the child must master in order to perform the subtraction algorithm. These are derivable directly from the 100 addition facts. The addition facts involve only one-digit addends. But since in subtraction the minuend is the sum of the related addition fact, the minuends of the subtraction facts include the two-digit numbers through 18.

As was true of the addition facts, certain generalizations will greatly facilitate mastery of the subtraction facts. By far the most important of these is the fact that *subtraction is the inverse of addition*. All of the remaining generalizations are subsumed by this one.

Subtracting zero from a number leaves the number unchanged. *Zero is the identity element* for subtraction. 5 − 0 = 5.

Counting backward by ones is equivalent to subtracting ones.

The remainder and the subtrahend may be interchanged. This derives from the fact that addition is commutative. It should be noted that in addition the two related facts produce the same result: 3 + 4 = 7 and 4 + 3 = 7. In subtraction the results are different: 7 − 3 = 4 but 7 − 4 = 3.

Subtracting a number from itself always gives zero. 5 − 5 = 0. This is a logical consequence of the second and fourth principles above.

It was shown in Section 4.10 that if successive subtractions are to be made one may instead add the subtrahends and subtract their sum:

$$18 - 6 - 3 = 18 - (6 + 3) = 18 - 9.$$

One may obviously reverse this procedure. *The subtrahend may be*

100 Subtraction Facts

0	1	2	3	4	5	6	7	8	9
0	0	0	0	0	0	0	0	0	0
—	—	—	—	—	—	—	—	—	—
0	1	2	3	4	5	6	7	8	9
1	2	3	4	5	6	7	8	9	10
1	1	1	1	1	1	1	1	1	1
—	—	—	—	—	—	—	—	—	—
0	1	2	3	4	5	6	7	8	9
2	3	4	5	6	7	8	9	10	11
2	2	2	2	2	2	2	2	2	2
—	—	—	—	—	—	—	—	—	—
0	1	2	3	4	5	6	7	8	9
3	4	5	6	7	8	9	10	11	12
3	3	3	3	3	3	3	3	3	3
—	—	—	—	—	—	—	—	—	—
0	1	2	3	4	5	6	7	8	9
4	5	6	7	8	9	10	11	12	13
4	4	4	4	4	4	4	4	4	4
—	—	—	—	—	—	—	—	—	—
0	1	2	3	4	5	6	7	8	9
5	6	7	8	9	10	11	12	13	14
5	5	5	5	5	5	5	5	5	5
—	—	—	—	—	—	—	—	—	—
0	1	2	3	4	5	6	7	8	9
6	7	8	9	10	11	12	13	14	15
6	6	6	6	6	6	6	6	6	6
—	—	—	—	—	—	—	—	—	—
0	1	2	3	4	5	6	7	8	9
7	8	9	10	11	12	13	14	15	16
7	7	7	7	7	7	7	7	7	7
—	—	—	—	—	—	—	—	—	—
0	1	2	3	4	5	6	7	8	9
8	9	10	11	12	13	14	15	16	17
8	8	8	8	8	8	8	8	8	8
—	—	—	—	—	—	—	—	—	—
0	1	2	3	4	5	6	7	8	9
9	10	11	12	13	14	15	16	17	18
9	9	9	9	9	9	9	9	9	9
—	—	—	—	—	—	—	—	—	—
0	1	2	3	4	5	6	7	8	9

broken up into parts and each part subtracted. This principle can be quite helpful in learning those facts which have for minuend a two-digit number. For example, the relationship $17 - 9 = 17 - 7 - 2$ should help the child learn the fact $17 - 9 = 8$.

The program of discovery and incidental learning of the subtraction facts must be complemented and reinforced with systematic intensive drill if the class is to master the subtraction algorithm. To this end, flash cards similar to those used in addition drill will prove valuable aids. Another type of card, containing families of related facts, is also useful. On one side of the card a fact without the answer is given, as $11 - 6 = ?$ On the reverse side the four related facts are given, as $11 - 6 = 5$, $6 + 5 = 11$, $11 - 5 = 6$, and $5 + 6 = 11$. Drill activities similar to those using the addition flash cards should be employed in mastering the subtraction facts.

$$
\begin{array}{cc}
11 & 6 \\
-\ 6 & +\ 5 \\
\hline
5 & 11 \\[2mm]
11 & 5 \\
-\ 5 & +\ 6 \\
\hline
6 & 11
\end{array}
$$

$$
\begin{array}{c}
11 \\
-\ 6 \\
\hline
\end{array}
$$

5.15 THE SUBTRACTION ALGORITHM

There are four methods of subtraction with which the teacher should be familiar. The superiority of each method has been the subject of much debate, yielding more heat than light. Experimental evidence concerning their relative merits is inconclusive. Nothing other than confusion can be gained by attempting to teach the child more than one method. However, in the upper grades alternative methods may be used as enrichment material and to motivate drill where needed. The prospective teacher should know all four methods since any one of them may be the prescribed one in the school system in which he teaches. Furthermore, transfer pupils are apt to have been taught any one of them.

A subtraction algorithm is needed whenever the process is extended beyond the 100 basic facts, that is, when the minuend exceeds 18 and/or the subtrahend has more than one digit. We can certainly subtract three from fifty, but we cannot subtract three ones from five tens and expect to get two ones or tens or one-tens or anything else. As was true with addition, in subtraction we must combine digits of the same order, ones with ones, tens with tens, and so on. Then we may think of the minuend and subtrahend as being broken into the components implied by its digits. For example:

$$876 = 8 \text{ hundreds} + 7 \text{ tens} + 6 \text{ ones}$$
$$342 = 3 \text{ hundreds} + 4 \text{ tens} + 2 \text{ ones}$$

We may then apply the basic subtraction facts to like digits. The above problem will be solved by the take-away method thus

		We think:
	876	$6 - 2 = ?$ (4) *ones*
	342	$7 - 4 = ?$ (3) *tens*
	534	$8 - 3 = ?$ (5) *hundreds*

Or by the additive method

		We think:
	876	$2 + ? = 6$ (4) *ones*
	342	$4 + ? = 7$ (3) *tens*
	534	$3 + ? = 8$ (5) *hundreds*

All goes well until we are confronted with a situation wherein a given digit of the subtrahend is greater than the corresponding digit of the minuend. For example:

	We think:
837	$7 - 9 = ?$ (Impossible with positive numbers)
259	$3 - 5 = ?$ (Impossible with positive numbers)

The additive method encounters the same impasse—$9 + ? = 7$, $5 + ? = 3$.

There are two ways out of this difficulty. One is the *decomposition* method, sometimes called the borrowing method. The other is the *equal additions* method, sometimes called the borrow and pay back method. Either of these may be used with either take-away subtraction or additive subtraction. These possible combinations yield the four methods mentioned at the beginning of this section. They are (1) *take-away—decomposition*, (2) *take-away—equal additions*, (3) *additive—decomposition*, and (4) *additive—equal additions*.

The decomposition method depends upon the fact that a number may be expressed as the sum of its components in a variety of ways. For example, $837 = 800 + 30 + 7$, but it also equals $763 + 72 + 2$ and $800 + 21 + 16$ and many other combinations. In the problem $837 - 259$ the usual components by digits

$$837 = 800 + 30 + 7$$
$$259 = 200 + 50 + 9$$

lead to difficulties. Since we cannot take 9 ones from 7 ones we "borrow" one of the tens, giving us 10 more ones or 17 ones in all. [This is really not borrowing at all. It is more properly making change—getting a ten-dollar bill changed into 10 ones. Who is the borrower, and who is the lender? Certainly not minuend or sub-trahend. Nor has the ones digit borrowed from the tens digit unless we use the word as the panhandler does.] This requires the following decomposition:

$$837 = 800 + 20 + 17$$
$$259 = 200 + 50 + 9$$

We can now take 9 ones from 17 ones, but we cannot take 5 tens from 2 tens. We must decompose the 8 hundreds into 7 hundreds and 10 tens:

$$837 = 700 + 120 + 17$$
$$259 = 200 + 50 + 9$$

and the subtraction can be performed, 9 ones from 17 ones, 5 tens from 12 tens, 2 hundreds from 7 hundreds. The problem is solved by take-away–decomposition as follows:

$$
\begin{array}{ll}
 & \text{We think:} \\
837 & 17 - 9 = 8 \\
259 & 12 - 5 = 7 \\
\overline{} & 7 - 2 = 5 \\
578 &
\end{array}
$$

or by the additive–decomposition method

$$
\begin{array}{ll}
 & \text{We think:} \\
837 & 9 + 8 = 17 \\
259 & 5 + 7 = 12 \\
\overline{} & 2 + 5 = 7 \\
578 &
\end{array}
$$

The equal-additions method depends upon the principle that if minuend and subtrahend are increased by the same amount the remainder is unchanged:

$$5 - 3 = 2 \text{ and } (5 + 7) - (3 + 7) = 2$$

The equal additions are made by adding 10 of a given digit, as 10 ones, 10 tens, to the minuend and adding 1 of the next higher digit to the subtrahend. Thus in the problem $837 - 259$ we add 10 ones to 837 and 1 ten to 259 for the first step

$$837 \rightarrow 800 + 30 + 17 + 10$$
$$259 \quad\ 200 + 60 + 9$$

and for the second step we add 10 tens to $800 + 30 + 17$ and add 1 hundred to $200 + 60 + 9$. This yields

$$837 \rightarrow 800 + 130 + 17$$
$$259 \quad\ 300 + 60 + 9$$

and the subtraction can be done.

The problem is solved by the take-away–equal-additions method as

	We think:
837	9 from 17 = 8
259	6 from 13 = 7
——	3 from 8 = 5
578	

and by the additive–equal-additions method as

	We think:
837	9 + ? = 17 (8)
259	6 + ? = 13 (7)
——	3 + ? = 8 (5)
578	

The popularity of the take-away–decomposition method undoubtedly stems from the fact that the take-away concept of subtraction is the most natural, the easiest for the child to grasp. Furthermore, decomposition is directly related to carrying in addition, they are inverse operations. In decomposition we convert a higher unit to ten of the next lower; in carrying we convert ten lower units into one of the next higher.

Regardless of the method used, such devices as implied by the terms *borrow*, *borrow and pay back*, and rules of thumb for carrying through the algorithm are at best a poor substitute for real insight into the true nature of the operation. "Borrow and pay back" is really "give and give." We give ten units to the minuend and give one of the next higher units to the subtrahend.

Money problems provide excellent means for making either decomposition or equal additions meaningful. Suppose the problem is to subtract 2 dimes 7 pennies from 5 dimes 3 pennies. The child is much more apt to discover for himself the decomposition method than equal additions.

Since there are not enough pennies in the minuend, the most obvious way to get more is to change one of the dimes into pennies.

If equal-additions is the official method the pupil must have already mastered the fact that the remainder is unaffected by the same increase in minuend and subtrahend. When this method is used we do not change one of the minuend dimes into pennies. We increase the minuend by ten pennies then subtract an extra dime.

The abacus is another excellent device for clarifying the concept involved here. In Figure 17 the decomposition method is used to find 53 − 27. In Figure 17a, 53 is registered.

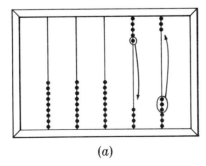

(a)

Figure 17a

The arrows indicate the direction in which the circled counters are moved to perform the subtraction in the ones digit. One counter on the tens line is moved down, leaving only 4 tens. Then we mentally combine 10 ones with the 3 ones present and subtract 7 ones. This means there must be 6 counters on the ones line. Thus the 3 circled counters are moved up. Figure 17*b* indicates the final step, subtracting 2 tens.

If we use the equal-additions method a ten would not be removed as a part of the first step, and in the final step 3 tens would be removed.

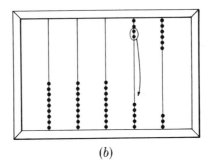

(*b*)

Figure 17*b*

Subtracting on the abacus affords an excellent means of motivating needed review drill in the upper grades.

5.16 OTHER ALGORITHMS

The child should not be expected to master for use any other than the official method of subtraction although other methods may be used as enrichment material. They may also be helpful in clarifying the meaning of the official method. Caution should be used to guard against creating confusion in the child's mind. This is most apt to occur among pupils who understand how but not why the method they are using works.

The *scratch* method holds some historical interest. It was used in the early days of our number system. It is adapted from computation on the abacus. Place value is preserved in the usual manner, by column alignment of all numbers of the same digit value. The usual order of subtraction of digits was from left to right although the algorithm works regardless of the order used:

Subtract: 1726 — 259

$$
\begin{array}{r}
46 \\
\cancel{5}7\cancel{7} \\
1\cancel{7}2\cancel{6} \\
\cancel{2}\cancel{5}\cancel{9}
\end{array}
$$

The minuend and subtrahend are first aligned in the usual manner. We first subtract 2 from 7, the 2 and 7 are canceled and 5 placed over the 7.

$$
\begin{array}{r}
5 \\
1\cancel{7}26 \\
\cancel{2}59
\end{array}
$$

We next subtract 5 (the tens digit in the subtrahend) from 52, leaving 47. In this step the 5, the 2 above it, and the 5 in hundreds place are canceled.

$$
\begin{array}{r}
4 \\
\cancel{5}7 \\
1\cancel{7}26 \\
\cancel{2}\cancel{5}9
\end{array}
$$

In the last step we take 9 from 76. The 9, 7, and 6 are canceled, leaving 6 over the canceled 7 and 7 over the canceled 6.

$$
\begin{array}{r}
46 \\
\cancel{5}7\cancel{7} \\
1\cancel{7}2\cancel{6} \\
\cancel{2}\cancel{5}\cancel{9}
\end{array}
$$

Everything is now canceled except the remainder, 1467.

There are a number of variations of the *complementary* method of subtraction. Its origin is also quite old. The operation of some calculating machines depends upon this principle. The idea is sometimes quite convenient in mental calculation; for example, rather than subtract 8 we can add 2 and subtract 10. This is what we really do on the abacus whenever we are confronted with the need for "borrowing." The method consists of adding the complement to ten (ten minus the number) of each digit in the subtrahend and subtracting ten from the sum:

Subtract 259 from 1726.

1726	(1) One is the complement of 9; therefore we add 1
259	to 6, giving 7 in the ones digit. Since this is less than
——	10 we must subtract a ten from the tens digit.
1467	

(2) Five is its own complement, therefore we add 5 to 1 [we used
1 of the 2 in step (1)] giving 6 in the tens digit. Again we have
less than 10 so we must reduce the 7 in the hundreds place to a 6.

(3) The complement of 2 is 8. We add $8 + 6 = 14$. Here, since
the sum is greater than 10, we subtract 10 from the sum, writing
4 in the hundreds place.

(4) We can still apply the rule to the last digit. Zero has 10 for
complement. Therefore we add 10 to 1 and subtract 10, leaving
1 in thousands place.

This scheme obviously gives the correct result since in each digit
we add ten minus the digit minus ten, which is equivalent to subtracting the digit.

The following is a slight variation of the complementary method:

Subtract 5361 from 7923.
Here we shall add the complement to *nine* of each digit of
the subtrahend.

7923   (1) 8 (the complement of 1) $+ 3 = 11$ we
5361   write 1 and carry 1.
——   (2) 3 (the complement of 6) $+ 2 + 1$ (carried)
①2561 $= 6$. We write 6.

2562

(3) 6 (the complement of 3) $+ 9 = 15$, we write 5 and carry 1.
(4) (4 the complement of 5) $+ 7 + 1$ (carried) $= 12$. We write
12. Now the highest digit, which must be a 1, is removed and
added to the ones digit, giving 2562, the correct remainder.

5.17 CHECKING SUBTRACTION

The most commonly used check for subtraction consists of performing
the inverse operation. The remainder plus the subtrahend equals the
minuend. If additive subtraction has been used the check becomes
merely a repetition of the original work.

Subtract and check.

                              CHECK
             4732 ←┐   931
              931 │   3801
             ———— │   ————
             3801 └→ 4732

During the developmental phase of learning subtraction counting backward is an appropriate check when the subtrahend is not too large. Dot drawings, loose counters, and the number line are also appropriate for this kind of situation.

A very good check consists of subtracting the remainder from the minuend, which should give the subtrahend for a check.

Subtract and check.

$$\begin{array}{cc} & \text{CHECK} \\ 837 & 837 \\ \underline{152} \leftarrow & \underline{685} \\ \overline{685} & \rightarrow \overline{152} \end{array}$$

The check of nines may be used with subtraction just as it is with addition except that we subtract the digit sum of the subtrahend from the digit sum of the minuend.

Subtract and check.

$$\begin{array}{c} 8365 \\ \underline{4728} \\ \overline{3637} \end{array}$$

CHECK.

$5 + 6 + 3 + 8 = 22 - 2 + 2 = 4$ (digit sum of minuend)
$8 + 2 + 7 + 4 = 21 - 2 + 1 = 3$ (digit sum of subtrahend)
$4 - 3 = 1$ (minuend minus subtrahend)

$7 + 3 + 6 + 3 = 19 - 1 + 9 = 10 - 1 + 0 = 1$ (digit sum of remainder)

Sometimes the digit sum of the subtrahend is greater than that of the minuend. When this occurs we can avoid negative numbers by increasing the minuend digit sum by 9.

Subtract and check.

$$\begin{array}{c} 34176 \\ \underline{8232} \\ \overline{25944} \end{array}$$

CHECK.

$6 + 7 + 1 + 4 + 3 = 21 - 1 + 2 = 3$ (digit sum of minuend)
$2 + 3 + 2 + 8 = 15 - 5 + 1 = 6$ (digit sum of subtrahend)
Since $6 > 3$ we increase the minuend by 9
$12 - 6 = 6$ (minuend minus subtrahend)
$4 + 4 + 9 + 5 + 2 = 24 - 4 + 2 = 6$ (digit sum of remainder)

The check of elevens is also applicable to subtraction. Negative numbers can be avoided by adding eleven at any point in the check where a negative number would otherwise be encountered:

Subtract and check.

$$
\begin{array}{r}
4731 \\
2193 \\
\hline
2538
\end{array}
$$

CHECK.

$1 - 3 + 7 - 4 = 1 + 7 - 3 - 4 = 1$ (excess of elevens in minuend)

$3 - 9 + 1 - 2 = 3 + 1 - 9 - 2 = 4 - 11$

Since this yields a negative number we add 11.

$11 + 4 - 11 = 4$ (excess of elevens in subtrahend)

Since $1 - 4$ is negative we add 11.

$11 + 1 - 4 = 8$ (difference of excesses)

$8 - 3 + 5 - 2 = 8$ (excesses of elevens in remainder)

Exercises

1   Discuss the issue of rote versus rational counting. Is there a place for rote counting in arithmetic instruction?

2   Which concept should come first, cardinal number or ordinal number?

3   Devise first-grade activities which may be used to distinguish cardinal from ordinal.

4   Why is it important for children to learn to count by groups of ten?

5   List activities in which the 100 chart may be utilized. State the objective of the activity.

6   Illustrate how 57 may be represented on the counting frame and on the abacus. What properties of number does each emphasize?

7   Describe a practice exercise utilizing the multiple counting chart.

8   Which is the more important concept, addition as combining groups or addition as regrouping?

9   Should the concepts of an empty group and a group of one be used in developing the addition facts?

10   Why is the commutative property important in learning the addition facts?

11   Why is it important for the child to know several methods for checking an operation?

12 Give examples, appropriate for use in the third grade, of each of the interpretations of subtraction.

13 Which method of subtraction is the easier for children to learn? Why?

14 Give arguments for and against teaching the subtraction facts concurrently with the addition facts.

15 Explain why the second complementary method of subtraction given on page 176 gives the correct answer.

16 List ways to check subtraction. Apply each method to check $7349 - 862 = 6487$.

17 By what principle may we say $38 - 23 = 40 - 25$?

18 Should subtraction be considered along with addition during the concept building foundation phase of the program? Should they be considered together during intensive drill for mastery of basic facts? Discuss.

19 What are the three possible interpretations of subtraction? Give appropriate examples to illustrate the three interpretations.

20 Show why subtraction is properly considered the inverse of addition in each of the examples of Exercise 19.

21 Why is the answer to a subtraction problem sometimes called a difference and sometimes called a remainder?

Suggested Supplementary Readings

Brueckner, Leo J., and Foster E. Grossnickle, *How to Make Arithmetic Meaningful*. Philadelphia: The John C. Winston Company, 1947. Chap. VI.

Buckingham, B. R., *Elementary Arithmetic: Its Meaning and Practice*. Boston: Ginn and Company, 1947. Chaps. V and VI.

Larson, Harold D., *Arithmetic for Colleges*. New York: The Macmillan Company, 1950. Chaps. III, V.

Morton, Robert Lee, *Teaching Arithmetic in the Elementary School*. New York: Silver Burdett Company, 1938. Vol. II, Chap. III.

Mueller, Francis J., *Arithmetic, Its Structure and Concepts*. Englewood Cliffs, N.J.: Prentice-Hall, Inc., 1956. pp. 48–68, 96–110.

Spitzer, Herbert F., *The Teaching of Arithmetic*. Boston: Houghton Mifflin Company, Third Edition, 1961. Chaps. III and IV.

Swain, Robert L., *Understanding Arithmetic*. New York: Rinehart and Company, Inc., 1957. Chap. IV.

Multiplication and Division

CHAPTER SIX

IN CHAPTER FOUR WE SAW that cardinal numbers, which we can consider synonymous with counting numbers, are definable in terms of sets. A cardinal number is a class of equivalent sets. We also defined addition of cardinal numbers in terms of the union of disjoint sets.

Addition can be described in terms of counting. Multiplication can be described as the addition of equal addends, $3 \times 4 = 4 + 4 + 4$. *successive addition* However, in this chapter we wish to consider multiplication in terms of set operations.

6.1 CARTESIAN PRODUCTS

A group of the boys and girls got together for some dancing. The set of boys was $B = \{$Tom, Jim, Ed, Rocky$\}$; the set of girls was

(181)

$G = \{\text{Alice, Sue, Martha}\}$. They decided that each boy would dance one number with each girl. What was the set of dancing partners? We can keep the list straight by starting with Tom, listing him with each girl, then doing the same for each of the remaining boys. We get the set of couples {(Tom, Alice), (Tom, Sue), (Tom, Martha), (Jim, Alice), (Jim, Sue), (Jim, Martha), (Ed, Alice), (Ed, Sue), (Ed, Martha), (Rocky, Alice), (Rocky, Sue), (Rocky, Martha)}.

This new set, the set of couples, is called the *Cartesian Product* of the sets B and G.

> *If A and B are sets, the symbol $A \times B$ indicates their Cartesian product, the set of ordered pairs obtained by pairing each element of A as first member with each of B as second member.*

EXAMPLE.

If $A = \{1, 3, 5\}$ and $B = \{2, 4, 6\}$
then $A \times B = \{(1, 2), (1, 4), (1, 6), (3, 2), (3, 4), (3, 6), (5, 2), (5, 4), (5, 6)\}$

We may upon occasion refer to a Cartesian product as merely a product. The qualifying word "Cartesian" is used because the intersection of two sets is referred to by some writers as a product of sets. Notice that the Cartesian product is not a union nor an intersection of sets. The elements of the product are pairs of elements, one from each of the original sets. The two sets do not have to be disjoint in order to have a Cartesian product.

$\{1, 2, 3\} \times \{2, 3, 5\}$
$= \{(1, 2), (1, 3), (1, 5), (2, 2), (2, 3), (2, 5), (3, 2), (3, 3), (3, 5)\}$

The elements of any set are distinct, $\{1, 2, 2, 2, 3\} = \{1, 2, 3\}$. In the notation $\{1, 2, 2, 2, 3\}$ we are merely repeating ourselves, its only elements are 1, 2, and 3. Since the pairs of a Cartesian product are ordered, its elements are unique even though the sets forming the product have common elements. In the above product each set has 2 and 3 for elements, but (2, 3) and (3, 2) are not the same *ordered* pair.

In fact, it is possible to find the product of a set with itself.

$\{1, 2, 3\} \times \{1, 2, 3\}$
$= \{(1, 1), (1, 2), (1, 3), (2, 1), (2, 2), (2, 3), (3, 1), (3, 2), (3, 3)\}$

Exercises

1 Find the Cartesian product $A \times B$ when sets A and B are each of the following:

(a) $A = \{a, b, c\}$; $B = \{1, 2\}$

(b) $A = \{1, a, x\}$; $B = \{a\}$
(c) $A = \{1, a, x\}$; $B = \{2, b, z\}$
(d) $A = \{1, 2\}$; $B = \{a, b, c\}$

2 In each part of Exercise 1 find the cardinal number of set A, set B, and set $A \times B$.

3 How many subsets are there of the set $\{a, b, c\}$? (Do not forget to count the empty set.)
How many elements are there of the set $\{a, b, c\} \times \{a, b, c\}$?

4 For any set A, how does the number of elements of A compare with the number of elements of $A \times A$?

5 What is the product $A \times B$ if $A = \{1, 2, 3\}$ and $B = $ the empty set?

6 Find $A \times A$ when $A = \{a\}$.

6.2 CARTESIAN PRODUCTS AND MULTIPLICATION

Every set has a cardinal number. The Cartesian product of two sets is a set, hence it has a cardinal number. We can now define the product of two cardinal numbers.

> Given set A *whose cardinal number is* a *and set* B *whose cardinal number is* b. *The product of the cardinal numbers* a *and* b, *written* a $\times$ b, a $\cdot$ b, *or* ab, *is the cardinal number of the Cartesian product* A $\times$ B *of the sets* A *and* B.

EXAMPLE. Set $A = \{0, 1, 2\}$ has the cardinal number 3. Set $B = \{0, 1, 2, 3\}$ has the cardinal number 4. By definition of multiplication, 3×4 is equal to the cardinal number of $A \times B = \{(0, 0), (0, 1), (0, 2), (0, 3), (1, 0), (1, 1), (1, 2), (1, 3), (2, 0), (2, 1), (2, 2), (2, 3)\}$. But the cardinal number of this set is 12. Then by definition, $3 \times 4 = 12$.

Under the usual interpretation of multiplication of whole numbers 3×4 does not mean the same as 4×3 although both equal 12. Is this consistent with the above definition of multiplication? Consider the two Cartesian products $\{a, b, c\} \times \{d, e\}$ and $\{d, e\} \times \{a, b, c\}$.

$$X = \{a, b, c\} \times \{d, e\} = \{(a, d), (a, e,) (b, d), (b, e), (c, d), (c, e)\}$$
$$Y = \{d, e\} \times \{a, b, c\} = \{(d, a), (d, b), (d, c), (e, a), (e, b), (e, c)\}$$

They certainly are not the same set. In fact, they are disjoint. However, they do have exactly the same set of pairs but the order of the elements in each pair is reversed. For example, the ordered pair (a, d) is an element of X and the ordered pair (d, a) is an element of Y. Thus, there is a one-to-one correspondence between the elements of X and the elements of Y. Any element (x, y) of X is paired with (y, x) of Y. This must be true of any two Cartesian products $A \times B$ and $B \times A$. In each case the elements of the product consist of each element of A paired with each element of B. We conclude that the number of elements of a Cartesian product is unaffected by changing the order of the sets.

The multiplication of cardinal numbers is *commutative*

$$a \times b = b \times a$$

Given set A with cardinal number a, set B with cardinal number b. The product $a \times b$ is the cardinal number of the Cartesian product $A \times B$. The product $b \times a$ is the cardinal number of the Cartesian product $B \times A$. Since the two Cartesian products have the same number of elements it follows that $a \times b = b \times a$.

In showing the commutativity of multiplication it was assumed that if sets A and B are finite then $A \times B$ is finite. We have shown, page 110, that the union of two finite sets is a finite set.

Let set A be a finite set with a elements; let x represent any one of its a elements. Let set B be a finite set with b elements; let y represent any one of its b elements. The set of (x_1, y) ordered pairs is a finite set since it has b elements. Call this set C_1. The symbol (x_1, y) means that we select a particular one of the a elements of A and pair it with each of the b elements of B. Similarly, the set of (x_2, y) ordered pairs is a finite set. Call it C_2. Continuing in this way there are a such sets of (x_i, y) ordered pairs. The union of these sets of ordered pairs is the Cartesian product $A \times B$

$$C_1 \cup C_2 \cup C_3 \ldots \ldots \cup C_a = A \times B$$

Now since the union of two finite sets is a finite set, $(C_1 \cup C_2) \cup C_3$ is a finite set; and $((C_1 \cup C_2) \cup C_3) \cup C_4$ is a finite set, and so on. This establishes the fact that *multiplication of cardinal numbers is closed*. That is, the product of two cardinal numbers is a cardinal number.

We know from experience with numbers that $3 \times (4 \times 5) = (3 \times 4) \times 5$. On the left we multiply $4 \times 5 = 20$ and then $3 \times 20 = 60$. On the right we find $3 \times 4 = 12$ and $12 \times 5 = 60$. This is called the *associative property* for multiplication. Can this be proved from our definition of multiplication?

We wish to show that for a, b, c the number of elements of sets A, B, C respectively

$$(a \times b) \times c = a \times (b \times c)$$

It is sufficient to show a one-to-one correspondence of the elements of the Cartesian products $(A \times B) \times C$ and $A \times (B \times C)$. Let x represent any element of set A, y any element of set B, and z any element of set C.

$A \times B$ is the set of all (x, y) pairs. $(A \times B) \times C$ is the set of all pairs whose first member is an (x, y) pair and second member is a z; that is, $(A \times B) \times C$ is the set of all pairs $((x, y), z)$.

$B \times C$ is the set of all (y, z) pairs. $A \times (B \times C)$ is the set of all pairs whose first element is an x and whose second element is a (y, z) pair; that is, $A \times (B \times C)$ is the set of all pairs $(x, (y, z))$.

Hence a one-to-one correspondence exists between the elements of $(A \times B) \times C$ and those of $A \times (B \times C)$. Corresponding to each $((x, y), z)$ in $(A \times B) \times C$ there is $(x, (y, z))$ in $A \times (B \times C)$ where x, y, and z have the same replacement value.

EXAMPLE. Let $A = \{a, b\}$, $B = \{c, d\}$, $C = \{e, f\}$

Then $A \times B = \{(a, c), (a, d), (b, c), (b, d)\}$
and $(A \times B) \times C = \{((a, c), e), ((a, c), f), ((a, d), e),$
$((a, d), f), ((b, c), e), ((b, c), f),$
$((b, d), e), ((b, d), f)\}$

But $(B \times C) = \{(c, e), (c, f), (d, e), (d, f)\}$
and $A \times (B \times C) = \{(a, (c, e)), (a, (c, f)), (a, (d, e)),$
$(a, (d, f)), (b, (c, e)), (b, (c, f)),$
$(b, (d, e)), (b, (d, f))\}$

We have the correspondence $((a, c), e) \leftrightarrow (a, (c, e))$ and so on. Since the one-to-one correspondence exists we know the two sets $(A \times B) \times C$ and $A \times (B \times C)$ have the same cardinal number. Since the cardinal number of $(A \times B) \times C$ is $(a \times b) \times c$ and the cardinal number of $A \times (B \times C)$ is $a \times (b \times c)$ it follows that $(a \times b) \times c = a \times (b \times c)$. That is, multiplication obeys the associative principle.

We know from experience with numbers that multiplication of whole numbers is equivalent to addition of equal addends. The product 3×5 means $5 + 5 + 5$. Is this result consistent with addition and multiplication as we have defined them in terms of sets?

This relationship can be proved with the aid of the *distributive property*. The distributive property is illustrated by

$$3 \times (4 + 5) = 3 \times 4 + 3 \times 5$$

We can justify this specific case by evaluating each side of the equality independently.

$$3 \times (4 + 5) = 3 \times 9 = 27 \text{ and}$$
$$3 \times 4 + 3 \times 5 = 12 + 15 = 27$$

The principle requires that for any whole numbers a, b, and c

$$a(b + c) = a \times b + a \times c$$

It can be generalized to any number of addends.

$$a(b + c + d + e + \ldots) = a \times b + a \times c + a \times d + a \times e + \ldots$$

With this principle we can prove $3 \times 5 = 5 + 5 + 5$

$5 + 5 + 5 = 5(1 + 1 + 1)$ by the distributive principle
$5(1 + 1 + 1) = 5 \times 3$ definition of addition
$5 \times 3 = 3 \times 5$ multiplication is commutative
$3 \times 5 = 5 + 5 + 5$ substitution of equals for equals

This brings us to the question: Can the distributive principle be proved from the definitions of addition and multiplication?

Let A, B, and C be sets with cardinal numbers a, b, and c respectively. Further, let B and C be disjoint sets. Then the number of elements in $B \cup C$ is $b + c$ by definition of addition. The number of elements in $A \times (B \cup C)$ is $a(b + c)$ by the definition of multiplication. Also by the definition of multiplication the number of elements in $A \times B$ is $a \times b$ and the number of elements in $A \times C$ is $a \times c$. Furthermore, since B and C are disjoint, $A \times B$ and $A \times C$ are disjoint. This is because the second components of the elements of $A \times B$ must all differ from the second components of the elements of $A \times C$. Then by definition of addition, the number of elements of the set $(A \times B) \cup (A \times C)$ is $a \times b + a \times c$. The distributive property is established, $a(b + c) = a \times b + a \times c$, provided the number of elements in $A \times (B \cup C)$ is the same as the number of elements in $(A \times B) \cup (A \times C)$. But this is surely true. The two sets are equal, they have exactly the same elements. In both cases the elements consist of the set of ordered pairs whose first components are the elements of A and whose second components are the elements of B and the elements of C.

EXAMPLE. To illustrate the fact that
$$A \times (B \cup C) = (A \times B) \cup (A \times C)$$
if B and C are disjoint consider $A = \{a, b\}$, $B = \{c, d\}$, and $C = \{e, f\}$

$$B \cup C = \{c, d, e, f\}$$

$$A \times (B \cup C) = \{(a, c), (a, d), (a, e), (a, f), (b, c), (b, d) \\ (b, e), (b, f)\}$$

$$A \times B = \{(a, c), (a, d), (b, c), (b, d)\}$$

$$A \times C = \{(a, e), (a, f), (b, e), (b, f)\}$$

$$(A \times B) \cup (A \times C) = \{(a, c), (a, d), (b, c), (b, d), (a, e), \\ (a, f), (b, e), (b, f)\}$$

But this is exactly the same set of elements as the elements of $A \times (B \cup C)$. (Remember that the order of listing of the elements of a set is of no significance.)

We are familiar with the fact that any number multiplied by zero has the product zero, $a \times 0 = 0 \times a = 0$. Is this consistent with the definition of multiplication developed here?

Consider the set $A = \{a, b, c\}$ and $B = \{\ \}$, that is, the empty set. The cardinal number of A is 3, the cardinal number of B is 0. Hence $3 \times 0 = 0 \times 3$ is equal to the cardinal number of the set $A \times B$. The elements of $A \times B$ are ordered pairs. Each pair has for first component a, or b, or c. The second component of each pair is an element of B. But B has no elements, hence there are no second components, there are no pairs. We must conclude that $A \times B$ is the empty set, whose cardinal number is 0. Hence $3 \times 0 = 0 \times 3 = 0$. One can readily see that if A is replaced by a set with any other cardinal number the result will be the same.

The product of any cardinal number and zero is zero.

$$a \times 0 = 0 \times a = a \quad 1 \quad 0$$

Suppose that rather than being the empty set $B = \{0\}$. We now have
$$A \times B = \{(a, 0), (b, 0), (c, 0)\}$$

But the cardinal number of B is now 1, not 0. If B were any other set containing one element the number of elements in $A \times B$ would be unaffected. Let $B = \{x\}$, then
$$A \times B = \{(a, x), (b, x), (c, x)\}$$

If the set B of the Cartesian product $A \times B$ has one element its cardinal number is 1. Since that one element is the only second component available for the pairs of the Cartesian product there must be the same number of elements in the Cartesian product as in set A. (Is this true if A is the empty set?) We conclude that

Any number times 1 equals that number.

$$a \times 1 = 1 \times a = a$$

SUMMARY: Combining the results on page 110 with those of this section, we can now list the properties of the cardinal numbers.

Addition

1. *Closure*—The sum of two cardinal numbers is a cardinal number.

2. *Commutativity*—The order of the addends does not affect the sum.

$$a + b = b + a$$

3. *Associativity*—The grouping of 3 addends does not affect the sum.

$$(a + b) + c = a + (b + c)$$

4. *Identity*—The sum of any number a and 0 is a

$$a + 0 = a$$

Multiplication

1′. *Closure*—The product of two cardinal numbers is a cardinal number.

2′. *Commutativity*—The order of the factors does not affect the product.

$$a \times b = b \times a$$

3′. *Associativity*—The grouping of 3 factors does not affect the product.

$$(a \times b) \times c = a \times (b \times c)$$

4′. *Identity*—The product of any number a and 1 is a.

$$a \times 1 = a$$

5. *Distributivity*—One factor can be distributed over the addends of another factor.

$$a(b + c) = a \times b + a \times c$$

We see that addition and multiplication are abstractly quite similar. They have properties 1 through 4 in common. The fifth, the distributive property, is the only one that links the two operations.

Another property of fundamental importance is the property of zero as a factor.

6. If a is any cardinal number

$$a \times 0 = 0$$

Exercises

Given $A = \{1, a, x\}$ $B = \{0, y\}$ $C = \{x, y\}$

1 Find $A \times B$.

2 Find $B \times A$.

3 Find $A \times C$.

4 Find $A \times (B \cup C)$.

5 Why is the cardinal number of $A \times B$ plus the cardinal number of $A \times C$ *not* equal to the cardinal number of $A \times (B \cup C)$?

6 Are $\{x, y\}$ and $\{y, x\}$ equal sets?
Are $\{x, y\}$ and $\{(x, y)\}$ equal sets?
Are $\{(x, y)\}$ and $\{(y, x)\}$ equal sets?
Explain your answers.

7 State the principle by which we may say that each of the following is an equality.

(a) $2 \times (3 + 7) = (2 \times 3) + (2 \times 7)$

(b) $2 \times (3 + 7) = (3 + 7) \times 2$

(c) $12 \times (3 - 3) = 0$

(d) $(3 + 5) + 9 = 3 + (5 + 9)$

(e) $(3 + 5) + 9 = (3 + 9) + 5$

8 In view of Exercise 7(a) and (b) what additional steps are required to reach the conclusion $(3 + 7) \times 2 = (3 \times 2) + (7 \times 2)$?

6.3 THE INVERSE OF MULTIPLICATION

Division is by definition the inverse of multiplication. This means that if we multiply by a number, then divide the result by the same number, the final result is the original number.

$$12 \times 3 = 36, \qquad 36 \div 3 = 12$$

We state the definition of division by means of the equations

$$a \div b = x, \text{ if and only if } x \times b = a \qquad (b \neq 0)$$

Hence $36 \div 3 = 12$ because $12 \times 3 = 36$.

Here we are saying the quotient $a \div b$ is whatever b must be multiplied by to get a. If we substitute the value of x, that is $a \div b$, from the first equation in the second we get

$$a \div b \times b = a \qquad (6.1)$$

If we divide a by b, then multiply the result by b, we obtain the original a.

Suppose we multiply by b first, then divide

$$a \times b \div b = x \qquad (6.2)$$

We may think of this as dividing the number $a \times b$ by the number b. Then by the definition of division we have $(a \times b) \div b = x$ implies that $x \times b = a \times b$. Now divide both sides of the equation by b and we have $x = a$. Substituting this in the first equation we have $a \times b \div b = a$.

Thus, whether we multiply by b, then divide by b, Equation (6.2), or divide by b then multiply by b, Equation (6.1), the end result is the original a. We can always divide by b if we have already multiplied by b as in Equation (6.2). But in Equation (6.1) we have no assurance that we can divide by b and get a cardinal number.

> EXAMPLE.   We know that $13 \times 7 \div 7 = 13$, since 13×7 is a cardinal number. But in $13 \div 7 \times 7$ we have no assurance that $13 \div 7$ is a cardinal number. In fact it is not.

This same situation exists relative to subtraction of cardinal numbers. In order that subtraction will always be possible we created negative numbers. Does this extension of number make division always possible? Before this question can be answered we must decide how we can multiply with negative numbers. However, the definition of division precludes the possibility of division *always* being possible. In the definition the possibility of zero as a divisor was excluded. Why was this done?

What does $5 \div 0$ equal? According to the definition of division, it must equal some number which multiplied by zero will equal 5. Symbolically, we are saying

$$5 \div 0 = a \text{ if and only if } a \times 0 = 5$$

But we saw in the previous section that zero multiplied by any number will equal zero. Hence, we can find no value for a which will satisfy the equation $a \div 0 = 5$. If 5 were replaced by any other number, except zero, the same situation would confront us. What if we do replace 5 with 0? We then have

$$0 \div 0 = a \text{ if and only if } a \times 0 = 0$$

In the equation $a \times 0 = 0$ any value whatever for a will make the equation true. This is just as undesirable as having no value. Hence division of any number by zero is undefined.

Exercises

1   If $A = \{\ \}$, the empty set, and $A \times B$ has the cardinal number 4 we can write $A \times B$ in dummy form as $\{(a, b), (a, b),$

$(a, b), (a, b)\}$ where a represents an element of A and b represents an element of B. Why is the above situation impossible?

2   If $A = \{\quad\}$ and $A \times B = \{\quad\}$ show why B can be any set one wishes to consider.

3   If neither A nor B is a unit set, that is, has one element, show why it is impossible for $A \times B$ to have the cardinal number 5.

4   Show with an example that it is impossible for $A \times B$ to have eight elements and A to have three elements.

5   If $B = \{a, b, c\}$ and $A \times B = \{(x, a), (x, b), (x, c), (y, a), (y, b), (y, c)\}$, what is set A?

6   If $m \times p = r$, from the definition of division what division fact is implied?

7   Since multiplication is commutative what other multiplication fact is implied in Exercise 6? What division fact is implied by this multiplication fact?

8   Since for any number a, $a \times 1 = a$ it follows that $a \div a = 1$ if $a \neq 0$. Why is this not true when $a = 0$?

6.4 MULTIPLICATION OF NEGATIVE NUMBERS

We introduced negative numbers in order that we may always subtract. Rules for the addition of positive and negative numbers were shown to be a consequence of the properties established for cardinal numbers. We now wish to extend this procedure to multiplication. We shall assume that the integers—positive, negative, and zero—are consistent with the properties established for cardinal numbers, page 188, and derive the rules for multiplication of positive and negative numbers.

There are three cases involving negative numbers. If a and b are positive we have (1) $a \times (-b)$, (2) $(-a) \times b$, (3) $(-a) \times (-b)$. First consider $a \times [b + (-b)]$

Since $b + (-b) = 0$, we have

$$a \times [b + (-b)] = a \times 0 = 0$$

But if we apply the distributive property

$$a \times [b + (-b)] = a \times b + a \times (-b)$$

Then by substitution

$$a \times b + a \times (-b) = 0$$

That is, $a \times (-b)$ is the negative of $a \times b$. But the negative of $a \times b$ is $-(a \times b)$. Hence,

$$a \times (-b) = -(a \times b) \qquad (6.3)$$

If we apply the commutative property we have

$$a \times (-b) = (-b) \times a$$

Since both a and b represent *any* positive integer $(-b) \times a$ can just as well be written $(-a) \times b$. Hence for Equation (6.4) we have

$$(-a) \times b = -(a \times b) \qquad (6.4)$$

Consider the product $(-a) \times [b + (-b)]$
Since $b + (-b) = 0$ we have

$$-a \times [b + (-b)] = -a \times 0 = 0$$

But, applying the distributive property,

$$-a \times [b + (-b)] = (-a) \times b + (-a) \times (-b)$$

Hence, applying Equation (6.3), and substituting on the left, we have

$$0 = -(a \times b) + (-a) \times (-b)$$

It follows that $(-a) \times (-b)$ is the negative of $-(a \times b)$. That is, for Equation (6.5) we have

$$(-a) \times (-b) = a \times b \qquad (6.5)$$

6.5 MULTIPLICATION ON THE NUMBER LINE

Multiplication can be illustrated on the number line when it is interpreted as successive addition of equal addends. For example, $3 \times 5 = 5 + 5 + 5$.

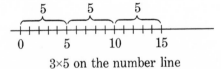

3×5 on the number line

With the proper conventions we can illustrate the laws of signs for multiplication on the number line.

Let $a \times b$ mean we move a steps to the right, b units per step. This is what we have done in the above illustration, showing $3 \times 5 = 15$. We agreed, page 123, that in adding a negative number (or subtracting a positive number) this should be interpreted as moving to the left. Hence, $3 \times (-5)$ we interpret as moving *to the left* five units at a time for 3 steps.

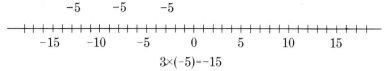

$$3\times(-5)=-15$$

We make the further convention that in the event we are required to make a given move for a negative number of steps, this shall mean make the corresponding move *in the opposite direction* that positive number of times. For example, $(-3) \times 5$ is interpreted: move 5 units to the right for -3 steps; we agree that it means the steps of 5 units are to be taken to the left and there are 3 steps. Hence, on the number line $(-3) \times 5$ will appear precisely the same as $3 \times (-5)$.

Using the same interpretation, how will $(-3) \times (-5)$ appear on the number line? The -5 means move to the *left* in steps of 5 units. The -3 means take -3 such steps. We have agreed that since this cannot be done we shall take 3 such steps in the opposite direction, or to the right. Hence, on the number line $(-3) \times (-5)$ appears precisely the same as 3×5.

Exercises

1 Evaluate each of the following.

(a) $-2 \times (3 + -4)$

(b) $-2 \times 3 + -2 \times -4$

(c) $-6 \times (-5 \times 9)$

(d) $(-6 \times -5) \times 9$

(e) $-4 \times (3 \times -12)$

(f) $3 \times -12 \times -4$

2 The interpretation of multiplication $a \times b = b + b + b +$ for a terms is meaningless when a is negative. If -3×4 must equal either 12 or -12 let us assume it is 12. Since $3 \times 4 = 12$, and if $-3 \times 4 = 12$, we have $3 \times 4 = -3 \times 4$. Then if we divide both sides by 4 we have $3 = -3$. We conclude that $-3 \times 4 = -12$.

Use an argument similar to this to show that $-3 \times -4 = 12$.

3 Evaluate $-a \times (b + -c)$ if a, b, and c are each of the following.

(a) $a = -5,\ b = -4,\ c = -7$

(b) $a = 3,\ b = -5,\ c = 2$

(c) $a = -3,\ b = 12,\ c = -5$

(d) $a = 4,\ b = 6,\ c = 3$

4 Since division is the inverse of multiplication, find each of the following:

(a) $(-12) \div (-3)$

(b) $6 \div (-2)$

(c) $15 \div 5$

(d) $(-20) \div 4$

5 Determine the sign of each of the following if a and b are positive:

(a) $a \div b$

(b) $(-a) \div b$

(c) $a \div (-b)$

(d) $(-a) \div (-b)$

6 As a result of Exercise 5, formulate a rule for division of positive and negative numbers.

7 If a greater than $b(a > b)$ means that a is further to the right on the number line than b, which is the greater? (a) -3×5 or -2×-4 (b) 6×-5 or 1×-2 (c) -10 or 2

8 What is the sign of $-a \times -b$ if a is positive and b is negative?

9 Use the number line to illustrate each of the following.

(a) $8 - 15 = -7$

(b) $3 - 8 = -5$

(c) $-5 + -3 = -8$

(d) $-5 - 3 = -8$

(e) $5 \times -2 = -10$

(f) $-3 \times -4 = 12$

10 Multiply a by $-b$ when a is 3 and b is -4.

11 Supply the missing numbers

(a) $3 + -5 + 8 = ? + 8 + 3$

(b) $2 \times -10 \times -5 = -5 \times (? \times -2)$

(c) $? \times -2 \times 3 = -3 \times (4 \times -2)$

6.6 MULTIPLICATION ON THE CIRCLE

In Section 6.4 we saw that multiplication of integers—that is, positive and negative whole numbers and zero—is always possible. Furthermore, the result is always an integer.

If the definition of division as the inverse of multiplication holds for integers, is division, other than division by zero, always possible?

Equations (6.3), (6.4), and (6.5) of Section 6.4 merely indicate whether the product is positive or negative. Otherwise multiplication is the same. For example, since $3 \times 4 = 12$, Equation (6.3) merely tells us whether 3×-4 is 12 or -12.

We know that division of natural numbers is not always possible. There is no natural number n such that $n \times 3 = 13$. Hence, $13 \div 3$ is not a natural number. Then neither is division of integers always possible, even with division by zero excluded. There can be no integer n such that $n \times -3 = -13$, and consequently, $-13 \div -3$ is not an integer.

Negative numbers were created in order that we have a system of numbers that is closed under subtraction. This merely means that subtraction is always possible in the system and the result is also in the system. In Chapter Eight we shall discuss the set of rational numbers, a system in which division other than by zero is always possible.

In Section 4.12 the idea of addition on a circle was introduced. We can extend the idea to multiplication. As on page 126, consider a circle with seven divisions, numbered 0, 1, 2, 3, 4, 5, 6.

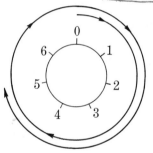

We interpret multiplication on the circle as we did on the number line, $a \times b$ means start at 0 and move clockwise b units, then b units more, and continue for a such steps. For example, to find 3×4, we go clockwise from 0 to 4, 4 to 1, and 1 to 5. Hence $3 \times 4 = 5$. The correctness of the following multiplication table should be verified by actual multiplication on the circle.

	0	1	2	3	4	5	6
0	0	0	0	0	0	0	0
1	0	1	2	3	4	5	6
2	0	2	4	6	1	3	5
3	0	3	6	2	5	1	4
4	0	4	1	5	2	6	3
5	0	5	3	1	6	4	2
6	0	6	5	4	3	2	1

It can be verified from the table that all of the properties of multiplication listed on page 188 for cardinal numbers also apply here. Furthermore, division other than by zero is always possible. From the definition of division $3 \div 2$ is equal to whatever 2 must be multiplied by to produce 3. In row 2 we find 3 in column 5, hence $3 \div 2 = 5$ because $2 \times 5 = 3$. It becomes apparent that division by nonzero numbers is always possible when we observe that in each row, and in each column, each of the numbers $0 - 6$ appears exactly one time. If this were not so, for example, if there were no 4 in row 3 it would be impossible to find $4 \div 3$ because there would be nothing by which to multiply 3 in order to produce 4. Note that in the table it is still true that 0 divided by anything other than 0 is equal to 0. Also, division by 0 is impossible. Why?

We can approach the question of division in another way. Recall, Section 4.9, that with the introduction of negative numbers we can always subtract—but we never have to—we can add the inverse of a rather than subtract a.

When we extend numbers to the rational numbers all nonzero numbers will have multiplication inverses, 5 and $\frac{1}{5}$ are inverses because $5 \times \frac{1}{5} = 1$, and 1 is the multiplication identity. (See Section 6.2.) Also, division by 5 and multiplication by its inverse $\frac{1}{5}$ produce the same result.

In multiplication on a circle of 7 divisions each nonzero number has its multiplication inverse. If we take steps of 2 units on the circle, 4 steps will bring us to 1. Hence $4 \times 2 = \widehat{1.}$

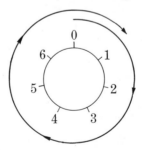

and it follows that 2 and 4 are multiplication inverses. Examination of the multiplication table reveals that 1 appears in each nonzero row and column exactly one time. Therefore, each nonzero number has a multiplication inverse.

From the table we find that 4 is the inverse of 2. Also, from the table we find $3 \times 4 = 5$. But above we found $3 \div 2 = 5$. This is one example of the general principle—division by a number produces the same result as multiplication by its inverse.

In Section 4.12 we saw that addition on a circle of seven divisions could be interpreted as the addition of residues, modulo 7, see page 130. The same interpretation can be given multiplication on the circle. The result $3 \times 5 = 1$ means any number whose remainder is 3 when divided by 7 multiplied by any number whose remainder is 5 when divided by 7 yields a product that has a remainder 1 when divided by 7.

EXAMPLE. $24 = 3 \times 7 + 3;\quad 24 \equiv 3, \bmod 7$
$47 = 6 \times 7 + 5;\quad 47 \equiv 5, \bmod 7$
$24 \times 47 = 1128 = 161 \times 7 + 1;$
$24 \times 47 \equiv 1, \bmod 7$

The idea of number congruence need not be restricted to the modulus 7. Any integer greater than 1 can be used as modulus.

EXAMPLE. $135 \equiv 21, \bmod 6$ because
$135 = 22 \times 6 + 3$ and
$21 = 3 \times 6 + 3$

Any two integers a, b are congruent, modulo c if they have the same remainder when divided by c.

$$a \equiv b, \bmod c.$$

Congruence is a reflexive, symmetric, and transitive relation. It may be characterized as a kind of equality, equality of remainders. All integers are congruent to some number 0 through 6, modulo 7, since 0 through 6 are the only possible remainders. As we move around the circle of 7 divisions we may think of each number as being its own remainder upon division by 7. For example, $5 \div 7 = 0$, remainder 5. When we get back to 0 we have the remainder of $7 \div 7$. Continuing, 1 is the remainder of $8 \div 7$, 2 the remainder of $9 \div 7$, and so on.

We interpret the addition table, page 127, as follows: $4 + 5 \equiv 2$ means $4 + 5$ has the remainder 2 upon division by 7. $6 + 6 \equiv 5$ means $6 + 6$ has the remainder 5 when divided by 7. The multiplication table, page 195, is interpreted in the same way: $6 \times 6 \equiv 1$ means 6×6 has the remainder 1 when divided by 7. $4 \times 4 \equiv 2$ means 4×4 has the remainder 2 when divided by 7.

From the addition table we find $5 + 4 \equiv 2$. This means of course that $9 \div 7$ gives a remainder 2. But it means more; the 5 represents any integer congruent to 5 modulo 7, and the 4 any integer congruent to 4 modulo 7. Let m, n be any two integers such that $m \equiv 5 \bmod 7$, and $n \equiv 4 \bmod 7$. This means that m is some integral multiple of 7 plus 5 and n is some integral multiple of 7 plus 4. Adding we get

$$
\begin{aligned}
m &= 7k_1 + 5 \\
n &= 7k_2 + 4 \\
\hline
m + n &= 7(k_1 + k_2) + 9 = 7(k_1 + k_2 + 1) + 2
\end{aligned}
$$

The sum $(m + n)$ is congruent to 2 just as the sum of their remainders is. The similar property holds for multiplication

$$
\begin{aligned}
m &= 7k_1 + 5 \\
n &= 7k_2 + 4 \\
\hline
m \times n &= 49k_1k_2 + 35k_2 + 28k_1 + 20 \\
&= 49k_1k_2 + 35k_2 + 28k_1 + 14 + 6 \\
&= 7(7k_1k_2 + 5k_2 + 4k_1 + 2) + 6
\end{aligned}
$$

Therefore $m \times n \equiv 6$, mod 7 and from the multiplication table we find $5 \times 4 \equiv 6$. We summarize these results by stating: If $a \equiv b$ and $c \equiv d$, then $a + c \equiv b + d$ and $a \times c \equiv b \times d$ (all modulo 7). As a matter of fact we can replace the 5, 4 and 7 in the illustrations with any arbitrary integers, and the summarizing statement applies to any modulus as well as to 7.

We illustrate the two principles above with numerical examples. Consider two numbers, 96 and 60. We may express 96 as $7 \times 13 + 5$ and 60 as $7 \times 8 + 4$. Now if we add the two:

$$
\begin{aligned}
96 &= 7 \times 13 + 5 \\
60 &= 7 \times 8 + 4 \\
\hline
156 &= 7 \times (13 + 8) + 5 + 4 = 7 \times 21 + 9
\end{aligned}
$$

But if we divide 156 by 7 we get a remainder 2, and if we divide 9 by 7, we also get 2 for remainder. Thus the sum of the numbers, 156, and the sum of their residues, 9, are congruent modulo 7 since each is congruent to 2.

Similarly for multiplication:

$$
\begin{aligned}
96 &= 7 \times 13 + 5 \\
60 &= 7 \times 8 + 4 \\
\hline
5760 &= 7 \times 8 \times 7 \times 13 + 7 \times 8 \times 5 + 7 \times 13 \times 4 + 5 \times 4 \\
&= 7(8 \times 7 \times 13 + 8 \times 5 + 13 \times 4) + 5 \times 4
\end{aligned}
$$

But if we divide 5760 by 7, we get 6 for remainder. We also get remainder 6 when we divide $5 \times 4 = 20$ by 7. Thus 5760, the product of the numbers, and 20, the product of their residues, are congruent, modulo 7 since each is congruent to 6.

If we choose a modulus other than 7 the result may and may not be a system closed to division. Let us construct addition and multiplication tables, modulo 4. To do this we merely divide the ordinary sums and products by 4. The remainders are the corresponding modulo 4 results. For example, $3 \times 3 = 9$, $9 \div 4 = 2$, remainder 1, therefore $3 \times 3 \equiv 1$.

Addition, modulo four

	0	1	2	3
0	0	1	2	3
1	1	2	3	0
2	2	3	0	1
3	3	0	1	2

Multiplication, modulo four

	0	1	2	3
0	0	0	0	0
1	0	1	2	3
2	0	2	0	2
3	0	3	2	1

Here $3 \div 2$ is meaningless. In row 2 we find no 3, hence there is no number n such that $2 \times n = 3$. Furthermore, there is no 1 in either row 2 or column 2, so 2 does not have a multiplication inverse.

The number nine has many fascinating properties. They do not stem from some mystic power as numerologists would have one believe. In the main, they stem from the fact that it is the largest integer below the base ten.

One of the interesting characteristics of nine is the fact that any number which is a multiple of nine has a digit sum which is also a multiple of nine.

$$2 \times 9 = 18 \qquad 1 + 8 = 9$$
$$3 \times 9 = 27 \qquad 2 + 7 = 9$$
$$4 \times 9 = 36 \qquad 3 + 6 = 9$$
$$11 \times 9 = 99 \qquad 9 + 9 = 18$$

This is a special case of a much more general property. Any number is congruent to the sum of its digits, modulo 9.

$$768 \div 9 = 85, \quad \text{remainder 3 or}$$
$$768 \equiv 3, \text{mod 9}$$
$$\text{but } 7 + 6 + 8 = 21 \equiv 3, \text{mod 9}$$

To show that this is true recall that we have shown that congruences may be added and multiplied just as equalities can. If $a \equiv b$ and $c \equiv d$ then $a + c \equiv b + d$ and $a \times c \equiv b \times d$ (all modulo 9). Further, recall that from our system of notation

$$768 = 7 \times 10^2 + 6 \times 10 + 8$$

But since $10 \equiv 1$, mod 9

$$768 \equiv 7 \times 1^2 + 6 \times 1 + 8 = 21 \equiv 3, \text{mod 9}$$

We note that $21 \equiv 3$ may be obtained by dividing by 9, but we can also apply the original idea to 21 and get $21 \equiv 2 + 1 = 3$.

The above illustration can easily be generalized to any integer. Express the integer in the form

$a_0 10^n + a_1 10^{n-1} + \ldots + a_n$ then
$a_0 10^n + a_1 10^{n-1} + \ldots + a_n \equiv a_0 1^n + a_1 1^{n-1} + \ldots a^n = a_0 + a_1 + \ldots + a_n$, the last expression being the sum of the digits of the original number.

This property shows why the "check of nines" works. We can check addition by adding the digits of each addend (and add the digits of each sum until a one-digit result is reached). The sum of these sums should agree with the sum of the digits in the answer.

EXAMPLE. Add and check (modulo 9)

$$786 \equiv 7 + 8 + 6 = 21 \equiv 2 + 1 = 3$$
$$359 \equiv 3 + 5 + 9 = 17 \equiv 1 + 7 = 8 \qquad 3 + 8 + 0 + 2 = 13$$
$$243 \equiv 2 + 4 + 3 = 9 \equiv \qquad\qquad 0 \qquad \equiv 1 + 3 = 4$$
$$407 \equiv 4 + 0 + 7 = 11 \equiv 1 + 1 = 2$$
$$\overline{1795} \equiv 1 + 7 + 9 + 5 = 22 \equiv 2 + 2 = 4$$

The same principle may be used to check multiplication, but we must multiply residues this time.

EXAMPLE. Multiply and check (modulo 9)

$$642 \equiv 6 + 4 + 2 = 12 \equiv 1 + 2 = 3$$
$$83 \equiv 8 + 3 = 11 \equiv 1 + 1 = 2 \qquad\qquad 3 \times 2 = 6$$
$$\overline{1926}$$
$$5136$$
$$\overline{53286} \equiv 5 + 3 + 2 + 8 + 6 = 24 \equiv 2 + 4 = 6$$

The check of nines may also be used to check subtraction and division. In subtraction we *subtract* the residues.

EXAMPLE. Subtract and check (modulo 9)

$$736 \equiv 7 + 3 + 6 = 16 \equiv 1 + 6 = \qquad 7$$
$$253 \equiv 2 + 5 + 3 = 10 \equiv 1 + 0 = \qquad 1$$
$$\overline{483} \equiv 4 + 8 + 3 = 15 \equiv 1 + 5 = 6 \leftrightarrow 6$$

It may happen in subtraction that the residue of the minuend is less than that of the subtrahend. In that case, if we wish to avoid negative numbers, we may increase the residue of the minuend by 9, then subtract.

EXAMPLE. Subtract and check (modulo 9)

$$893 \equiv 8 + 9 + 3 = 20 \equiv 2 + 0 \equiv 2 \equiv 11$$
$$251 \equiv 2 + 5 + 1 = \qquad\qquad\qquad 8 = \quad 8$$
$$\overline{642} \equiv 6 + 4 + 2 = 12 \equiv 1 + 2 = 3 \leftrightarrow \overline{3}$$

When we check division by inverse operations we multiply the quotient by the divisor, then add the remainder to secure the dividend. When the check of nines is used with division it is better to apply the above check, using the residues in the place of the numbers.

EXAMPLE. Divide and check (modulo 9)

$$
\begin{array}{r}
49 \\
17\overline{)836} \\
68 \\
\hline
156 \\
153 \\
\hline
3
\end{array}
$$

CHECK:

(quotient) $49 \equiv 4 + 9 = 13 \equiv 1 + 3 = 4$
(divisor) $17 \equiv 1 + 7 = \qquad\qquad\qquad 8$
$$32 \equiv 3 + 2 = 5$$
(remainder) 3 $\qquad\qquad\qquad\qquad\qquad\qquad 3$
(dividend) $836 \equiv 8 + 3 + 6 = 17 \equiv 1 + 7 = 8 \longleftrightarrow 8$

If the division example is checked by performing the direct operations with the residues we have

$836 \div 17 = 49 + (3 \div 17)$ implies
$8 \div 8 \equiv 4 + (3 \div 8)$,   but $3 \div 8 = 6$
because $6 \times 8 = 48 \equiv 12 \equiv 3$.
$1 \equiv 4 + 6 = 10 \equiv 1$

However, this procedure will not always work.

EXAMPLE.   Divide and check (modulo 9)

$$
\begin{array}{r}
39 \\
21 \overline{\smash{\big)}\ 836} \\
63 \\
\hline
206 \\
189 \\
\hline
17
\end{array}
$$

$836 \equiv 8$
$21 \equiv 3$
$39 \equiv 3$
$17 \equiv 8$

The check requires that $8 \div 3 \equiv 3 + (8 \div 3)$. But $8 \div 3$ equals that number which, multiplied by 3, gives a result congruent to 8, and there is no such number. Any number multiplied by 3 gives a result which is congruent to 0, 3, or 6, modulo 9.

As was true of modulo 4, division is not always possible in the modulo 9 system even though division by 0 is not considered.

Exercises

1 Each number except 0 on a circle of 7 divisions has a multiplication inverse. Find the inverse of each of them.

2 Start at 0 on a circle of 5 divisions and take steps of 3 units each. What is the smallest number of steps required to stop at 0?

3 Start at 0 on a circle of 6 divisions and take steps of 4 units each. What is the smallest number of steps required to stop at 0?

4 Use the table on page 195 to find the following.
(a) $2 \div 5$ (b) 2×3 (c) $4 \div 6$ (d) 4×6

5 In Exercise 4(c) and (d) you should have found that $4 \div 6 = 4 \times 6$. We would expect $4 \div 1$ to equal 4×1. Is this property true of any numbers other than 1 and 6? Explain why it is true of 6?

6 Construct addition and multipication tables for the integers, modulo 2. There will be two elements, 0 and 1.

7 In the tables of Exercise 6 replace 0 with *even* and 1 with *odd*. Are the results consistent with the behavior of even and odd numbers under addition and multiplication?

8 A perfect square is the product of an integer multiplied by itself. $5 \times 5 = 25$; 25 is a perfect square. Since any number is congruent to 0, 1, 2, or 3, modulo 4, prove that any odd perfect square is 1 more than a multiple of 4.

9 In modulo 12 multiplication find $3 \times 8 \equiv ?$ $4 \times 6 \equiv ?$ Do the numbers 0, 1, 2, 3, 4, 5, 6, 7, 8, 9, 10, 11, modulo 12 constitute a set whose nonzero elements are closed with respect to multiplication? To division?

10 Which of the numbers in modulo 12 multiplication have inverses? What is the inverse of each?

11 Use the addition and multiplication tables, modulo 7 to check the following.
(a) $32 \times 73 \equiv 16 \times 41$, mod 7
(b) $15 \times (65 + 18) \equiv 23 \times (20 + 9)$, mod 7

12 Use the addition and multiplication tables, modulo 7 to check for the distributive property with the following.
(a) $4 \times (5 + 3) \equiv 4 \times 5 + 4 \times 3$
(b) $2 \times (6 + 4) \equiv 2 \times 6 + 2 \times 4$

13 Add and check (modulo 9):

$$493 + 871 + 639$$

14 If we use octonal notation the above scheme can be applied to 7. Add and check in base 8:

$$463_{\text{eight}} + 721_{\text{eight}} + 542_{\text{eight}}$$

15 Multiply and check (modulo 9):
(a) 543×657
(b) 321×47

16 If we square the numbers 0–8 and express the results as residues, modulo 9, we get $0^2 = 0$, $1^2 = 1$, $2^2 = 4$, $3^2 = 9 \equiv 0$, $4^2 = 16 \equiv 7$, $5^2 = 25 \equiv 7$, $6^2 = 36 \equiv 0$, $7^2 = 49 \equiv 4$, $8^2 = 64 \equiv 1$. We may then conclude that any perfect square will be congruent to 0, 1, 4, or 7, mod 9. Which of the following numbers might possibly be a square:

$$\text{(a) } 183{,}436 \quad \text{(b) } 72{,}603 \quad \text{(c) } 843{,}675$$

17 Prove that any perfect cube is a multiple of nine, one more than a multiple of nine, or one less than a multiple of nine. *Hint:* Any integer is congruent to 0, 1, 2, 3, 4, 5, 6, 7, or 8, mod 9. Now cube each one of these residues.

18 Subtract and check (modulo 9):
(a) $18{,}546 - 8328$
(b) $63{,}524 - 3760$

19 Construct the modulo 9 multiplication table. What numbers other than zero do not have multiplication inverses?

20   Divide and check (modulo 9); check the direct operation if possible as well as the inverse:
(a) $543 \div 88$
(b) $2974 \div 278$

21   Construct addition and multiplication tables for base seven notation. How does this differ from the modulo seven tables? Explain.

22   Find three numbers that are congruent to 7, modulo 12. Find three numbers that are congruent to 12, modulo 7.

23   Find the smallest multiple of 6 which is congruent to 0, modulo 11.

24   Give an illustration to demonstrate that congruence is a reflexive, symmetric, and transitive relation.

25   Find a modulus for which the following is true.
$$3 + 4 + 6 \equiv 2 \times 7 + 4$$

26   Supply the missing numbers.
(a) $15 \times (65 + 18) \equiv 23 \times (20 + 9)$, modulo?
(b) $4 \times 6 \equiv 0$, modulo?
(c) $127 \equiv 7$, modulo?

6.7   THE FUNDAMENTAL THEOREM OF ARITHMETIC

If $a \times b = c$, a is called the *multiplier*, b the *multiplicand*, and c the *product*. We call a and b the *factors* of c. When dealing with integers, "factor" and "integral factor" are used interchangeably. Thus, we refer to 3 and 4 as the factors of 12. But $\frac{6}{5}$ and 10 are also factors of 12 in the sense that they are two numbers whose product is 12. From this point of view, any number has infinitely many sets of factors. But if we restrict "factor" to integers this is not the case. The only sets of positive integral factors of 12 are 2, 2, 3; 4, 3; 6, 2; and 12, 1.

A positive prime number is a number greater than one that has no set of positive integral factors other than itself and 1.

Five is a prime number because no set of positive integers other than 1 and 5 give the product 5. Our definition excludes 1 from the prime numbers. Two is the only even prime because any other even number has two as a factor. Integers greater than one which are not prime are called *composite* numbers.

All prime numbers less than a given number can be isolated by means of a simple device known as the Sieve of Eratosthenes. We shall illustrate the method by finding the prime numbers less than 20. First write down the integers 2 through 20. Two is a prime, so we circle it. We next cross out every second number after two, that is 4, 6, 8, ... Three is a prime; we circle it. We then cross out every third number after three, 6, 9, 12, ... Some of them will have been crossed out already but they are counted in getting every third number.

②③✕⑤✕⑦✕✕✕ ⑪ ✕ ⑬ ✕ ✕ ✕ ⑰ ✕ ⑲ ✕

As we continue, the first number remaining in the sequence is always a prime. Five is a prime and every fifth number after 5 has already been crossed out. Obviously the remaining numbers 11, 13, 17, 19 are prime because the eleventh number after 11 goes beyond 20.

When we test a number for prime factors it is sufficient to test only those primes whose squares are equal to or less than the given number. For example, suppose we wish to determine whether 97 is a prime. We test and find that neither 2, 3, 5, 7, nor 11 is a factor. We need go no further because 11 × 11 is greater than 97 and if 97 had a prime factor greater than 11 it would have to have one less than 11 also.

> *The* Fundamental Theorem of Arithmetic *asserts: any positive integer greater than one may be factored into primes in essentially one way.*

That is, the order of the primes may differ but the same primes must be present, and each prime must appear the same number of times. For example: $24 = 3 \times 8 = 4 \times 6$ but 8, 4, and 6 are not prime. If they are factored into primes we get

$$24 = 3 \times 2 \times 2 \times 2 = 2 \times 2 \times 3 \times 2$$

and the two representations of 24 in prime factors differ only in the order in which the primes appear. This theorem is as important as it seems obvious. But the obviousness of a statement has no necessary relationship to the ease with which it can be proved. For that matter, history is filled with "obvious facts" that have been disproved. In the following proof we designate the integer to be factored as a. If a is prime, the truth of the theorem follows from the definition of prime numbers. If a is not prime it can be expressed as the product of two factors, $a = b \times c$, with b, c each less than a. If b and c are prime $b \times c$ is the required factorization. If b is composite it can be expressed as the product of two factors less than b; similarly for c. Repetition of this argument a finite of times produces prime factors, for there are only a finite number of positive integers less than a. This shows that any integer a may be expressed as a product of primes. To show the primes are the same for any factorization consider a factored into two sets of primes.

$$a = p_1 \times p_2 \times p_3 \times \ldots = q_1 \times q_2 \times q_3 \times \ldots$$

Since p_1 is a factor of a it is also a factor of $q_1 \times q_2 \times q_3 \times \ldots$. But the qs are prime, therefore p_1 must equal some one of the qs. We may now apply the cancellation principle and get the product $p_2 \times p_3 \times \ldots =$ the product of the remaining qs. By a repetition of the same argument we can show there is a q equal to p_2, and similarly for all the ps. Having eliminated all ps, we have on that side of the equation 1, and on the other side a product of the remaining qs. But since the qs are all integers we know they have been canceled and 1 remains on that side. It follows that the products $p_1 \times p_2 \times p_3 \times \ldots$ and $q_1 \times q_2 \times q_3 \times \ldots$ differ only in the order in which the factors appear.

Exercises

1 Use the Sieve of Eratosthenes and find all positive prime numbers less than 100.

2 Illustrate the Fundamental Theorem of Arithmetic with $40 \times 63 = 35 \times 72$.

3 The *lowest common multiple* (l.c.m.) of two numbers, as the name implies, is the smallest number that is an exact multiple of each. For example, 60 is the lowest common multiple of 12 and 15. Use the Fundamental Theorem of Arithmetic to find the l.c.m. of 144 and 216.

4 Determine whether each of the following is prime or composite.
(a) 97   (b) 163   (c) 159   (d) 311   (e) 517

5 If n is a factor of a does it follow that n is a factor of a^2? Why?

6 If n is divisible by a does it follow that n is divisible by a^2? Why?

6.8 DIVISION OF INTEGERS

We can subtract in the set of positive integers and zero only if the subtrahend (number subtracted) is equal to or less than the minuend.

Knowledge of the system of numeration is sufficient to determine when subtraction is possible. We can divide in the set of integers only if the divisor is a factor of the dividend. We know that $12 \div 4 = 3$ because $3 \times 4 = 12$. But $12 \div 5$ is meaningless unless there is an integer a such that $a \times 5 = 12$. It is not as simple a matter to determine whether division of two specific numbers is possible as was the case with subtraction.

We can, of course, determine divisibility by trial. In fact, in its practical application we are as much concerned with division that does not come out even as otherwise. But any time we have a remainder the division is impossible in the sense that we divide two *integers* and get for quotient an *integer*. There are tests for divisibility by small numbers, including all of the one-digit integers except 7, which are easy to apply and which will prove useful.

In Section 6.6 it is shown that the excess of nines in a number is equal to the excess of nines in its digit sum. If a number is divisible by 9 its excess of nines is zero. From this we may infer the rule:

An integer is divisible by nine if and only if the sum of its digits is divisible by nine.

We may, of course, apply the rule to the digit sum if necessary. For example, to test 89,783,946 for divisibility by nine we add $8 + 9 + 7 + 8 + 3 + 9 + 4 + 6 = 54$. And we can apply the test to the digit sum $54: 5 + 4 = 9$. We conclude the original number is divisible by nine because 9 certainly is.

The test is more than a test for divisibility; it gives the remainder upon division by nine in case the number does not have 9 for a factor. For example: 4875 has a digit sum of $4 + 8 + 7 + 5 = 24$ and 24 has a digit sum of $2 + 4 = 6$. Therefore when 4875 is divided by nine the remainder is 6.

An integer is divisible by two if and only if its ones digit is divisible by two.

In applying this rule we merely have to know that 0, 2, 4, 6, and 8 are the one-digit multiples of two. Any two or more digit number may be considered ten times an integer plus the ones digit; for example, $1276 = 10 \times 127 + 6$. Let us express the number $N = 10 \times a + b$ where a is an integer and b a one-digit integer. If 2 is a factor of N it must be a factor of $10 \times a + b$, by the Fundamental Theorem of Arithmetic, Section 6.7. But 2 is a factor of $10 \times a = 2 \times 5 \times a$. Then by the distributive property 2 must also be a factor of b:

$$N = 2[5 \times a + b/2]$$

On the other hand, if b does not have the factor 2, that is, it is odd, $10 \times a$ would have to be odd if N is even. But $10 \times a$ cannot be odd.

The rule for divisibility by five:

An integer is divisible by five if and only if its ones digit is divisible by five.

This rule follows from the above argument. Express the number $N = 10 \times a + b$. The term $10 \times a$ having the factor 10 must have the factor 5. Then by the distributive law N has the factor 5 if and only if b does. Then the number must have for ones digit either 5 or 0 if it is divisible by five.

These rules are also rules for determining the remainder upon division by two or five. Any integer is either divisible by two or has remainder one when divided by two. In the case of five the number has the same remainder upon division by five as the ones digit has. This is evident from the fact that the number minus its ones digit must be an exact multiple of five. For example, we know that $86,357 \div 5$ has a remainder 2 because $7 \div 5$ has remainder 2.

The rule for divisibility by three:

An integer is divisible by three if and only if the sum of its digits is divisible by three.

The test here is analogous to the test for the factor nine. It can be derived in the same manner. We know that 10 has remainder 1 when divided by 3. Or, in the terminology of Section 6.6, $10 \equiv 1$, mod 3. It follows that any integral power of 10 also has remainder 1: $10^n \equiv 1^n \equiv 1$ mod 3, and any multiple a of a power of 10 has remainder a:

$$a \times 10^n \equiv a \times 1^n = a, \text{ mod } 3.$$

For example, 50 and 5 have the same remainder, 2, upon division by 3. Since an integer is the sum of multiples of powers of 10 it has the same remainder upon division by three as does the sum of its digits. If the remainder is zero the number is divisible by 3. For example, 454,326 is a multiple of 3 because $4 + 5 + 4 + 3 + 2 + 6 = 24$ is; and we know 24 is because $2 + 4 = 6$ is. We know that 0, 3, 6, 9 are the one-digit multiples of three; the test is no help here.

We may derive a test for four patterned after the test for five. Or a slightly different test patterned after the test for three may be developed.

Following the test for five, we have the rule:

An integer is divisible by four if and only if the number represented by the tens and ones digit is divisible by four.   4

This rule follows from the fact that a three or more digit integer is an integral multiple of 100 plus a two-digit integer. For example, $7618 = 100 \times 76 + 18$. The integral multiple of 100 must be divisible by four because 100 has the factor 4. The entire number is then divisible by 4 if and only if the two-digit number is. Let N be a three or more digit integer, a an integer and b a two-digit integer. Then

$$N = 100a + b = 4 \times (25a + b/4)$$

and the number in parentheses is an integer if and only if b has 4 for a factor.

If we pattern after the rule for three the test for four becomes:

An integer is divisible by four if and only if the ones digit plus 2 times the tens digit is divisible by four.   4

To establish this rule we note that 10 is 2 more than a multiple of 4:

$$10 \equiv 2, \text{mod } 4$$

Then $10^2 = 100$ is 2×2 or 4 more than a multiple of 4. It is a multiple of 4:

$$10^2 \equiv 2^2 = 4 \equiv 0, \text{mod } 4$$

All higher powers of 10, having 10^2 for a factor, must be multiples of 4. Then any integer is congruent to 2 times its ten digit plus its ones digit, modulo 4.

EXAMPLE. Test 839,672 for divisibility by 4. By the first rule we may divide $72 \div 4 = 18$ and thus the original number has 4 for a factor.

By the second rule we find $2 \times 7 + 2 = 16$ (and if we wish we may apply the rule to 16, $2 \times 1 + 6 = 8$); since 16 (or 8) is a multiple of 4, so is the original number.

Since $6 = 2 \times 3$ we may combine the tests for two and for three to obtain a test for divisibility by six.

An integer is divisible by six if and only if its ones digit is divisible by two and the sum of its digits is divisible by three.   6

EXAMPLE. Test 634,254 for divisibility by six. The ones digit is divisible by 2. The sum of the digits $6 + 3 + 4 + 2 + 5 + 4 = 24$ is divisible by 3. Therefore the number is divisible by 6.

Unlike the other tests, the test for six does not indicate the remainder in case the number does not have six as a factor. This stems from the fact that we have combined two tests into one.

Each of the rules for divisibility by 4 may be extended to give a test for 8. Since 1000 is a multiple of 8 we have the rule:

An integer is divisible by 8 if and only if the number represented by the hundreds, tens, and ones digits is divisible by 8.

Ten being 2 more than a multiple of 8, 100 is $2 \times 2 = 4$ more than a multiple of 8, and 1000 is $2 \times 2 \times 2 = 8$ more than a multiple of 8, that is, a multiple of 8.

$$10 \equiv 2, \text{ mod } 8$$
$$10^2 \equiv 2^2 = 4, \text{ mod } 8$$
$$10^3 \equiv 2^3 = 8 \equiv 0, \text{ mod } 8$$

This justifies the rule:

An integer is divisible by 8 if and only if the ones digit, plus 2 times the tens digit, plus 4 times the hundreds digit is divisible by 8.

EXAMPLE. Test 867,312 for divisibility by 8. Since $312 \div 8 = 39$ we know that 867,312 is divisible by 8. By the other rule we have $4 \times 3 + 2 \times 1 + 2 = 16$ and $2 \times 1 + 6 = 8$, therefore the original number is a multiple of 8.

The test for divisibility by eleven is known as the skip rule:

An integer is divisible by eleven if and only if the sum of the odd placed digits, beginning with the ones digit, minus the sum of the even placed digits is divisible by eleven.

EXAMPLE. Test 53,621,348 for divisibility by eleven.

$$8 + 3 + 2 + 3 = 16$$
$$4 + 1 + 6 + 5 = 16$$
$$16 - 16 = 0 = 11 \cdot 0$$

Therefore the original number is divisible by eleven.

The justification for this rule follows. Since 10 is one less than a multiple of 11 we may express the fact as $10 \equiv -1, \text{ mod } 11$. Then 100 must be one more than a multiple of 11 since $10^2 \equiv (-1)^2 = 1, \text{ mod } 11$. But $1000 = 10^3 = 10^2 \times 10$, therefore $10^3 \equiv 1 \times (-1) = -1, \text{ mod } 11$. Each higher power of 10 has remainder alternately $+1$ and -1 upon division by 11, depending on whether the power of ten is even or odd.

For example, $700 = 7 \times 10^2$ has remainder 7 on division by 11, but $7000 = 7 \times 10^3$ has remainder -7 (which is equivalent to 4) on division by 11. The rule now follows from the fact that a number is the sum of the numbers represented by its digits, and the sum of the remainders has a remainder equal to the remainder of the sum.

We have given no test for divisibility by seven. One can be developed, using the ideas of congruence but it is easier to divide the number out than to apply the test. Note the following congruences:

$$10 \equiv 3, \text{mod } 7$$
$$10^2 \equiv 3^2 = 9 \equiv 2, \text{mod } 7$$
$$10^3 = 10^2 \times 10 \equiv 2 \times 3 = 6 \equiv -1, \text{mod } 7$$
$$10^4 = 10^3 \times 10 \equiv -1 \times 3 = -3, \text{mod } 7$$
$$10^5 = 10^4 \times 10 \equiv -3 \times 3 = -9 \equiv -2, \text{mod } 7$$
$$10^6 = 10^5 \times 10 \equiv -2 \times 3 = -6 \equiv 1, \text{mod } 7$$
$$10^7 = 10^6 \times 10 \equiv 1 \times 3 = 3, \text{mod } 7$$

The cycle $3, 2, -1, -3, -2, 1, 3 \ldots$ obviously continues. This suggests the rule for divisibility by 7: If the sum of the ones digit, 3 times the tens digit, 2 times the hundreds digit, -1 times the thousands digit, and so on, is divisible by seven, the number itself is.

EXAMPLE. Test 83,629 for divisibility by 7.
$$9 + 3 \times 2 + 2 \times 6 + (-1) \times 3 + (-3) \times 8 = 27 - 27 = 0$$
Therefore the number is divisible by 7.

The test for divisibility by 6 combines the tests for 2 and for 3, the factors of 6. In this same fashion, we may devise tests for divisibility by larger numbers. If the number may be factored into *relatively prime* (see Section 6.9) factors we may test for divisibility by testing for divisibility by the factors. For example, a number is divisible by 24 if it is divisible by 3 and by 8. But we may not say it is divisible by 24 if it is divisible by 4 and by 6. Obviously, 36 is divisible by 4 and by 6 but not by 24. Since 4 and 6 have the common factor 2 they are not relatively prime. A number may be divisible by both 4 and 6 and contain the factor 2 only two times. On the other hand if a number is divisible by 3 and by $8 = 2^3$ it must have the factor 2 three times.

Divisibility by 3 and by 5 constitutes divisibility by 15 but divisibility by 3 and by 15 does not constitute divisibility by 45. Divisibility by 15 implies divisibility by 3.

all but six remainders
indicate

Exercises

1 Test the following for divisibility by 2, 3, 5, 9 and 11; if they are not divisible, find remainders:

(a) 47,801

(b) 3510

(c) 635,822

(d) 2970

2 Test the following for divisibility by 2, 4, and 8; if not divisible, find remainders:

(a) 36,104

(b) 9696

(c) 8310

(d) 2501

3 Since a number is divisible by 6 if it is divisible by 2 and by 3, why can we not say it is divisible by 8 if it is divisible by 2 and by 4?

4 Using the congruence idea, devise a test for divisibility by 13. The result will be comparable to the test for 7.

5 State a test for divisibility by 12. Apply the test to 10,032.

6 Is it possible for a number to end in 14 and be divisible by 12? By 21? Why?

7 Give a test for divisibility by 22. *2 ψ 11*

8 If a number is divisible by 99 what does this tell us about its digits?

9 Supply the missing digit which will make the following divisible by 2, by 3, by 4, by 5, by 6, by 9, and by 11. In those cases where this is impossible state why.

(a) 4636_82   (b) 731656_4_   (c) 837_61_3

10 Consider the digits of a number expressed in base ten to have *position* values in the base three scale. If the resulting number is divisible by 7 the original number is also. For example: Applying the rule to 245 we have $2 \times 9 + 4 \times 3 + 5 = 35$. Applying the rule to 35 we have $3 \times 3 + 5 = 14$. And finally applying the rule to 14 we have $1 \times 3 + 4 = 7$. Therefore 245 is divisible by 7. Is this rule correct? Why?

11 How can you tell whether a number is divisible by 25 without dividing by 25? Justify your answer.

6.9 THE EUCLIDEAN ALGORITHM

Two integers are *relatively prime* if they have no prime factors in common. If they have no prime factor in common they obviously have no integral factor in common except 1. The Euclidean algorithm is a convenient device for finding the greatest factor common to two integers. First we shall illustrate the method:

EXAMPLE. Find the greatest factor common to 368 and 1081.
Divide 1081 by 368

$$
\begin{array}{r}
2 \\
368 \overline{\smash{)}1081} \\
736 \\
\hline
345
\end{array}
$$

Then divide the 368 by the remainder 345

$$
\begin{array}{r}
1 \\
345 \overline{\smash{)}368} \\
345 \\
\hline
23
\end{array}
$$

Continuing, $345 \div 23$

$$
\begin{array}{r}
15 \\
23 \overline{\smash{)}345} \\
23 \\
\hline
115 \\
115 \\
\hline
0
\end{array}
$$

The last nonzero divisor, 23, is the greatest factor common to 1081 and 368.

The process consists of dividing the larger of the two original numbers by the smaller, then on each succeeding step dividing the previous divisor by the previous remainder.

If a remainder 1 is reached, the next step will yield a remainder zero, and the greatest common factor is 1. The numbers are relatively prime.

EXAMPLE. Show that 391 and 113 are relatively prime.

$$
\begin{array}{cccccc}
3 & 2 & 5 & 1 & 3 & 2 \\
113\overline{\smash{)}391} & 52\overline{\smash{)}113} & 9\overline{\smash{)}52} & 7\overline{\smash{)}9} & 2\overline{\smash{)}7} & 1\overline{\smash{)}2} \\
339 & 104 & 45 & 7 & 6 & 2 \\
\hline
52 & 9 & 7 & 2 & 1 & 0
\end{array}
$$

Therefore the greatest factor common to 391 and 113 is 1.

We shall examine the first example to discover why the method works. Since we got no remainder when 345 was divided by 23 we know that 345 has 23 for a factor. The next to the last step reveals that

$$368 = 1 \times 345 + 23$$

But the distributive law tells us that any factor common to 368 and 345 must be a factor of 23. Then the only factors common to 368 and 345 are 23 and 1. By the first step we know that

$$1081 = 2 \times 368 + 345$$

Again the distributive law tells us that any factor common to 1081 and 368 must also be common to 368 and 345, namely 23 and 1. Thus we have shown not only that 23 is a common factor of 1081 and 368 but that it is the highest common factor. The generality of the reasoning is evident.

We follow the same reasoning in the second example. From the next to the last step we know

$$7 = 3 \times 2 + 1$$

and 7 and 2 have no common factor other than 1. Then, since $9 = 1 \times 7 + 2$, all factors common to 9 and 7 are also common to 7 and 2, namely 1. Continuing this reasoning, we reach the conclusion that 391 and 113 have as common factors only those factors common to 113, 52, 9, 7, 2, namely 1.

Exercises

1 Use the Euclidean algorithm to find the greatest common divisor (g.c.d.) of 180 and 252.

2 Use the Euclidean algorithm to show that 76 and 207 are relatively prime.

3 If two numbers are relatively prime can they be congruent with respect to any modulus? Illustrate.

4 If two numbers are relatively prime can each be congruent to zero with respect to any modulus? Explain.

5 Show that 163 and 227 are relatively prime.

6 Explain the difference between relatively prime and prime.

7 Find the greatest factor common to 2048 and 326.

8 In using the Euclidean algorithm what does it signify if we get a remainder 1?

9 Are 38265 and 956 relatively prime? Use the Euclidean algorithm.

10 Compute in base eight and determine the greatest common divisor of 217_{eight} and 130_{eight}.

6.10 TESTS FOR DIVISIBILITY IN OTHER BASES

The rules given in the previous section are a function of the base of notation. *Forty-six* is divisible by 2 regardless of the base in which it is written. The above test for divisibility by 2 will not apply to all bases. If forty-six is expressed in base five it is written 1 4 1, but it is still divisible by 2. The symbol 1 1 1, interpreted as a base-twelve number, is not divisible by three although the sum of its digits is $1 + 1 + 1 = 3$.

The analogy to the test for nine in base ten will serve as a test for the number one less than the base. For example, to test 3245_{six} for divisibility by 5 we add the digits:

$$3 + 2 + 4 + 5 = 22 \text{ }_{six}; \qquad 2 + 2 = 4_{six}$$

We conclude that 3245_{six} has a remainder 4 when divided by five. To check this we may convert 3245_{six} to base ten:

$$3245_{six} = (3 \times 6^3 + 2 \times 6^2 + 4 \times 6 + 5)_{ten} = 749_{ten}$$

But, using the base ten test for 5, 749 has remainder 4 upon division by 5 because 9 does.

The skip rule gives a test for the number one more than the base. We test 3245_{six} for divisibility by seven by the skip rule:

$$5 + 2 = 11_{six}; \qquad 4 + 3 = 11_{six}; \qquad 11_{six} - 11_{six} = 0;$$

therefore seven is a factor. We may verify this by observing that 749 is divisible by 7.

The tests for 2 and 5 were obtained by merely inspecting the ones digit. This was possible because 2 and 5 are the factors of the base 10. If we use twelve for base we may test for division by 2, 3, 4, and 6 by determining whether the ones digit is a multiple of each. For example, 1276_{twelve} is divisible by 2, 3, and 6 because the ones digit is a multiple of each; but it is not divisible by 4 because the ones digit, 6, is not. On the other hand, 378_{twelve} is divisible by 2 and 4 but not by 3 or 6.

If the number is written in base five we would not add the digits to test for three. We would add the ones digit, 2 times the 5s digit, the 5^2 digit, 2 times the 5^3 digit, and so on. For example, to test $342,341_{five}$ for divisibility by 3, we get

$$1 + 2 \times 4 + 3 + 2 \times 2 + 4 + 2 \times 3$$
$$= 1 + 13_{five} + 3 + 4 + 4 + 11_{five}$$
$$= 101_{five} \quad \text{then} \quad 1 + 2 \times 0 + 1 = 2.$$

We conclude that $342{,}341_{\text{five}}$ has remainder 2 when divided by 3. On the other hand, if seven is base the test for 3 is the same as the base ten test, that is, the sum of the digits must be a multiple of three if the number is. For example, we test 6254_{seven} for divisibility by three by adding the digits $6 + 2 + 5 + 4 = 23_{\text{seven}}$ then $2 + 3 = 5_{\text{seven}}$. We conclude that 6254_{seven} has remainder 2 on division by 3 because 5 has remainder 2.

Both of these results, the test for divisibility by 3 in base five and in base seven, are obtained by considering the powers of the base, modulo 3. In the case of five we have

$$5 \equiv 2, \bmod 3$$
$$5^2 \equiv 2^2 = 4 \equiv 1, \bmod 3$$
$$5^3 = 5^2 \times 5 \equiv 1 \times 2 = 2, \bmod 3$$
$$5^4 = 5^3 \times 5 \equiv 2 \times 2 = 4 \equiv 1, \bmod 3$$

and the cycle 2, 1, 2, 1 continues. With seven as base, we have

$$7 \equiv 1, \bmod 3$$
$$7^2 = 7 \times 7 \equiv 1 \times 1 = 1, \bmod 3$$
$$7^3 = 7^2 \times 7 \equiv 1 \times 1 = 1, \bmod 3$$

and we conclude that any power of seven has remainder one upon division by 3.

Exercises

1   (a) Add and check, modulo 3 $121_{\text{four}} + 123_{\text{four}}$
(b) Multiply and check, modulo 6 $322_{\text{seven}} \times 15_{\text{seven}}$
(c) Divide and check, modulo 4 $312_{\text{five}} \div 14_{\text{five}}$
2   Devise appropriate tests and check the following.
(a) 960753_{twelve} for divisibility by 11_{ten}.
(b) 427_{eight} for divisibility by 9.
(c) 3264_{seven} for divisibility by 5; for divisibility by 3.
(d) 27314_{eight} for divisibility by 5; for divisibility by 4.
3   If a number ends in 6 can it be divisible by 6 if it is written in base ten? Must it be?
4   If a number ends in 6 can it be divisible by 6 if it is written in base twelve? Must it be?
5   If a base twelve number ends in 5 must it be divisible by 5? Can it be divisible by 5?
6   A number is written in base five. Prove that it is even if it has an even number of odd digits.
7   Under what conditions will a base-five number be odd?

8 If the base six is used what is the test for divisibility by three? by two ? by four?

9 Test $73{,}626_{\text{nine}}$ for divisibility by 8. Convert the number to base ten and check.

10 Use any base and show that an odd number can end in an even digit and that an even number can end in an odd digit.

11 Write $1^2, 2^2, \ldots 5^2$ in modulo 5 and thus show that any perfect square is a multiple of 5, one more than a multiple of 5, or one less than a multiple of 5.

6.11 PROPERTIES OF DIVISION

Does division, being the inverse of multiplication, obey the same rules? Until we enlarge our number system to include rational numbers (fractions) the operation is not always possible in the sense that the quotient is an integer. However, we can examine the behavior of division in those cases where it is possible.

First, is division commutative? If so, $a \div b = b \div a$. When we examine a specific example, $20 \div 4 = 5$, but $4 \div 20 = ?$ It certainly does not equal 5 because $5 \times 20 = 100$, not 4. It cannot equal any integer, for if it did this would mean that if we use 20 as an addend an integral number of times the sum would be 4. But let us assume that division is commutative and see what conclusion we are forced to accept.

By definition of division, $a \div b = x$ implies $b \times x = a$ and $b \div a = x$ implies $a \times x = b$. Using this value of b in the first implication, we get $a \times x \times x = a$. This implies that $x \times x$ is the multiplication identity element 1 and therefore $x = 1$. But if $a \div b = 1$, then $1 \times b = a$. We conclude that division is commutative only if the dividend and the divisor are identical.

Consider continuous division such as $24 \div 6 \div 2$. Does this equal $24 \div 2 \div 6$? The answer is yes, in this specific case; $24 \div 6 \div 2 = 4 \div 2 = 2$ and $24 \div 2 \div 6 = 12 \div 6 = 2$. But this is not an example of commutative division. Neither the 6 nor the 2 plays the role of dividend. They are divisors in both cases. We have not commuted dividend and divisor; we have commuted two division operations, dividing by 6 and dividing by 2.

To show that this property holds for the general case we must show that

$$(a \div b) \div c = (a \div c) \div b$$

To show this let $a \div b = x$. The left member of the equation becomes $x \div c$. But $a \div b = x$ implies $b \times x = a$. Substituting for a in the right member, the equation becomes

$$x \div c = (b \times x \div c) \div b$$

Consider $x \div c$ as one factor in the parentheses and commute the two factors and we have

$$x \div c = (x \div c) \times b \div b$$

But, as we have seen in Section 6.3, the right member also becomes $x \div c$.

Had we not restricted ourselves to those integers with which exact division is possible, a simpler argument could be used. If we grant that division by an integer is equivalent to multiplication by its reciprocal, that is $a \div b = a \times 1/b$, the following argument could be used:

$$(a \div b) \div c = (a \times 1/b) \times 1/c.$$

But since multiplication is both associative and commutative (these properties hold for fractions just as they do for integers) we can say

$$(a \times 1/b) \times 1/c = a \times (1/b \times 1/c) = a \times (1/c \times 1/b)$$
$$= (a \times 1/c) \times 1/b = (a \div c) \div b.$$

We conclude that *in continuous division the order in which the divisors are used is immaterial.*

If division is associative, $(a \div b) \div c = a \div (b \div c)$. A numerical example is sufficient to show that this property does not exist:

Consider $(24 \div 4) \div 2$ as compared to $24 \div (4 \div 2)$.

$(24 \div 4) \div 2 = 6 \div 2 = 3$ but $24 \div (4 \div 2) = 24 \div 2 = 12$

However, we note that in the successive division $24 \div 4 \div 2 = 3$ we obtain the same result as we do if we *multiply* the successive divisors 4 and 2 and use the product for divisor:

$$24 \div 4 \div 2 = 24 \div (4 \times 2) = 24 \div 8 = 3$$

To show the general case we must show that

$$a \div b \div c = a \div (b \times c)$$
$$\text{If } a \div (b \times c) = x \text{ then } x \times b \times c = a$$

Replace a in the left member of the equation by $x \times b \times c$ and we get $x \times b \times c \div b \div c = x \times c \times b \div b \div c = x \times c \div c = x$. Then, since both members of the equation equal x, we have shown that the equality holds.

Again, a more direct argument results if we admit fractions:

$$a \div b \div c = a \times 1/b \times 1/c = a \times \frac{1}{b \times c} = a \div (b \times c)$$

We conclude from the above that *we may replace successive division with division by the product of the successive divisors*. Or, otherwise stated, *we may divide by each factor of the divisor rather than the divisor itself*. For example:

$$96 \div 8 \div 4 = 96 \div (8 \times 4) = 96 \div 32 = 3, \quad \text{and}$$
$$63 \div 21 = (63 \div 7) \div 3 = 9 \div 3 = 3$$

Since multiplication is commutative we know that

$$a \times (b + c) = (b + c) \times a$$

If we apply the distributive law to $a \times (b + c)$ we get

$$a \times (b + c) = a \times b + a \times c$$

Then, commuting the factors in each term,

$$a \times b + a \times c = b \times a + c \times a$$

The final expression being equal to $(b + c) \times a$ indicates that we can "enter the parentheses through the back door," so to speak. The relationship $a \times (b + c) = a \times b + a \times c$ is properly known as the left-hand distributive law. And the other relationship $(b + c) \times a = b \times a + c \times a$ is known as the right-hand distributive law. Although both properties hold for integers (and other ordinary numbers) they are not necessarily equivalent. There are mathematical systems wherein this is not true.

Numerical examples will indicate that the left distributive law *does not* hold for division but the right does:

$96 \div (16 + 32) = 96 \div 48 = 2$ does not equal $(96 \div 16) +$
$(96 \div 32) = 6 + 3 = 9$, as it would if the distributive law held.

However

$(16 + 32) \div 4 = 48 \div 4 = 12$, and $(16 + 32) \div 4 = 16 \div 4$
$+ 32 \div 4 = 4 + 8 = 12$

In this one case at least, the right-hand distributive law does hold.

To show why the left-hand does not but the right does apply in the general case we reduce the problem to multiplication:

$$c \div (a + b) = c \times \frac{1}{a + b} = \frac{c}{a + b} \text{ which does } \textit{not} \text{ equal } c/a + c/b$$
$$= c \div a + c \div b$$

as required by the distributive law. On the other hand,

$$(a + b) \div c = (a + b) \times 1/c = \frac{a + b}{c} \text{ which } does \text{ equal } a/c + b/c$$
$$= a \div c + b \div c$$

as required by the distributive law.

We conclude that *we can distribute the divisor over the terms of the dividend but we cannot distribute the dividend over the terms of the divisor.*

One further property of division follows from the fact that its inverse, multiplication, is commutative. If $a \div b = c$ then $b \times c = a$ and $c \times b = a$, but this implies that $a \div c = b$. In other words, *any division fact, dividend divided by divisor equals quotient, implies another division fact, dividend divided by quotient equals divisor.* We know that if $a \div b = c$ then $a \div c = b$.

In multiplication, if either factor is multiplied by a number the product is multiplied by the same number. For example, $12 \times 5 = 60$ and $12 \times (3 \times 5) = (3 \times 60)$. From this it follows that in division we may *multiply both dividend and divisor by the same number not zero without changing the quotient.* For example, since $30 \div 6 = 5$, we know that $(3 \times 30) \div (3 \times 6) = 5$ also. In general, if $a \div b = c$ then $(n \times a) \div (n \times b) = c$. We know that $a \div b = c$ implies $c \times b = a$. Multiplying this by n we get $n \times c \times b = n \times a$, which may be written $c \times (n \times b) = n \times a$. This implies $(n \times a) \div (n \times b) = c$.

We note that $n \times c \times b = n \times a$ can be written $(n \times c) \times b = n \times a$, and this implies $(n \times a) \div b = n \times c$. This establishes the principle *multiplying the dividend by a number produces the same effect on the quotient*:

$$30 \div 6 = 5 \text{ implies } (3 \times 30) \div 6 = (3 \times 5)$$

Finally, we wish to determine the effect on the quotient if we multiply the divisor. To this end we divide both sides of the equation

$$c \times n \times b = n \times a$$

by n in order that a be intact. This gives

$$(c \div n) \times (n \times b) = a, \text{ which implies } a \div (n \times b) = c \div n$$

Multiplying the divisor by a nonzero number divides the quotient by the same number:

$$100 \div 5 = 20 \text{ implies } 100 \div (5 \times 5) = (20 \div 5)$$

The three preceding arguments can be reversed, yielding the same principles with multiplication replaced by division:

If $(n \times a) \div (n \times b) = c$
then $c \times n \times b = n \times a$, but this implies
$c \times b = a$, which implies $a \div b = c$.

We may divide both dividend and divisor by the same nonzero number without changing the quotient.

In a similar manner we can establish the principle, *dividing the dividend by a nonzero number produces the same effect on the quotient* and *dividing the divisor by a nonzero number multiples the quotient by the same number*:

$$60 \div 15 = 4 \text{ implies } 20 \div 5 = 4$$
$$60 \div 15 = 4 \text{ implies } 30 \div 15 = 2$$
$$60 \div 15 = 4 \text{ implies } 60 \div 3 = 20$$

Subtraction and division do not behave by the same rules as their inverses addition and multiplication. We have observed a parallel between addition and multiplication of positive integers. Both operations are commutative and associative. The positive integers are closed under both operations, that is, addition and multiplication are always possible. The two operations are related by the distributive law.

A similar parallel exists between subtraction and division. The properties of the two are summarized below:

Subtraction	*Division*
The order of successive subtrahends can be changed:	The order of successive divisors can be changed:
$a - b - c = a - c - b$.	$a \div b \div c = a \div c \div b$.
Successive subtractions may be performed by subtracting the sum of the subtrahends:	Successive division may be performed by dividing by the product of the divisors:
$a - b - c = a - (b + c)$.	$a \div b \div c = a \div (b \times c)$.
If the same number is added to (or subtracted from) minuend and subtrahend the remainder is unchanged:	If dividend and divisor are multiplied (or divided) by the same *nonzero* number the quotient is unchanged:
$a - b = (n + a) - (n + b)$ $= (a - n) - (b - n).$	$a \div b = (m \times a) \div (m \times b)$ $= (a \div m) \div (b \div m).$

Adding to (or subtracting from) the minuend produces the same change in the remainder:
If $a - b = c$
then $(n + a) - b = n + c$
and $(a - n) - b = (c - n)$.

Multiplying (or dividing) the dividend produces the same change in the quotient:
If $a \div b = c$
then $n \times a \div b = n \times c$
and $a \div n \div b = c \div n$.

From any subtraction fact another may be obtained by interchanging subtrahend and remainder:
If $a - b = c$, then $a - c = b$.

From any division fact another may be obtained by interchanging divisor and quotient:
If $a \div b = c$, then $a \div c = b$.

Multiplication is distributive with respect to subtraction:
$a \times (b - c) = a \times b - a \times c$.

Division obeys only the right-hand distributive law relative to addition (or subtraction):
$(a + b) \div c = (a \div c) + (b \div c)$
$(a - b) \div c = (a \div c) - (b \div c)$.

Exercises

State whether each of the proposed equalities in Exercises 1–29 is true. If true, state the principle(s) involved. If the equality holds but represents a special case rather than demonstrates a general principle, so indicate:

1 $28 \div 4 \div 7 = 28 \div 7 \div 4$

2 $5 \times (6 - 3) = 5 \times 6 - 5 \times 3$

3 $125 - 256 = 256 - 125$

4 $3 \times (7 + 6) = 3 + (7 \times 6)$

5 $3 \times (9 + 4) = 3 + (9 \times 4)$

6 $25 \div 5 = 75 \div 15$

7 $(60 \div 12) \div 5 = 60 \div (12 \div 5)$

8 $(25 \div 5) \div 1 = 25 \div (5 \div 1)$

9 $(20 - 5) \div 3 = 20 \div 3 - 5 \div 3$

10 $6 - (30 \div 5) = (30 \div 5) - 6$

11 $48 \div 6 \div 2 = 48 \div 12$

12 $30 \div (6 + 5) = 30 \div 6 + 30 \div 5$

13 $(7 - 3) \times 2 = 7 \times 2 - 3 \times 2$

14 $(3 - 2) \times 3 = 3 \times 2 - 3$

15 $(5 - 3) \times 4 = 5 \times 3 - 4$

16 $36 - 7 - 5 - 4 = 36 - (7 + 5 + 4)$

17 $18 \times 12 \div 18 \times 4 = 12 \div 4$

18 $18 \times (6 \div 3) = (18 \times 6) \div (18 \times 3)$

19 $(25 + 6) - 12 = (13 + 6) - 0$

20 $(48 \div 12) \div (24 \div 12) = 48 \div 12$

21 $13 - (6 - 4) = 13 - (4 - 6)$

22 $42 \div (4 + 3) = 42 \div 4 + 42 \div 3$

23 $(14 + 28) \div 7 = (14 \div 7) + (28 \div 7)$

24 $12 - 8 = 12 - (5 + 2 + 1)$

25 $(29 - 13) - 6 = 29 - (13 - 6)$

26 $17 \times (5 + 8) = (17 \times 5) + (17 \times 8)$

27 $96 \div 16 = (96 \div 8) \div 2$

28 $(40 - 8) - 12 = 28 - 8$

29 $18 - 9 = (72 - 36) \div 4$

30 Give an example to illustrate that the left hand distributive law does not hold for division.

31 Which, if any, of the following are correct?

(a) $(36 \div 6) \div 3 = 36 \div (6 \div 3)$

(b) $7 \div (4 + 9) = 7 \div 4 + 7 \div 9$

(c) $(6 + 5) \div 8 = 6 \div 8 + 5 \div 8$

(d) $(3 + 4) \div 14 = 3 \div 14 + 4 \div 14$

32 The following is true if the numbers are interpreted in base ten. Is it true if we are using base 12?

$$3 \times (9 + 4) = 3 + (9 \times 4)$$

33 Find other triples of numbers which behave as those in Exercise 32.

Suggested Supplementary Readings

Banks, J. Houston, *Elements of Mathematics*, Second Edition. Boston: Allyn and Bacon, Inc., 1961. Pp. 100–113, 135–148.

Buckingham, B. R., *Elementary Arithmetic: Its Meaning and Practice.* Boston: Ginn and Company, 1947. Chaps. VII, VIII.

Larsen, Harold D., *Arithmetic for Colleges.* New York: The Macmillan Company, 1950. Chaps. IV, VI.

Mueller, Francis J., *Arithmetic, Its Structure and Concepts.* Englewood Cliffs, N.J.: Prentice-Hall, Inc., 1956. Pp. 69–95, 117–141.

Bell, Clifford, Clela D. Hammond, Robert B. Herrera, *Fundamentals of Arithmetic for Teachers.* New York: John Wiley and Sons, Inc., 1962. Chaps. IV, VI.

Dutton, Wilbur H. and L. J. Adams, *Arithmetic for Teachers.* Englewood Cliffs, N.J.: Prentice-Hall, Inc., 1961. Chaps. IV, V.

Richardson, Moses, *Fundamentals of Mathematics.* New York: The Macmillan Company, 1941. Pp. 58–63.

Swain, Robert L., *Understanding Arithmetic.* New York: Rinehart and Company, Inc., 1957. Chap. V.

Teaching Multiplication
and Division

MULTIPLICATION AND DIVISION ARE logically in as close proximity to each other as are addition and subtraction. However, in the development of algorithms and, for that matter, learning of basic facts, this logical connection cannot be utilized to nearly so great an extent. If the child has insight into the meaning of the symbols he can with a minimum of difficulty associate $8 - 5 = 3$ and $3 + 5 = 8$ as merely two ways to express one basic fact. But in terms of visualization of a physical model $15 \div 3 = 5$ and $5 \times 3 = 15$ presents a more difficult situation.

A far more significant cause for the greater difficulty in relating multiplication and division is the fact that subtraction never leads us outside the integers, but division does. Closely associated with this is the relative ease with which one can determine whether subtraction is possible in the set of nonnegative integers as compared to whether division is possible. For example, one can tell at a glance that 489372 − 489296 is possible. But what about 489372 ÷ 326?

Nevertheless, in teaching the operations of multiplication and division their inverse nature should be developed. And, the fact of this relationship should be utilized.

7.1 PREPARING FOR MULTIPLICATION

Systematic formal work on multiplication is usually deferred until Grade 3. However, preparation for it should be an integral part of the number readiness program of the earlier grades. Two concepts of multiplication should be developed before any attempt is made to master the basic multiplication facts as such. In fact these concepts should be developed before the term *multiplication* is introduced.

First, multiplication should be developed as a special kind of addition, addition of equal addends. There are many situations in the child's experience which call for the solution of this type of addition problem. For example: "Four boys and four girls dance together in a set. Two sets dance at a time. How many children dance at one time?" "Six children brought 3 cents each today for our aquarium fund. How much does that make?" "We want to buy three new goldfish. They cost 20 cents each. How much do we need?" "We wrote letters to the 4 children who are out with measles. How much will 5-cent stamps for the letters cost?" The number line, one hundred chart, counting frame, loose counting materials, all such aids should be employed freely where needed. To the child this is simply solving a problem in addition. At first, problem situations of this kind should be referred to as finding four 3s or six 2s and so on, rather than 4 times 3 or 3 multiplied by 4. As the children learn this is a special kind of addition situation the term *times* should be introduced gradually to establish the fact that four 3s and 4 times 3 convey the same meaning.

The second multiplication meaning which should be developed may be called the "ratio to one" meaning. For example, when we find 4×3 we are finding that number which has the same ratio to 3 that 4 has to 1:

$$4 : 1 = 12 : 3$$

In developing this meaning it is better to refer to $4 \times 3 = ?$ as finding the number that is four times as large as 3 rather than to refer to finding four 3s.

Why do we find the cost of three 5-cent ice cream cones by find-ing 3 × 5? Because we want a quantity 3 times as large as 5 cents. In the terminology of ratio, we have 3 is to 1 as 15 cents is to 5 cents. We can think of the ratio 3:1 as a comparison between a set of three elements and a unit set.

and the ratio 15¢:5¢ as a comparison between two sets, the first containing 15 cents and the second 5 cents.

A set with three elements has three times as many elements as a unit set, and a set with 15 cents has three times as many cents as a set with 5 cents.

It is not difficult to find situations in the child's experience which require the second interpretation of multiplication. Addition and subtraction are used in comparing two quantities in a "more than" or "larger than" manner. We use multiplication and division in comparing two quantities in a "times as many" or "times as large" manner. For example: "Bill lives 2 blocks from school but Mary lives 3 times as far." "Jack's father said he was 3 times as heavy as Jack." "His kite string is 2 times as long as mine."

Specific types of number activities which help provide the foun-dation for multiplication include counting by equal groups—counting by twos, by fives, by tens, and so on. In this connection we refer again to the multiple counting chart, Section 5.6. A thorough study of the discoverable relationships present on the chart will prove very helpful in learning the multiplication facts.

Many comparisons, such as comparing counting by 3s to 12 with counting by 4s to 12 should be made in order to establish the com-mutative property of multiplication. This can be forcefully illustrated on the number line. Similar comparisons of addition of equal addends also should be made. Concrete situations involving an interchange of the roles of multiplier and multiplicand are more meaningful than the mere observation that $3 + 3 + 3 + 3 + 3 = 5 + 5 + 5$. For example: "Jane bought 5 small balloons at 3 cents each. Bill bought 3 larger balloons at 5 cents each. Compare the amounts that each spent."

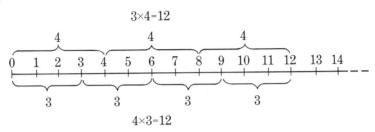

MULTIPLICATION IS COMMUTATIVE.

The associative and distributive properties should be used as aids in *discovering* multiplications facts. Later they will be essential to an *understanding* of the multiplication algorithms. The associative property is simply a matter of regrouping. We are utilizing the associative property when we find $7 + 8 = 15$.

$$7 + 8 = 7 + (3 + 5) = (7 + 3) + 5 = 10 + 5 = 15$$

There is a variety of ways the associative property can be applied to $7 + 8$. For example $7 + 8 = 7 + (1 + 7) = (7 + 1) + 7 = 8 + 7$, a result we could have gotten from the commutative property. The possibilities are somewhat more limited in multiplication. A number usually has fewer pairs of factors than pairs of addends. The associative property is all that is necessary to discover that $15 \times 3 = 45$ provided that we know $5 \times 9 = 45$.

$$5 \times 9 = 5 \times (3 \times 3) = (5 \times 3) \times 3 = 15 \times 3$$

5×6

The making of such discoveries need not depend upon the pupils' ability to factor. Loose counting materials can be manipulated to find other possibilities for grouping. For example, 5×6 will be represented as 5 sets, 6 to a set. But we can split each set of 6 into

$$5 \times (2 \times 3)$$

two sets of 3. We have 5 sets of 2 sets of 3. This is $5 \times 6 = 5 \times (2 \times 3)$. But concentrating only on the number of sets of 3, we have 5×2

$$(5 \times 2) \times 3$$

such sets. That is $5 \times 6 = 5 \times (2 \times 3) = (5 \times 2) \times 3 = 10 \times 3$.

Counting materials can be used to good purpose to show such relationships as four 8s equal four 10s less four 2s, and

$$4 \times 10 - 4 \times 2 = 4 \times 8$$

and four 8s equal four 5s plus four 3s.

$$4 \times 5 + 4 \times 3 = 4 \times 8$$

The purpose of such activities is two fold: discovery of unknown facts (or verification of uncertain ones) and establishment and reinforcement of the associative and distributive *ideas*. Applied to whole numbers these ideas, as well as commutativity, can be illustrated merely as regrouping.

$3\times4=4\times3$

Commutativity

$4\times(3+2)=4\times3+4\times2$

Distributivity

Development of the concepts themselves is the important consideration. Although they can be useful in mastery of the basic facts, these concepts have a far more pervasive value. Ability to verbalize the concept is not essential to its mastery or application. A few people even think verbalization is a hindrance to understanding. In any event, verbalization should not be an end in itself. Children certainly should be encouraged to explain the ideas in their own words, rather than memorize correct statements of principles which are meaningless to them. Children would be expected to express the commutative concept in a manner something like: "It doesn't matter which number comes first" or "You can swap the number of sets with the number of members in the set." Distributivity might be expressed as: "It doesn't matter whether you add and then multiply or multiply each addend then add." Associativity might be expressed as: "It makes no difference which two factors are multiplied first." Of course this really assumes more than just associativity, but it is a correct generalization. It is true that

$$(3 \times 4) \times 7 = (3 \times 7) \times 4$$

But it cannot be justified from the associative property alone.

There should be a gradual transition from groups of objects to numbers themselves. When the child is ready for mastery of the multiplication facts the commutative property applied to 3×4 should mean the equivalence of 3 groups of 4 each and 4 groups of 3 each. But it should also mean that the number which is three times as large as 4 is the same number that is four times as large as 3:

$$3:1 = 12:4 \quad \text{and} \quad 4:1 = 12:3$$

Finally, he should accept as an automatic response $3 \times 4 = 4 \times 3 = 12$. The associative and distributive properties will continue to be applied in a more deliberately reasoned manner, but they too should ultimately be applied to *numbers* rather than groups of things. For example, the child should come to realize that 8×52 is the same as $8 \times 50 + 8 \times 2$ simply because the multiplicand 52 can be separated into the addends 50 and 2 and the multiplier 8 applied to each addend. He should also be familiar with the idea of breaking one or both factors up into factors. For example, $14 \times 15 = 2 \times 7 \times 3 \times 5 = 2 \times 3 \times 7 \times 5 = 6 \times 35$. Here the two-digit by two-digit problem is changed into a two-digit by one-digit problem.

7.2 THE MULTIPLICATION FACTS

There are 100 one-digit by one-digit multiplication facts. Before progress can be made with the multiplication algorithms these must be mastered. They, like the basic addition facts, ultimately should be reduced to automatic responses. The facts which involve zero should not be ignored but they should cause no great difficulty. The child should not consider multiplication by zero as not multiplying. The same remark was made relative to the addition of zero. If $5 + 0$ means we do not add anything to the 5 and therefore still have 5 why should we not say that 0×5 means we do not multiply the 5 by anything and therefore still have the 5?

One source of difficulty with the zero facts for the thinking pupil stems from his observation that in general multiplying by a number causes a greater increase than adding the same number. That is 5×3 is greater than $5 + 3$. This is not true with zero. When we add zero we at least break even, but when we multiply by zero we get less than we started with. The same kind of difficulty applies to multiplication by 1. We get an increase when we add 1 but no change when we multiply by 1. When work on the multiplication facts enters the memorization stage major emphasis should still be on understanding with regard to the *zero* facts and the *one* facts. In this way the child can better make the generalizations that any number times zero equals zero and any number times one equals the number. The child will experience no need for these facts until two-digit multiplication is encountered. The wise procedure is to wait until he sees the need for them, then show him that the above generalizations are consistent with the previously accepted meanings of multiplication. That is, 5×1 means $1 + 1 + 1 + 1 + 1$ and 1×5 means one set of 5. And in the case of zero, 5×0 means $0 + 0 + 0 + 0 + 0$. While we might rationalize 0×5 as meaning we add no fives, the better approach is to emphasize the fact that 0×5 must mean whatever 5×0 means. In other words commutativity applies to zero just as to other numbers.

Aside from the zero and one facts there remain 64 multiplication facts to be memorized. Of these there are 28 facts and their reversals, and 8 squares. It would be entirely erroneous to assume that there are therefore 36 unrelated facts to learn. Ten of the 36 facts are related in pairs in that they give the same product:

$2 \times 6 = 3 \times 4 = 12,$ $2 \times 8 = 4 \times 4 = 16,$ $2 \times 9 = 3 \times 6 = 18,$
$3 \times 8 = 4 \times 6 = 24,$ $6 \times 6 = 4 \times 9 = 36.$

These facts, as well as all those indicated in Section 5.6 in connection with the multiple counting chart, should be utilized by the pupil as aids in committing the multiplication facts to memory. In fact, learning the multiplication tables in sequence is a good memory device provided the facts have already been developed and understood. This activity should be the final step rather than the initial one, as has been true of so much instruction in the past.

The point has been made repeatedly that the introduction of a new topic should be an outgrowth of pupil experience. Problem situations that are real to the pupil provide excellent motivation. But we have made a fetish of utility when we ignore the possibility that the child may derive satisfaction and pleasure from arithmetic for its own sake, given the chance.

Study of the multiplication tables affords many such opportunities. For example, consider the squares of the numbers 1 through 9. 1, 4, 9, 16, 25, 36, 49, 64, 81. The final digits are arranged

100 Multiplication Facts

0	1	2	3	4	5	6	7	8	9
0	0	0	0	0	0	0	0	0	0
0	0	0	0	0	0	0	0	0	0

0	1	2	3	4	5	6	7	8	9
1	1	1	1	1	1	1	1	1	1
0	1	2	3	4	5	6	7	8	9

0	1	2	3	4	5	6	7	8	9
2	2	2	2	2	2	2	2	2	2
0	2	4	6	8	10	12	14	16	18

0	1	2	3	4	5	6	7	8	9
3	3	3	3	3	3	3	3	3	3
0	3	6	9	12	15	18	21	24	27

0	1	2	3	4	5	6	7	8	9
4	4	4	4	4	4	4	4	4	4
0	4	8	12	16	20	24	28	32	36

0	1	2	3	4	5	6	7	8	9
5	5	5	5	5	5	5	5	5	5
0	5	10	15	20	25	30	35	40	45

0	1	2	3	4	5	6	7	8	9
6	6	6	6	6	6	6	6	6	6
0	6	12	18	24	30	36	42	48	54

0	1	2	3	4	5	6	7	8	9
7	7	7	7	7	7	7	7	7	7
0	7	14	21	28	35	42	49	56	63

0	1	2	3	4	5	6	7	8	9
8	8	8	8	8	8	8	8	8	8
0	8	16	24	32	40	48	56	64	72

0	1	2	3	4	5	6	7	8	9
9	9	9	9	9	9	9	9	9	9
0	9	18	27	36	45	54	63	72	81

symmetrically 1, 4, 9, 6, 5, 6, 9, 4, 1. If we extend the squares beyond 9^2 we see the next digit ending in 0 ($10^2 = 100$) and then the whole sequence repeats itself endlessly. No perfect square can end in 2, 3, 7, or 8.

Among the odd tables 1, 3, 5, 7, 9, with the exception of the table of 5s, each possible digit ending appears in each table. As we move down to table of 8s at each step, the tens digit goes up one and the ones digit down 2, except in moving from 40 to 48. These and many similar relationships which may be discovered from the tables hold an intrinsic interest for the child aside from their value as aids to learning the tables.

7.3 THE MULTIPLICATION ALGORITHM

The multiplication algorithm depends upon two properties, the distributive principle and place value. Preparation for multiplication must include an understanding of these two ideas as well as mastery of the basic multiplication facts.

Multiplication of a two-digit number by a one-digit number, with no carrying involved, should be studied first. Counting by tens furnishes the background for problems involving even tens as the two-digit number. Since 20 means 2 tens, 3×20 means 3×2 tens, or 6 tens, or 60. It is not difficult to establish the generalization that multiplying by ten is equivalent to attaching a zero. It is important to present all forms in which this may appear.

$$
\begin{array}{ccc}
10 & 5 & 5 \\
\underline{5} & \underline{10} & \underline{10} \\
50 & 50 & 50
\end{array}
$$

In all three cases we are finding five 10s or its equivalent, ten 5s. The product is simply 5×1 with a zero in ones place so that the 5 may represent tens. Note that here we are not faced with multiplication by zero, nor with the distributive property. The extension to multiples of ten should cause no difficulty.

$$
\begin{array}{ccc}
30 & 5 & 5 \\
\underline{5} & \underline{30} & \underline{30} \\
150 & 150 & 150
\end{array}
$$

In this case we are finding the product 5×3 tens, then the result is 5×3 with a zero attached to make the 5×3 be tens.

As a preliminary to learning the method for two-digit multiplication the class should be confronted with finding a product such as 8×31 in any way they can. The following are likely solutions.

$$31 + 31 + 31 + 31 + 31 + 31 + 31 + 31 = 248$$

31	31	30	1
$\times 10$	$+31$	$\times 8$	$\times 8$
310	62	240	8
-62		8	
248		248	

When these and other correct solutions are analyzed and compared it is not difficult for the pupils to select the most efficient method. The pupil should see the problem as $8 \times (3$ tens $+ 1$ one$) = 8 \times 3$ tens $+ 8 \times 1$ ones. This suggests the algorithm

$$
\begin{array}{r}
31 \\
8 \\
\hline
24\,0 \\
8 \\
\hline
248
\end{array}
$$

which should then be shortened to

$$
\begin{array}{r}
31 \\
8 \\
\hline
248
\end{array}
$$

Here the partial products are obtained from left to right rather than in the usual order, right to left. This has merit for a number of reasons: (1) The procedure is a correct one. There is more than one correct way to solve a problem. (2) The use of the distributive principle is emphasized. (3) The necessary preservation of place value is emphasized. The 4 in 24 is aligned under the 3, in the tens place. It is more obvious that this is done when starting on the left than is the case with the usual method. (4) Its inadequacy when carrying is required helps establish understanding of carrying. A motive for the right-to-left procedure is provided.

When the pupil attempts a problem involving carrying, such as 6×87, the left-to-right order may still be followed.

$$
\begin{array}{r}
87 \\
6 \\
\hline
48 \\
42 \\
\hline
522
\end{array}
$$

But when he attempts to shorten this to a single step the advantage of the right-to-left order is evident. The term *carry* is an unfortunate choice of names. Carrying is really only an application of the associative property. It is regrouping. When we find 6×87 in the usual way we take advantage of commutativity of addition, and the distributive property:

$$6 \times 87 = 6 \times (80 + 7) = (80 + 7) \times 6 = (480 + 42)$$
$$= [400 + (80 + 40) + 2] = (400 + 120 + 2)$$
$$= [(400 + 100) + 20 + 2] = (500 + 20 + 2) = 522$$

While the child is learning the method his thought process in solving the above problem should be "$6 \times 7 = 42$ which is 4 tens and 2, so I write the 2 in the ones place under the 7. I must add the 4 tens in with the other tens I get. 6×8 tens $= 48$ tens. I add the 4 tens from the first step. 48 tens $+ 4$ tens $= 52$ tens (higher decade addition) but that is 5 hundreds and 2 tens, so I write the 2 in the tens place under the 8, and the 5 in the hundreds place." Detailed analyses of this sort should be carried out only long enough to establish the meaning of the operation. The ultimate objective with this, as well as many-digit multiplication, is to reduce the operation to finding partial products of one-digit factors, and letting the algorithm itself take care of place value. For example, in finding 1835×63 the child should not have to be burdened with recalling that the 6 means 6 tens and the 8 means 8 hundreds when he gets the partial product 8×6. He should know that the algorithm keeps track of its place value for him. This of course presupposes that he knows why and how the algorithm serves this purpose.

As each new step is made toward the general algorithm the pupil should be encouraged to devise a method for himself. All different methods should then be reviewed by the group. Any that are incorrect as to *method* should be so identified, showing why the method is wrong. Any incorrect solution using a correct method should be corrected. A comparison of the correct methods should then indicate the next step in the development of the general algorithm.

To illustrate this, suppose the class has learned the algorithm for one-digit multipliers, which presupposes ability to multiply by ten by merely attaching a zero on the right. The class is asked to find the answer to 18×53 in any way they can. The following correct solutions are all perfectly logical extensions of their current mastery of multiplication.

A.		B.		C.		
53	53	53	53	53	53	53
×20	×2	×10	×8	×10	×5	×3
1060	106	530	424	530	265	156
−106		+424		+265		
				+156		
954		954		954		

D.	E.	F.	
53	53	18	18
×6	×9	×50	×3
318	477	900	54
×3	×2	+54	
954	954	954	

Solutions A, B, C, and F all employ the distributive property. Solutions D and E are based upon the fundamental theorem of arithmetic. The advantage of B and F over the other methods can be demonstrated by refining them so that they become the algorithms for   53   and   18   respectively.
   × 18   × 53

This procedure suggests using the digits of the multiplier from left to right

$$\begin{array}{r} 53 \\ \times 18 \\ \hline 53 \\ 424 \\ \hline 954 \end{array}$$

The method does have some advantages over the usual right-to-left order. It is the natural outgrowth of the conception of the problem as $53 \times (10 + 8)$. Proper placing of the partial product 53 is more apt to be thought of as belonging one place to the left of the ones digit in 424 rather than that it belongs under the 1 in 18 (because we are multiplying by 1 *ten*). The usual right-to-left order has the advantage of being in agreement with the method employed in addition. The above method is recommended only as a developmental procedure; it is useful in establishing understanding of the algorithm.

If the child understands why he multiplies as he does with a two-digit multiplier extension to more than two digits offers no difficulty. If 76 × 23 means 76 × 20 + 76 × 3 in the algorithm

$$
\begin{array}{r}
76 \\
23 \\
\hline
228 \\
152 \\
\hline
1748
\end{array}
$$

(76 × 3)
(76 × 20)

the pupil should without difficulty attack 476 × 323 by treating it as 476 × 300 + 476 × 20 + 476 × 3, suggesting the algorithm

$$
\begin{array}{r}
476 \\
323 \\
\hline
1428 \\
952 \\
1428 \\
\hline
153748
\end{array}
$$

(476 × 3)
(476 × 20)
(476 × 300)

Filling in the terminal zeros in the partial products

$$
\begin{array}{r}
238 \\
173 \\
\hline
714 \\
16660 \\
23800 \\
\hline
41174
\end{array}
$$

has been recommended as an aid in preserving place value. This, as well as the following practices,

$$
\begin{array}{r}
137 \\
105 \\
\hline
685 \\
000 \\
137 \\
\hline
14385
\end{array}
\qquad
\begin{array}{r}
137 \\
360 \\
\hline
000 \\
822 \\
411 \\
\hline
49320
\end{array}
$$

should be used sparingly to the extent that they aid in understanding the algorithm. But the teacher should insist that they be abandoned in favor of more efficient methods as soon as they have served their purpose. All of the algorithms are merely devices for *systematizing* and *simplifying* computation.

To recapitulate, the multiplication algorithm should be developed as a series of steps, each new step being reduced to an application of the previous one. We begin with the basic one-digit by one-digit multiplication facts. Multiplication with a one-digit multiplier is reduced to use of the basic facts and addition with the aid of the distributive and associative properties. Multiplication with a many-digit multiplier is reduced to a series of one-digit multiplications.

7.4 CHECKING MULTIPLICATION

A variety of checks on multiplication are possible. The pupil should be aware of them. He should avoid falling into the habit of using the same check constantly (though this is better than none at all). The best check from the standpoint of ease of application varies with the particular problem.

The check by addition is cumbersome. Its appropriateness is inversely related to the pupil's proficiency. The following is an appropriate check early in the multiplication program.

```
      853        CHECK:  853
     ×4                  853
     ─────               853
     3412               +853
                        ─────
                        3412
```

We may use the distributive property to check the following:

```
     76          CHECK: 76 × 25 = 1900
    ×28                 76 × 3  =  228
    ─────                         ─────
     608                         2128
     152
    ─────
    2128
```

The associative property is the basis for the following check

```
       76         CHECK:    76
      ×28                  ×7
      ─────                ─────
       608                 532
       152                 ×4
      ─────                ─────
      2128                 2128
```

The commutative property provides the check

```
       76         CHECK:    28
      ×28                  ×76
      ─────                ─────
       608                 168
       152                 196
      ─────                ─────
      2128                 2128
```

This check provides different higher decade addition but, unlike the others, the same basic multiplication facts are involved. This reduces its efficiency since in the event of error the same mistake may be made in the check.

The check of nines described in Section 5.12 is a quick, interesting, and effective multiplication check. We may also employ the check of elevens with the same reservations that applied when checking addition. Any time the skip rule gives a negative result we may avoid it by increasing the number by eleven:

$$
\begin{array}{r}
76 \\
\times 28 \\
\hline
608 \\
152 \\
\hline
2128
\end{array}
$$

$8 - 2 + 1 - 2 = 5$

CHECK: Since 6 is less than 7 we add $6 + 11$
and proceed $\quad 6 + 11 - 7 = 10$
$$8 - 2 \qquad = 6$$

Since 0 is less than 6

$$60$$
$$0 + 11 - 6 = 5$$

Any discussion of checks should of course include estimating the answer. We know the answer to the above problem should be less than 2800 (100×28) and more than 1400 (50×28). In fact, it should be about halfway between the two, about 2100.

7.5 OTHER MULTIPLICATION ALGORITHMS

Our present algorithms are the result of much trial and error. They are an example of survival of the fittest. Study of earlier methods provides interesting motivation for needed added practice or remedial drill in the upper grades. One such method is the Russian Peasant method, described in Section 2.12.

Two other interesting methods are essentially the same as our present one in that the partial products of each digit in the multiplier by each digit in the multiplicand are added. The difference lies in the manner in which place value is preserved.

The first of these is known as the scratch method:

EXAMPLE.   Multiply 456 by 231.
Step one:

$$
\begin{array}{r}
9 \\
824 \\
456 \\
231
\end{array}
$$

In the first step we align the ones digit of the multiplier with the highest digit of the multiplicand. Then the partial products 2×4, 3×4, and 1×4 are obtained, each being written over the corresponding multiplier digit. When we reach 3×4 we enter the 1 in 12 by changing the 8 over the 2 to a 9, scratching out the 8. As each digit 2, 3, and 1 are used they are scratched. At the conclusion of this step the 4 in 456 is scratched. In general, when a digit is no longer needed it is scratched.

Step two: We shift the multiplier 231 to align the 1 under the 5, then

```
9                        0
824          becomes     939
   456                  18245
 2311                      456
  23                     2311
                          23
```

Here the first product 2×5 is entered over the 2 in 824, but this leaves the 2 undisturbed, changes the 9 to 0 and places a 1 at the extreme left. The next product 3×5 is entered by changing the 4 over the 3 to 9 and the 2 to the left of the 4 to 3. The last product 1×5 is entered over the 5.

Step three: We shift the multiplier again, aligning the 1 under the 6, then

```
0                        3
939          becomes     52
18245                    041
   456                   9393
 23111                  182456
  233                      456
   2                     23111
                          233
                           2
```

The first product 2×6 is added in two steps. The 3 is changed to 4, then 2 added to 49 gives 51. Similarly with 3×6. We scratch the 1, giving 2, then add 8 to 25, making 33. The final product 1×6 entered over the 6 completes the multiplication. The only thing unscratched is the answer 105336.

Further interest may be aroused by demonstrating that any order may be used in obtaining the partial products of each step. If we reverse the order used above, the complete solution will be

$$
\begin{array}{r}
3 \\
5\text{\textit{1}} \\
0\text{\textit{4}}0 \\
19\text{\textit{3}}93 \\
12\text{\textit{4}}56 \\
45\text{\textit{6}} \\
2\text{\textit{3}}111 \\
2\text{\textit{33}} \\
2 \\
\end{array}
$$

One obvious shortcoming of this scheme is the well-nigh impossible task of reviewing the work.

Another quite popular former scheme, known as the lattice method, did not have that disadvantage. In fact, except for the required grid, it has much to recommend it. We work the above problem by this method.

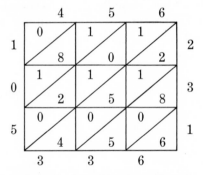

Here each partial product is placed in the cell under and opposite the two factors. For example, the product of 3 × 5 is placed in the second column and second row. The diagonals separate each cell; tens go in the upper left half and units in the lower right. The answer is obtained by adding along the diagonals, carrying when necessary to the next diagonal just as we ordinarily carry to the next column. Obviously, with this method the partial products can be obtained in *any* order. We know we have all the partial products only when the rectangular array is filled.

Critical analysis of these methods should help pupils gain a clearer insight into the significance of the steps in our own. It is quite helpful for the pupils to identify corresponding steps when the same multiplication is also carried out in the usual way.

Exercises

1 Multiplication should be approached through problem situations.
(a) Give an appropriate problem involving multiplication as addition of equal addends.
(b) Give an appropriate problem involving multiplication as finding the "ratio to one."

2 Do 5×3, and $5 + 5 + 5$ appear the same on the number line? Why?

3 Use dot drawings to illustrate the equivalence of:
(a) 3×5 and 5×3
(b) $3 \times (2 + 4)$ and $3 \times 2 + 3 \times 4$
(c) $(2 \times 3) \times 4$ and $2 \times (3 \times 4)$

4 If tens are multiplied by tens is the product always tens? Justify your answer.

5 Show how higher decade addition is necessary in multiplication.

6 Show how the distributive property is used in the multiplication algorithm.

7 Devise four checks, based on different principles, and apply them to

$$\begin{array}{r} 34 \\ \times 75 \\ \hline 2550 \end{array}$$

8 Use the lattice method to find $321_{seven} \times 61_{seven}$.

9 Compare the steps involved in multiplying 649 by 486 by the scratch method with those in using the lattice method.

10 Multiply 342 by 513 using as many different algorithms as you know.

11 What advantages and what disadvantages does the check of elevens have over the check of nines?

12 Multiply and check by the check of nines and by the check of elevens:

$$596 \times 831$$

13 Show how the associative and distributive properties are utilized when we multiply 23×47 in the usual way.

14 List ways to check multiplication. Give advantages of each.

15 Use the lattice method to multiply 463 by 47. Show how the method preserves place value.

16 Check Exercise 15 by casting nines.

7.6 INTERPRETATION OF DIVISION

We may define division quite simply as the inverse of multiplication. Then division means the undoing of whatever multiplication means. But we interpret multiplication in terms of addition, and the undoing of addition is subtraction. Shall we then interpret division in terms of subtraction? Since $15 \div 5$ means that number by which 5 must be multiplied to give 15, and 3×5 means $5 + 5 + 5$, then could we not find $15 \div 5$ by finding how many times 5 can be subtracted if we start with 15?

It is quite important that both conceptions of division, the undoing of multiplication and successive subtraction, be developed. Both interpretations are essential to understanding problem situations requiring division. If the division algorithm is ever to be understood the pupil must have developed the successive subtraction concept of division.

When we add two numbers, each number represents the count of one of the sets to be combined. Each addend plays the same kind of role. But when we multiply two numbers one of them represents the count of each of the equivalent sets to be combined and the other represents the number of sets. The two factors play different kinds of roles. Then, when we divide do we find the count of the equivalent sets or the number of such sets?

We interpret $3 \times 4 = 12$ to mean 3 sets of 4 combined to give a set of 12. Then we should interpret $12 \div 4 = 3$ to mean that 12 separated into sets of 4 will yield 3 sets. Since multiplication is commutative we know that $4 \times 3 = 12$ also. And now we should interpret $12 \div 4 = 3$ to mean if 12 is separated into 4 sets there will be 3 to a set. We conclude, in answer to the above question, that we may be doing either one.

If our objective is to determine the number of sets of a specified size we can obtain from a given quantity we are doing *measurement* division. When we measure a line with a yardstick we are determining the number of 36-inch intervals the total distance contains. The total distance (in inches) is the dividend, 36 inches the divisor, and the obtained number of yards is the quotient. The divisor is the unit of measure; in terms of sets it specifies the number of elements in each of the equivalent sets.

In addition and subtraction we combine only like things, tens with tens, pounds with pounds, quarts with quarts. Both addends as well as the sum are *like* quantities in that they give the number property of the same kind of thing. Similarly for minuend, subtrahend, and remainder in subtraction. When we multiply, the multiplicand and the product are like numbers. The multiplier, designating how many sets, is an abstract number. "If Tom, Joe, and Bob each have 4 marbles how many do they have in all?"

$$3 \times 4 \text{ (marbles)} = 12 \text{ (marbles)}$$

The abstract 3 tells how many sets. The 4 and 12 each give the number property of a set of the same sort in that the elements of each are the same kind of thing (marbles). In measurement division the dividend and divisor are like numbers. The quotient is an abstract number telling how many sets. "If I have 12 marbles how many boys can I give 4 marbles each?"

$$12 \text{ (marbles)} \div 4 \text{ (marbles)} = 3$$

We have "measured" 12 marbles with 4 marbles as the unit of measure in that we find the number of times 4 marbles is contained in 12 marbles. The pupil is apt to interpret the answer "3 boys." We should emphasize the fact that the answer to the question posed in the problem is "3 boys," but the quotient is simply a number telling how many sets of 4 are obtained. The problem could have required the number of piles of 4 marbles each or bags of 4 marbles each.

The problem may require that the dividend be broken up into a predetermined number of equivalent sets. In this case we have *partition* division. The divisor in this case gives the number of sets and the quotient determines the number of elements in each. Quotient and dividend are like numbers and the divisor is an abstract number. "How many marbles will each get if I divide 12 marbles equally between Tom, Joe, and Bob?"

$$12 \text{ (marbles)} \div 3 = 4 \text{ (marbles)}$$

Division is used to make "times as many" comparisons. "If Jane brought 6 dolls to school and Faye brought 3, Jane brought how many times as many as Faye?" This is measurement division. Jane's dolls are measured against Faye's dolls as the unit of measure. We can also measure Faye's dolls, using Jane's as the unit of measure. Jane brought 2 times as many as Faye and Faye brought $\frac{1}{2}$ times as many as Jane.

When finding an arithmetic average, the sum of the terms divided by the number of terms, we use partition division. The average would be the size of each addend if they were all equal. We partition the sum equally among the addends.

Considered from the standpoint of subdividing a set of objects into constituent sets, division frequently does not come out even. We cannot separate 13 objects into 3 equivalent sets of objects unless the individual objects can themselves be subdivided. Thirteen children cannot be divided into 3 equivalent sets. The part of the dividend which is not used, which is not a part of one of the equivalent sets formed is called the *remainder*. When a remainder exists the division is *incomplete*. Complete division requires that the remainder be partitioned among the equivalent sets also. Thirteen quarts of milk can be separated into 3 equal parts. But each part will not be an integral number of quarts. Each subdivision will contain $4\frac{1}{3}$ quarts, and the division is complete.

The same situation exists relative to measurement division. We cannot change 13 quarters to dollars. If we attempt to separate 13 objects into sets of 4 we obtain 3 such sets with 1 object left over, the remainder. In this case, the division can be completed only if we are willing to admit the concept of a *part of* a constituent set. Thirteen quarters changed to dollars yields $3\frac{1}{4}$ dollars. However, this is a subterfuge. If we are changing quarters to dollar bills we simply cannot use more than 12 of the quarters in the exchange. The extra quarter is the unavoidable remainder. On the other hand, a vessel containing 13 quarts can be completely converted to gallon jugs; we get 3 full jugs and another jug $\frac{1}{4}$ full.

Counting materials and the number line can be used to make the distinction between measurement division and partition division. Suppose we wish to find out how many 4s there are in 52. We count out the 52 counters into piles of 4, then count the piles. This is measurement division. There are 13 tricks in a hand of bridge. On the other hand, suppose we wish to divide 52 into 4 equal groups. We count out the objects in rotation into 4 piles. This is partition division. A bridge hand contains 13 cards.

Incomplete division with a remainder may be demonstrated in the same way. Suppose we wish to divide 25 cards among 6 people. There are enough to go around 4 times with 1 card left. We cannot complete the division unless we are willing to tear up the last card. Card games using a "widow" illustrate this idea. If we wish to separate 25 cards into groups of 4 we can count out 6 piles of 4 but 1 card will remain.

The number line may be used to illustrate the idea of division as successive subtraction of equal groups, which is measurement division.

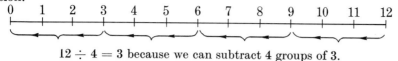

$12 \div 4 = 3$ because we can subtract 4 groups of 3.

This is complete division on the number line.

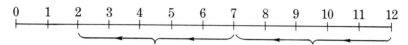

$12 \div 5 = 2$, remainder 2, because we can subtract 2 groups of 5 and have 2 left.

This is incomplete division with a remainder.

The number line is a good device to use in emphasizing the fact that although division is subject to the two interpretations there is but one division process. It can be used to illustrate partition division as well as measurement, but not so conveniently.

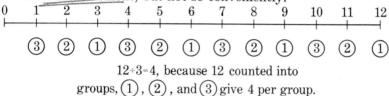

$12 \div 3 = 4$, because 12 counted into groups, ①, ②, and ③ give 4 per group.

7.7 CAUSES OF DIFFICULTY WITH DIVISION

A clear understanding of both the significance of the operation and why the algorithm works will go far toward alleviating difficulty with division. However, for a number of reasons it remains by far the most difficult of the four fundamental operations.

In the first place, the division facts are more difficult. Compare the corresponding situation in division with the multiplication fact $4 \times 8 = 32$. There is the corresponding division fact $32 \div 8 = 4$. But the pupil must recognize as well the following incomplete division facts: $33 \div 8 = 4$, $34 \div 8 = 4$, ..., $39 \div 8 = 4$. The advisability of teaching the subtraction facts as the inverse of addition facts may be debatable. But there is hardly room for doubt relative to the division facts. Complete mastery of the multiplication facts is the best insurance against difficulty with the division facts. If the child knows that $4 \times 8 = 32$ and $5 \times 8 = 40$ he knows he can get only 4 complete 8s from any of the numbers 32 through 39. This of course presupposes that he knows the meaning of multiplication and division.

Although the dual interpretation of division need not add to the difficulty of the algorithm itself, it undoubtedly contributes to difficulty in correctly applying the operation. When the child is in the first stages of learning division, problem situations should be chosen in which the dividend is larger than the divisor. But at later stages, particularly after decimals are introduced, this is no longer the case. In addition the roles of the addends can be reversed, in multiplication multiplier and multiplicand can be interchanged, in subtraction we must subtract the smaller number from the larger. We have no such guides in division. It is imperative for the child to identify correctly dividend and divisor from the context of the problem. To be able to do this he must have a clear grasp of both the measurement and partition aspects of the operation.

Success with the division algorithm presupposes facility with the other operations. We cannot hope to divide unless we can multiply and subtract.

Unlike the other operations, division requires some unavoidable guessing in obtaining trial divisors. Intelligent guessing, it is to be hoped, but guessing nevertheless.

It is less apparent how place value is preserved in the quotient than in the sum, difference, or product.

The correct interpretation of the result in incomplete or uneven division poses a special problem which has no counterpart in the other operations. Consider $25 \div 6$. Is the answer 4, 4 with remainder 1 (usually written 4 R 1), $4\frac{1}{6}$, or 5? In the abstract mathematical sense there is only one correct answer, $4\frac{1}{6}$. In terms of its application to a concrete problem any one of the above answers may be correct. If a class of 25 children is divided into 6 teams for a relay race the correct answer is 4 (children per team) with 1 (child) remainder. The division is incomplete; we have not divided 25 by 6. We have divided 24 of the 25 by 6 and the one child left out is still there. If we have a 25-foot rope from which we wish to cut 6-foot lengths for jumping ropes, the correct answer is 4 (jumping ropes). The extra foot of rope is not relevant to the question "How many jumping ropes?" The class of 25 children are going to the zoo. If 6 can ride in a car how many cars are needed? Here the correct answer to $25 \div 6$ is 5 (cars). A bus gets 6 miles to the gallon of gasoline. How many gallons are used on a 25-mile trip? Here the correct answer is $4\frac{1}{6}$.

7.8 BEGINNING DIVISION

Discovery of the basic division facts should be attacked concurrently with the corresponding multiplication facts. In neither case should technical terminology be used until after the concept of the operation begins to emerge. Rather than "six times seven equals what?" the child is discovering "seven sixes are how many?" Similarly, with division the child should conceive his problem as finding "how many sevens are in 42?" rather than "42 divided by seven equals what?" Only after the idea of division emerges should the technical terminology be used. This approach will make the foundation work more meaningful and should minimize confusion arising from the dual interpretation of division. Measurement division is the easier of the two concepts to grasp and it is more readily related to multiplication. Hence it should receive the greater attention early in the foundation, discovery phase of the program.

The child who is using loose counters will see the two kinds of division as distinct problems. There is quite a difference between counting out one complete pile of seven, then another, and so on, and counting into seven equal piles. Only after he sees the equivalence of the two should they both be tagged division.

The idea of equal sharing should be the dominant theme in problem situations illustrating partition division. We know how many sharers are to receive a portion of the dividend. The problem is to determine the size of the equal portions.

Problems from the children's experience illustrative of both types of division should first be solved by the two kinds of counting. Count into complete sets for measurement division and count in rotation into the required number of groups for partition division.

| 1, 2, 3, 4 | 5, 6, 7, 8 | 9, 10, 11, 12 | $12 \div 4$ (measurement)
3 sets |

| 1, 5, 9 | 2, 6, 10 | 3, 7, 11 | 4, 8, 12 | $12 \div 4$ (partition)
3 per set |

When subtraction has been mastered, measurement division can readily be understood as successive subtraction of equivalent sets. But the child can rationalize partition division as successive subtraction only after he accepts the equivalence of the two types of counting.

The introduction of multiplication as successive addition of equal addends should be accompanied by the corresponding idea of division as successive subtraction; the basic division facts should be associated with the corresponding multiplication facts. Drill cards displaying families of related facts can be used effectively when the facts are being committed to memory.

$$7 \times 8 = \,?$$

$$7 \times 8 = 56$$
$$8 \times 7 = 56$$
$$56 \div 7 = 8$$
$$56 \div 8 = 7$$

Although formal instruction in division is usually deferred until the third or fourth grade, preparation for it should begin with meaningful counting experiences and continue through the development of subtraction and multiplication.

7.9 THE DIVISION FACTS

The division facts (complete division) are derivable from the corresponding multiplication facts. The basic addition and multiplication facts consist of all possible one-digit number combinations, yielding 100 facts. The subtraction facts do not include all possible one-digit number combinations, but there is a subtraction fact to correspond to each addition fact. The combinations involve numbers up to 18. The division facts are similar to subtraction in that dividends are not restricted to one-digit numbers; they go as high as 81. It is also true that we do not use all possible one-digit number combinations. But, unlike subtraction, we do not get a division fact to correspond to every multiplication fact. Multiplication facts involving a zero multiplier do not have their counterpart in division since division by zero is impossible. Thus, there are only 90 basic division facts.

90 Division Facts

quotient	0	1	2	3	4	5	6	7	8	9
divisor 1	1)0	1)1	1)2	1)3	1)4	1)5	1)6	1)7	1)8	1)9
divisor 2	2)0	2)2	2)4	2)6	2)8	2)10	2)12	2)14	2)16	2)18
divisor 3	3)0	3)3	3)6	3)9	3)12	3)15	3)18	3)21	3)24	3)27
divisor 4	4)0	4)4	4)8	4)12	4)16	4)20	4)24	4)28	4)32	4)36
divisor 5	5)0	5)5	5)10	5)15	5)20	5)25	5)30	5)35	5)40	5)45
divisor 6	6)0	6)6	6)12	6)18	6)24	6)30	6)36	6)42	6)48	6)54
divisor 7	7)0	7)7	7)14	7)21	7)28	7)35	7)42	7)49	7)56	7)63
divisor 8	8)0	8)8	8)16	8)24	8)32	8)40	8)48	8)56	8)64	8)72
divisor 9	9)0	9)9	9)18	9)27	9)36	9)45	9)54	9)63	9)72	9)81

When the horizontal form is used the symbolism for all four fundamental operations is read in the usual left-to-right manner. We read $2 + 3$ "two plus three," $5 - 1$ "five minus one," 6×4 "six times four," and $8 \div 2$ "eight divided by two." The last of these is meaningless to the child until the meaning of division is well established. The operational forms are recommended as the better forms to use in the introductory stage of development. The forms and method of reading are $\begin{array}{r} 2 \\ + 3 \\ \hline \end{array}$ "two *and* three," $\begin{array}{r} 5 \\ - 1 \\ \hline \end{array}$ "five *take away* one,"

$\begin{array}{r} 4 \\ \times 6 \\ \hline \end{array}$ "six 4s," and $2\overline{)8}$ "(The number of) 2s in 8." Note that in 6×4 the multiplier comes first, $6 \times 4 = 4 + 4 + 4 + 4 + 4 + 4$, but $\begin{array}{r} 4 \\ \times 6 \\ \hline \end{array}$ is not properly read "four times six," but correctly "four *multiplied by* six." However, no serious harm is done if it is read "four times six" since it is essential for the child to know the equivalence of $\begin{array}{r} 4 \\ \times 6 \\ \hline \end{array}$ and $\begin{array}{r} 6 \\ \times 4 \\ \hline \end{array}$. But in reading $2\overline{)8}$ in the "divided by" form we must begin with 8, "eight divided by two." "Two divided by eight" is an entirely different matter.

The need for division facts involving 0 dividends or 1 divisors will not arise until they occur in the division algorithm. Learning of these facts should be postponed until need for them arises. When they are studied they should be treated in a different manner from the other facts. In the physical sense of division we cannot divide nothing into equal parts. If there is nothing to divide we do not declare a dividend. Dividing nothing up into subnothings is not an idea which children can visualize. From the standpoint of measurement division we are a little better off. In this case $0 \div 12$ poses the question "How many twelves in zero?" "How many dozen oranges in an empty sack?" From this point of view it is not unreasonable to make the generalization "zero divided by any number (other than zero) equals zero." If division is understood as the inverse of multiplication there is another approach to the question "Zero divided by a number equals what?" It must equal whatever the divisor must be multiplied by to give zero. If the divisor is not zero the quotient must be.

The question of division by zero is not likely to arise. It certainly would not occur in connection with problems within the children's experience. It does not grow out of consideration of the division algorithm. The closest thing to it is a division problem involving a two or more digit divisor containing a zero. However, since we cannot distribute the dividend over the parts of the divisor, we still are not faced with a zero divisor. The unusually observant pupil in the middle or upper grades may discover this discrepancy between multiplication and division, the fact that zero has no multiplication inverse. On such rare occasions it is much better to give the logically correct explanation—$12 \div 0$ must equal some number such that when multiplied by zero it yields a product 12. But we know that any number multiplied by zero equals zero. Then $12 \div 0$ cannot equal anything; it is meaningless, it is undefined. The pupil with sufficient insight to require an explanation will more readily accept this approach than he will a consideration of what happens if we divide 12 objects into no equal parts or how many nothings are contained in 12.

The generalization "any number divided by 1 equals the number" should not cause difficulty. From the standpoint of partition division, we count the total set to be divided into a single pile. The one sharer gets it all. From the standpoint of measurement division, if each set is to contain 1 object we certainly shall get as many one object sets as we have objects to begin with.

The zero divided facts and the 1 divisor facts should not be learned as 18 unrelated facts. The two above generalizations should be established when need for these facts arises. Care should be exercised to insure that the generalization becomes a complete generalization in the child's mind. It does not apply merely to the 90 basic division facts. Zero divided by *any* nonzero number equals zero. *Any* number divided by one equals the number.

Those facts involving division of a number by itself should be handled in a similar fashion. The child should generalize "any number divided by itself equals one." This applies not merely to the basic facts but to numbers in general. The child should not have to learn $4 \div 4 = 1$ and as a separate unrelated fact $5 \div 5 = 1$. This generalization raises a difficult question. Should the child be led to believe that any number divided by itself equals one? Ultimately he may discover that he has been deceived because $0 \div 0$ does not equal one. But for the present it is better that he not be confused by the $0 \div 0$ issue. Those teachers who need it may salve their consciences with the contention that the generalization implies the division is possible.

When we remove from consideration the zero dividend facts, the 1 divisor facts, and the number divided by itself facts, there remain 64 different facts to be mastered. These are, however, not unrelated. Further generalization can facilitate the child's task immensely. Eight of the remaining facts have dividends which are squares and have divisor and quotient equal, as $6\overline{)36}$ (quotient 6). The remaining 56 combinations consist of 28 pairs so related that either may be obtained from the other by interchanging divisor and quotient, as $7\overline{)56}$ (quotient 8) and $8\overline{)56}$ (quotient 7). The generalization "from any division fact another fact is obtained by interchanging divisor and quotient" is as important to learning the division facts as the commutative property, from which it is derived, is to learning the multiplication facts.

Other division properties may be utilized as aids in learning the 28 pairs of basic facts. For example, *multiplying the dividend produces the same change in the quotient*. This property relates such facts as $5\overline{)15}$ (quotient 3) and $5\overline{)45}$ (quotient 9); $6\overline{)18}$ (quotient 3), $6\overline{)36}$ (quotient 6), and $6\overline{)72}$ (quotient 12). *Multiplying dividend and divisor by the same number leaves the quotient unchanged*. Awareness of this principle enables the pupil to recognize that $2\overline{)14}$, $4\overline{)28}$, $6\overline{)42}$, $8\overline{)56}$ all have the same quotient. The distributive principle enables one to recall the quotient of $7\overline{)56}$ from the fact that $56 = 35 + 21$. $7\overline{)35}$ (quotient 5) and $7\overline{)21}$ (quotient 3), therefore $7\overline{)56}$ equals $5 + 3$.

Although the distributive principle is not of as great value as some of the other generalizations in learning the basic facts it is indispensable to understanding of the division algorithm.

The above generalizations should not be rules handed down to the pupil. They should be an outgrowth of his experience in discovering and learning the basic facts. They should serve as unifying principles to reinforce his learning. Their usefulness does not end with mastery of the basic facts. They are applicable to all numbers. The pupil should be able to generalize from $3\overline{)27}$ (quotient 9) to $3\overline{)270}$ (quotient 90), $30\overline{)270}$ (quotient 9), $9\overline{)2700}$ (quotient 300), and the like.

7.10 DIVISION WITH ONE-DIGIT DIVISORS

It is neither necessary nor advisable to withhold learning the division algorithm until all basic division facts are mastered. We should begin with problems involving known facts and no remainders.

The former practice of teaching short division before long division has lost favor. The difference between the two is a matter of form. The same thought processes are involved. We merely carry more of the work mentally when we use the short form. The long form should be used first since it gives a better picture of the steps in the operation. The short form should never be taught *as a form* but can be used later as a short cut after the general method involving divisors containing more than one digit has been mastered. This is something the pupil should be permitted to do if he discovers it for himself.

Initial instruction with the algorithm should stress two principles, the distributive property and division as successive subtraction. For example, in finding $2 \overline{\smash{)}84}$ the child should see the problem as finding $2 \overline{\smash{)}80}$ and $2 \overline{\smash{)}4}$. The dividend is expressed as $80 + 4$ and the divisor distributed over the terms. The first step should be

$$
\begin{array}{r}
40 \\
2 \overline{)84} \\
80 \\
\hline
4 \\
\hline
\end{array}
$$

The child's thinking is: "Forty 2s is 80, take away forty 2s leaves 4." The second step becomes

$$
\begin{array}{r}
2 \\
40 \\
2 \overline{)84} \\
80 \\
\hline
4 \\
4
\end{array}
$$

The child thinks "Two 2s in 4, take away 4."

Incomplete division should be introduced early; the existence of a remainder helps develop insight into *what* is happening as the division is performed—that is, successive subtraction of the divisor. When that which remains is less than the divisor we can no longer subtract the divisor.

To divide 698 by 3 we think of 698 as 600 + 90 + 8

```
              2
             30
            200
         3 | 698
            600
            ———
             98
             90
            ———
              8
              6
            ———
              2
```

The child thinks: "Two hundred 3s in 600, take away 600; thirty 3s in 90, take away 90; two 3s in 8, take away two 3s (6) leaves 2." When we leave a remainder the child should see this as incomplete division. We did not divide the remaining 2 by 3. The remainder should not be written as the numerator of a fraction with divisor as denominator unless the child has sufficient insight into fractions to realize that the fraction is an implied division. When this is done the fraction should *not* be referred to as a remainder. It is not a remainder, it is a part of the quotient. The division is then complete.

The next obstacle to be encountered is illustrated below. Find 4 | 416. Here we cannot think of 416 as 400 + 10 + 6 and obtain each partial quotient as the result of exact division. Here we subdivide 416 into 400 + 16. The child should think:

```
              4
            100
         4 | 416
            400
            ———
             16
             16
            ———
```

"One hundred 4s in 400, take away 400 leaves 16; 4s in 10? there are no exact 4s in 10, so 4s in 16? 4, take away 16." This situation illustrates the desirability of writing the partial quotients in the form given above. If the child thinks "4s in 400?" he knows his partial quotient is 1 *hundred*, similarly "4s in 16?" gives 4 *ones*. There is no necessity to think "4 into 1 zero time, zero from 1 leaves 1" in the tens digit.

The next extension should be to the following type of situation. Find 4 | 456. Here, as before, we think "4s in 400? 100." Then we consider 4s in 50. There are 4s in 50 but not exact 4s. This is a crucial point in a meaningful development of the algorithm. A quite plausible procedure at this point would be to subtract all the exact 4s which are contained in 50. This is mathematically sound and would lead to the correct answer thus:

$$
\begin{array}{r}
2 \\
12 \\
100 \\
4\overline{)\,456} \\
400 \\
\hline
50 + 6 \\
48 \\
\hline
2 + 6 \\
8 \\
\hline
\end{array}
\qquad
\begin{array}{r}
2 \\
12 \\
100 \\
\hline
114
\end{array}
$$

Past experience with division, in the concept-development program, should have established the fact that the dividend may be separated in a variety of ways. For example, $2\overline{)\,20} = 2\overline{)\,10} + 2\overline{)\,10}$, $2\overline{)\,20} = 2\overline{)\,16} + 2\overline{)\,4}$, and $2\overline{)\,20} = 2\overline{)\,12} + 2\overline{)\,8}$. We do not wish to subtract as many 4s as possible from 50, we wish to subtract as many groups of ten 4s as possible. In other words, we want to subtract even 10s which are also even 4s. Since 50 gives even 10s but not even 4s, try 40. Since 40 is four 10s but four 10s is the same as ten 4s we subtract 40, leaving 10 ones to combine with the original 6 ones. The procedure is summarized below. The child should think "One hundred 4s in 400, take away 400; ten 4s in 50, take away 40; four 4s in 16, take away 16."

$$
\begin{array}{r}
4 \\
10 \\
100 \\
4\overline{)\,456} \\
400 \\
\hline
56 \\
40 \\
\hline
16 \\
16 \\
\hline
\end{array}
$$

This rationale of the process combined with writing the partial quotients will aid materially in correctly preserving place value in the quotient, particularly when zeros occur.

For example $6\overline{)\,84362}$.

(1) 6s in 80,000 (8 ten thousands)? 10,000 (1 ten thousand), take away 60,000.

$$
\begin{array}{r}
10000 \\
6\overline{)84362} \\
60000 \\
\hline
24362
\end{array}
$$

(2) 6s in 24,000 (24 thousands)? 4,000 (4 thousands) take away 24,000.

$$
\begin{array}{r}
4000 \\
10000 \\
6\overline{)84362} \\
60000 \\
\hline
24362 \\
24000 \\
\hline
362
\end{array}
$$

(3) 6s in 300? less than 100 (1 hundred). 6s in 360 (36 tens)? 60, take away 360. No 6s in 2, remainder 2.

$$
\begin{array}{r}
60 \\
4000 \\
10000 \\
6\overline{)84362} \\
60000 \\
\hline
24362 \\
24000 \\
\hline
362 \\
360 \\
\hline
2
\end{array}
$$

When the partial quotients are added

$$
\begin{array}{r}
60 \\
4000 \\
10000 \\
\hline
14060
\end{array}
$$

the zeros in the quotient should offer no difficulty.

Using the above problem for illustration we may summarize the procedure. By inspection we note the order of the dividend, ten thousands in our example. Next, we determine the greatest integral multiple of this order which the dividend contains and such that the integer is a multiple of the divisor. In our example we seek the greatest number of ten thousands in the dividend in which the *number* the rational number. Thus $\frac{4}{8}$ is just another way to write the rational number $\frac{1}{2}$.

Two ratios a/b and c/d are two names for the same rational number if and only if they are equivalent ratios. That is, if and only if $a = kc$ and $b = kd$, where $k \neq 0$. Since $b = kd$ is equivalent to $kd = b$ we can multiply these equal numbers by the equal numbers $a = kc$ and obtain $akd = bkc$. Since k cannot be zero we can divide both sides by k and obtain $ad = bc$. Hence the rational numbers a/b and c/d are the same number if and only if $ad = bc$.

We should make a distinction between a *fraction*, a *ratio*, and a *rational number*. The word "fraction" has to do with the form of a number. Although $\frac{8}{4} = 2$, 2 is not a fraction, but $\frac{8}{4}$ is a fraction. A fraction is a number that has two parts, a numerator and a denominator. It is an implied division, numerator divided by denominator. The fraction $\frac{8}{4}$ means $8 \div 4$. It is by no means always possible to carry through the division; in fact it is not necessary for either numerator or denominator to be an integer. For example, $\frac{1}{\sqrt{2}}$ and $\frac{\sqrt{2}}{\sqrt{3}}$ are fractions.

A ratio is simply a set of comparable measures of some kind. A ratio is not restricted to two numbers, nor are the numbers restricted to integers. For example, $1 : \sqrt{2} : -5$ is a ratio. For this reason we cannot say in general that a ratio is an implied division. If a ratio were always an implied division how would we interpret $8 : 4 : 2$? Does it mean $(8 \div 4) \div 2 = 2 \div 2 = 1$ or does it mean $8 \div (4 \div 2) = 8 \div 2 = 4$? In truth, it means neither. It merely states a comparison of three comparable measures, the first is twice as large as the second and the second is twice as large as the third.

However, *if the ratio compares only two magnitudes*, the second of which is not zero, it can be considered as an implied division. We may think of $8 : 4$ as $8 \div 4 = 2$ in the sense that $8 : 4$ and $2 : 1$ are equivalent ratios.

We have technically defined a rational number as an equivalence class of ratios of two integers, $a : b$, with the restriction that $b \neq 0$. However, we agree that any element of the equivalence class may be used as a symbol for the rational number. Thus $\frac{1}{2}$ and $\frac{2}{4}$ are but two symbols for the same rational number.

Then what is $\frac{1}{2}$, or for that matter a/b where a and b are integers and $b \neq 0$? It may be interpreted as a fraction, numerator a and *of* ten thousands is a multiple of 6. Since the dividend contains 6 ten thousands but not 12 ten thousands, the number we seek is 60,000. We know the divisor will go into this an integral number of *ten thousands* times. We subtract ten thousand 6s. We then repeat the process with the remainder of the dividend. The dividend contains many multiples of 6 greater than 60,000, but they are not also multiples of 10,000. Even if 70,000 were a multiple of 6 we would not want to remove 70,000 as the first step since it is not an integral multiple of ten thousand 6s. The steps consist of subtracting the largest possible integral number of ten thousand 6s, then the largest possible integral number of one thousand 6s, then one hundred 6s, then ten 6s, and finally 6s.

This is the ultimate form that we seek. However the child should be aware of two points. (1) We want this form for convenience. This provides in an orderly fashion the *digits* of the quotient. (2) This does not alter the fact that we are actually subtracting the divisor from the dividend and succeeding remainders as many times as possible. In fact the child should have ample time to develop this refinement. He should have ample opportunity to grasp the real significance of the algorithm by being permitted to subtract multiples of the divisor in any kind of order. For example, as a learning device there is nothing wrong with the algorithm

$$
\begin{array}{r}
7 \\
30 \\
50 \\
110 \\
700 \\
\hline
7\,\overline{\smash{\big)}\,6279} \\
4900 \\
\hline
1379 \\
770 \\
\hline
609 \\
350 \\
\hline
259 \\
210 \\
\hline
49 \\
49 \\
\hline
\end{array}
\qquad
\begin{array}{r}
7 \\
30 \\
50 \\
110 \\
700 \\
\hline
897
\end{array}
$$

After the procedure has been followed long enough for the child to see *how* and *why* the dividend is separated (in the above example

$84,362 = 60,000 + 24,000 + 360 + 2 = 1 \times 6 \times 10,000 + 4 \times 6 \times 1000 + 6 \times 6 \times 10 + 2)$ as it is, the standard long form should be adopted:

$$
\begin{array}{r}
14060 \\
6\overline{\smash)84362} \\
6 \\
\overline{} \\
24 \\
24 \\
\overline{} \\
36 \\
36 \\
\overline{} \\
2
\end{array}
$$

It is of course true that one may much more easily merely instruct the child to divide each digit of the divisor starting at the left, write the quotient number directly above, and in the case of incomplete division "carry" the remainder to the next digit. In fact, this is the procedure which ultimately should be adopted.

The proposed method requires more time to learn, it is longer and slower. But it gives the pupil an opportunity to see the *why* of what he is doing. This approach will make division with larger divisors much more intelligible. As a purely mechanical process, division is difficult to learn. There are so many diverse steps in the process, with the possibility of false starts and repetitions, that it is easy to get lost if the process is not meaningful. The child who knows why he takes the steps he does is much less apt to stumble.

7.11 DIVISORS WITH TWO OR MORE DIGITS

Division with divisors of more than one digit should not be attempted until the process is well understood with one-digit divisors.

When applicable, some of the properties of division may be used to reduce the problem to one-digit divisors. For example, we may apply the rule of successive divisors to solve $72\overline{\smash)1152}$. We may divide by 8, then divide the quotient by 9. Or we may reduce $14\overline{\smash)876}$ to $7\overline{\smash)438}$ by dividing both numerator and denominator by 2.

Many such problems should be solved by the application of these principles. They provide one-digit division practice. They reinforce understanding of the principles involved, principles which are invaluable in the study of fractions. They develop the habit of seeking more than one way to solve a problem. Finally, they provide motivation for learning to extend the algorithm to the more complicated situations.

When division with two-digit divisors is introduced, the first problems encountered should have divisors that are exact tens. This will enable the pupil to master a part of the task presented by two-digit divisors unencumbered by the most difficult part. Consider the two problems $3\overline{\smash{\big)}576}$ and $30\overline{\smash{\big)}576}$. The first step of the first problem requires the answer to the question: How many hundreds of 3s in 576? The first step in the second problem requires the answer to: How many tens of 30s in 576? In other words, it is apparent that the quotient figure is 1 in each case. The only question is: One what? There should be considerable practice provided for division with the divisor even tens before the general case is considered. This will enable the pupil to learn how to position the quotient figure before he has to worry about rounding off to find nonapparent quotient figures.

After considerable work of this sort, the class should be challenged with a problem like $79\overline{\smash{\big)}8321}$; that is, one whose divisor is a prime number, not a factor of the dividend. Although successive division is of no help and there is no factor to divide numerator and denominator by, we may still use the distributive principle. The dividend is a little over 100 times the divisor. This suggests separating the dividend into $7900 + 421$. Since 79 is about 80 and 421 is about 400 we further separate the dividend into $7900 + 395 + 26$. By the distributive principle this suggests $79\overline{\smash{\big)}8321} = 79\overline{\smash{\big)}7900} + 79\overline{\smash{\big)}395} + 79\overline{\smash{\big)}26}$. If we had a one-digit divisor we would be concerned with how many thousands of the divisor we can subtract from the dividend. But inspection tells there are none if the divisor is a two-digit number. We are concerned with how many hundreds of 79s can be subtracted from 83 hundred, rather than how many thousands of 79s can be subtracted from 8 thousand. The first step in the algorithm

$$
\begin{array}{r}
100 \\
79\overline{\smash{\big)}8321} \\
7900 \\
\hline
421
\end{array}
$$

should be seen by the pupil as: 79 into 8300? 100 times, subtract 7900. The zeros should be omitted from the algorithm as soon as the child has confidence in what he is doing. In the second step the child should think "How many tens of 79s in 421? Since 421 is less than 790 there are none. How many 79s in 421 ?'' The estimate, 5, is obtained by considering about 80 into about 400.

$$
\begin{array}{r}
105 \\
79\overline{)8321} \\
7900 \\
\hline
421 \\
395 \\
\hline
26
\end{array}
$$

If the child has thought of the quotient figure *1* as 1 *hundred* and *5* as *5* *ones* and placed them in their respective places relative to the dividend there is less likelihood of overlooking the 0 in tens place.

The procedure is the same if the first two digits of the dividend are less than the divisor. For example, $67\,\overline{)1537}$. We know the dividend contains no thousands of 67s (67,000) or hundreds of 67s (6700). Then our first step concerns the number of tens of 67s (670s) in 153 tens (1530). We estimate the quotient figure by approximating 67 and 1530. Since 67 is about 70 and 1530 about 1500 we know there are about 20 67s in 1530. Then we subtract 20×67 from the dividend

$$
\begin{array}{r}
20 \\
67\overline{)1537} \\
1340 \\
\hline
197
\end{array}
$$

and proceed. Our next concern is with 67s in 197. Again we approximate about 70 and about 200. Since it will go nearly 3 times we try 3. On multiplication we find $67 \times 3 = 201$, which is too much, so we take our quotient figure as 2.

The same approach should be used with divisors of any size. For example, the first step in $483\,\overline{)67285}$ should be "about 500 into about 67000," which is equivalent to "about 5 into about 670." In other words, we first find how many hundreds of times the divisor may be subtracted.

It is not proposed that the above procedure be adopted as a permanent method of division. But it should be followed long enough for the child to understand the significance of the mechanics of the usual algorithm. That is, he should realize that he is subtracting multiples of powers of ten times the divisor. In the first step we subtract the divisor times the highest possible multiple of ten as many times as possible. On each subsequent step precisely the same thing is done to that part of the dividend which remains after the preceding subtraction. The procedure continues until there remains a quantity less than the divisor.

The proposed method gives an evaluation of the position value of each quotient digit which will give meaning to the rule to be used later for placing the quotient.

If the child has a basis for understanding, the conventional division algorithm can be mastered as a refinement, a short cut to the earlier method. For example, in analyzing the process when dividing $483 \overline{\smash{)}67285}$ he can readily see that finding how many times 483 will go into 672 is equivalent to finding how many *hundred* times 483 will go into 67,200. Then placing the quotient digit 1 over the 2 makes it *hundreds* because the 2 is in hundreds place. The alignment of the product of quotient digit by divisor is no mystery. It is dictated by the fact that we are dealing with so many *hundreds*.

Much of the difficulty with division stems from the fact that the child gets lost. He does not see the continuing process as a repetition of the basic step—subtract as many times as possible the highest possible power of ten multiplied by the divisor. The proposed developmental approach emphasizes this aspect of the operation. If with the usual algorithm *all* of the remaining part of the dividend is brought down each time this will emphasize the fact that we are proceeding exactly as at the beginning except that we have for dividend that part of the original dividend which has not been used:

$$
\begin{array}{r}
1495 \\
56\,\overline{\smash{)}83746} \\
56 \\
\hline
27746 \\
224 \\
\hline
5346 \\
504 \\
\hline
306 \\
280 \\
\hline
26
\end{array}
$$

7.12 TRIAL DIVISORS

None of the operations—addition, subtraction, multiplication—requires the exercise of judgment. It is possible for one to follow the rules in machine-like fashion and secure the correct answer. Division requires the making of estimates and appraising their appropriateness.

The algorithm requires that we determine the number of times the divisor of n digits will go into the number represented by the n highest digits of the dividend, or if the divisor is the greater into the $(n + 1)$ highest digits of the dividend. At times this is quite apparent from an examination of the first digits of dividend and divisor. The highest quotient digit is apparent for the following: $36\overline{\smash{\big)}\,4291}$, $231\overline{\smash{\big)}\,5576}$, $827\overline{\smash{\big)}\,18346}$; 36 into 42 one time, 231 into 557 two times, 827 into 1834 two times. On other occasions the quotient digit is not apparent. In this case we must make an estimate and try it out. The correct quotient digit is not apparent in the following: $563\overline{\smash{\big)}\,16734}$, $17\overline{\smash{\big)}\,11936}$, $256\overline{\smash{\big)}\,10739}$. There are two widely used rules for finding the trial quotient digit. By the first rule the highest digit of the divisor is divided into the highest digit of the dividend, or if the divisor of n digits is greater than the first n digits of the dividend, the first two digits of the dividend. If we apply the rule to the above cases the quotient digits indicated are 3, 11, and 5, respectively, 5 into 16, 1 into 11, and 2 into 10. In the second case we get 11 as trial quotient digit, which is impossible. In cases of this sort 9 is taken as trial quotient. Multiplication shows that all three trial quotients are too large. When this happens the rule requires that we reduce the trial quotient by 1 and try again. When we try 2, 8, and 4 we find 2 and 4 are correct but 8 is still too large. We reduce the 8 to 7 and try again. When this rule is followed unsuccessful trial quotients are invariably too large.

The second rule is the same as the above if the second digit of the divisor is 0, 1, 2, 3, 4, or 5. If the second digit is 6, 7, 8, or 9 we increase the first digit by 1 and proceed as before. In the above cases the trial divisors are $16 \div 6$, $11 \div 2$, and $10 \div 3$, giving the trial quotient figures of 2, 5, and 3. Trial shows the 2 is correct but the 5 and the 3 are too small. Then we increase by 1 and try 6 and 4. The 6 is still too small so we try 7.

There is no doubt that the second rule will result in fewer unsuccessful trials. However, under the first rule we always correct by subtracting 1, but under the second rule we add or subtract depending on whether we did or did not increase the divisor digit.

The first rule, though less efficient, is easier for children to remember and to apply. It has an added advantage. If the trial quotient is too large the fact becomes apparent as soon as it is multiplied by the divisor. If it is too small we must subtract this product and compare the remainder with the divisor, for example:

$$\begin{array}{cc} 8 & 4 \\ 173\overline{\smash{\big)}\,8694} & 173\overline{\smash{\big)}\,8694} \\ 1384 & 692 \\ & \overline{177} \end{array}$$

Neither of the two procedures is too good; both are substitutes for thoughtful analysis of the situation. The one-rule procedure is perhaps the better of the two, to be taught as a scheme that will invariably give the correct quotient figure ultimately. However, the children should be encouraged to devise improvements on the procedure. When the two-part rule is employed we are really rounding off the divisor. There is no reason why the dividend cannot also be rounded off. After some experience the child will learn to let the individual problem dictate how far the rounding off should go. For example, in the problem $563\overline{\smash{\big)}\,16734}$ the correct quotient digit is obtained when we round off to $600\overline{\smash{\big)}\,17000}$ but this is so close to 30 that greater confidence in the estimate is obtained when we consider $560\overline{\smash{\big)}\,16700}$. If we round $17\overline{\smash{\big)}\,11936}$ to $20\overline{\smash{\big)}\,12000}$ we still get an incorrect quotient digit, but the result 6 is a better estimate than was obtained from either of the other methods. We get the correct result immediately when we round $256\overline{\smash{\big)}\,10739}$ to $250\overline{\smash{\big)}\,11000}$.

7.13 CHECKS ON DIVISION

The traditional check for division consists of multiplying the quotient by the divisor and adding the remainder, if any, to the product. The result should be the dividend. Although this is a check by inverse operations, it is almost a check by repetition since the same multiplication must occur in the division and in the check.

Checking by subtraction is not feasible except for very simple problems in the early grades. Although a legitimate check, it would hardly be considered an efficient one to count the number of times 67 can be subtracted from 17,864 as a check on $67\overline{\smash{\big)}\,17864}$.

If the divisor is not a prime we can check by successive division. For example:

$$836\overline{\smash{\big)}\,93528} = (209\overline{\smash{\big)}\,93528}) \div 4$$

The distributive principle may be used for a check. For example:

$$18\overline{\smash{\big)}\,216} = 18\overline{\smash{\big)}\,90} + 18\overline{\smash{\big)}\,90} + 18\overline{\smash{\big)}\,36}$$

Fifth- and sixth-graders will find the check of nines both interesting and useful. You will recall that we cannot always perform the division operation with the excesses of nines. Instead we find the excess of nines in dividend, divisor, quotient and remainder. Then we perform the usual check with the excesses, quotient times divisor plus remainder equals dividend:

$$
\begin{array}{r}
53 \\
156\overline{)8372} \\
780 \\
\hline
572 \\
468 \\
\hline
104
\end{array}
$$

CHECK:

Excess of divisor: $1 + 5 + 6 = 12; 1 + 2 = 3$

Excess of quotient: $5 + 3 = 8$

Excess of remainder: $1 + 0 + 4 = 5$

Excess of product of excesses of divisor and quotient plus excess of remainder: $3 \times 8 + 5 = 29; 9 + 2 = 11; 1 + 1 = 2$ ⟵⟍

Excess of dividend: $8 + 3 + 7 + 2 = 20; 2 + 0 = 2$ ⟵⟋

The excess of elevens is applied to division in the same manner. We check the same problem by the check of elevens. Recall that at any point where subtraction leads to a negative number we may add eleven and proceed:

Excess of divisor: $6 - 5 + 1 = 2$

Excess of quotient: $3 + 11 - 5 = 9$

Excess of remainder: $4 - 0 + 1 = 5$

Excess of product of excesses of quotient and divisor plus excess of remainder: $2 \times 9 + 5 = 23; 3 - 2 = 1$ ⟵⟍

Excess of dividend: $2 + 11 - 7 + 3 - 8 = 1$ ⟵⟋

Perhaps the most useful check of all consists of estimating the answer. The estimate, to be unprejudiced, should be made before the computation. This is simply a matter of looking to the reasonableness of the result, a habit which should be fostered at every opportunity.

7.14 OTHER WAYS TO DIVIDE

Other methods of dividing can be used to advantage in the upper grades as motivation for needed review of the process and for enrichment purposes. When items of this sort are used they should not be taught for complete mastery and efficient use. The objective should be to lead the child to see the principles involved which make the method work. The child will have the opportunity to see that any algorithm is merely a device which utilizes the structure of the number system as an aid in performing the operation. By comparison with present-day methods he can appreciate the evolutionary struggle which produced the method he uses.

We know of the method used by the ancient Egyptians through papyri which have been discovered and translated. They used similar devices for both multiplication and division. The Russian Peasant method of multiplication is an adaptation of it. By this method we find $73 \overline{\smash{)}8647}$ as follows:

1	73
2	146
4	292
8	584
16	1168
32	2336
64	4672

In the left column we start with 1 and double each number to obtain the number below. In the right column we start with the divisor and double to obtain the next number below. The process terminates when one more step will give a result in the right column which exceeds the dividend. Now begin with the last number in the right column and add to it all those numbers and only those numbers which give a sum equal to or less than the dividend, working from the bottom. For example, we add 2336 because $4672 + 2336 = 7008$ is less than 8647. We add $1168 + 7008 = 8176$. But we reject 584 since $8176 + 584 = 8760$, which is too large. Adding $292 + 8176 = 8468$. Then we add $146 + 8468 = 8614$. But if we add $73 + 8614 = 8687$ we exceed the dividend, so we reject 73. We have added $4672 + 2336 + 1168 + 292 + 146 = 8614$, which is 33 less than the dividend. Then, if we add the corresponding numbers in the left column, we get

$$64 + 32 + 16 + 4 + 2 = 118$$

and we have discovered that $118 \times 73 = 8614$ which differs from 8647 by 33, less than the divisor 73. Then the problem is solved:

$$8647 \div 73 = 118\tfrac{33}{73}$$

Sixth-grade children can appreciate the fact that this is just *another* way to find the maximum number of times 73 can be subtracted from 8647. It is not necessary to go into the Egyptian system of notation to point out that they could not have used our system because their notation system did not employ place value. If we were restricted to their kind of notation system this method of division would appear quite clever.

The scratch method represents one of the early attempts at utilizing the place-value principle of the notation system. It is also indicative of the influence of the abacus, an indispensable tool for computation with notation systems which do not have place value.

We shall illustrate the method using the same problem: 73⟌8647.

Step 1.
$$
\begin{array}{c|c}
13 & \\
\cancel{8647} & 1 \\
\cancel{73} &
\end{array}
$$

Write the divisor under the dividend, aligned on the left. Determine how many times 73 will go into 86. This is the first quotient digit, written to the right of the vertical line. Subtract 73 from 86, scratching digits as they are used.

Step 2.
$$
\begin{array}{cc}
6 & \\
\cancel{1}31 & \\
\cancel{8647} & 11 \\
\cancel{733} & \\
\cancel{7} &
\end{array}
$$

Shift the divisor one digit to the right. Repeat the above procedure: 73 into 134 goes 1 time. Subtract 73 from 134. Again scratch digits as they are used.

Step 3.
$$
\begin{array}{cc}
\cancel{5}3 & \\
\cancel{6}9 & \\
\cancel{1}3\cancel{1}3 & \\
\cancel{8647} & 118 \\
\cancel{7333} & \\
\cancel{7}7 &
\end{array}
$$

Shift the divisor one more place to the right and proceed as before. 73 into 617 goes 8 times. (This method involves trial divisors just as our own does. It is advisable to do your trying mentally so as to be sure the correct quotient digit is used before writing it down.) Subtract 8 × 73 from 617, again scratching used digits. The quotient 118 is to the right of the vertical line and the remainder 33 is the unscratched digits on the left.

It is interesting to note that both of these methods, as well as our own, enable us to subtract the highest power of some base number multiplied by the divisor the greatest possible number of times. We then repeat the process with that part of the dividend which remains after each subtraction. Under the scratch method, as well as our own, the algorithm enables us to find $8647 \div 73$ by subtracting $1 \times 10^2 \times 73$, then $1 \times 10^1 \times 73$, and finally $8 \times 10^0 \times 73$. The Egyptian method utilizes powers of 2 rather than 10. By that method we subtract $1 \times 2^6 \times 73$, then $1 \times 2^5 \times 73$, then $1 \times 2^4 \times 73$, then $1 \times 2^2 \times 73$, and finally $1 \times 2^1 \times 73$.

In other countries forms somewhat different from the one used in the United States are preferred. The following method is taught in the schools of Brazil. We illustrate with the problem, $58700 \div 246$:

$$
\begin{array}{l|l}
58700 & 246 \\
0950 & \overline{238} \\
2120 \\
0152
\end{array}
$$

The method lends itself quite well to the additive–equal-additions method of subtraction. The trial quotients are found in the usual way. The multiplication of quotient digit by divisor and the subtraction of this product from the dividend are done mentally. Only the remainders are written down. The first step in the above problem,

$$
\begin{array}{l|l}
58700 & 246 \\
095 & 2
\end{array}
$$

is obtained as follows: $2 \times 6 = 12$. The ones digit $2 + 5$ (written under 7) $= 7$. (Here we have used additive subtraction) $2 \times 4 = 8$; $8 + 1$ (carried) $= 9$; $9 + 9$ (written under 8) $= 18$. $2 \times 2 = 4$; $4 + 1$ (to compensate for the 1 in 18) $= 5$. Here we use equal addition rather than decomposition or "borrowing." $5 + 0$ (written under 5) $= 5$. The 0 in tens place in the dividend is then drawn down

$$
\begin{array}{l|l}
58700 & 246 \\
0950 & 2
\end{array}
$$

and the process is repeated, using 950 for dividend. To the individual who subtracts by the take-away–decomposition method, this method seems to require a burdensome amount of mental calculation. But that is really not the case when subtraction is done by the additive–equal-addition method.

Exercises

1 Illustrate with an example that addition, subtraction, and multiplication may all be required to perform a problem in division.

2 Describe the two rules for finding trial quotient digits. Under which rule will wrong digits always be in the same direction, that is, always too large or always too small?

3 Is division as successive subtraction consistent with partition division? Measurement division?

4 There is no better way to be acutely aware of the difficulties inherent in the division algorithm that dividing in a base other than ten. Perform the following in the indicated base.

$$32_{\text{six}} \overline{)2532_{\text{six}}}$$

5 Is there any value in learning short division? Discuss.

6 Distinguish between measurement division and partition division. Which concept should be developed first? Why?

7 Why is it incorrect to say $13 \div 5 = 2$, with $\frac{3}{5}$ remainder?

8 Why is division the most difficult of the four fundamental operations?

9 How would you explain to a seventh-grade pupil why he cannot divide by zero?

10 How do you think the child should be taught to find trial divisors?

11 Divide $4372 \div 159$ by the ancient Egyptian method. Check by the check of nines.

Suggested Supplementary Readings

Clark, John R., and Laura K. Eads, *Guiding Arithmetic Learning*. Yonkers-on-Hudson, N.Y.: World Book Company, 1954. Chap. V.

Morton, Robert L., *Teaching Children Arithmetic*. New York: Silver Burdett Company, 1953. Pp. 115–192.

Spencer, Peter L., and Marguerite Brydegaard, *Building Mathematical Concepts in the Elementary School*. New York: Henry Holt and Company, 1952. Pp. 121–137.

Spitzer, Herbert F., *The Teaching of Arithmetic*. Boston: Houghton Mifflin Company, third edition, 1961. Chaps. V, VI.

Stokes, C. Newton, *Teaching the Meanings of Arithmetic*. New York: Appleton-Century-Crofts, Inc., 1951. Pp. 135–150.

Wheat, Harry G., *How to Teach Arithmetic*. Evanston, Illinois: Row, Peterson and Company, 1951. Chap. V.

Rational Numbers

CHAPTER EIGHT

IN CHAPTER FOUR WE SAW that the cardinal numbers, the natural numbers and zero, are closed with respect to addition and multiplication. But they are not closed with respect to subtraction or division. The motive for the creation of negative numbers was to produce a system closed with respect to subtraction. The set of integers, positive, negative, and zero, is such a set. The existence of additive inverse elements, or opposites, is equivalent to closure for subtraction. We have seen that subtraction of an integer is equivalent to addition of its opposite.

The integers are not closed under division, even with division by zero excluded. In this chapter we shall make another extension of number to produce a system that is closed with respect to division, except that division by zero is not permissible. The set of rational numbers is such a set.

8.1 RATIOS

Jim has 6 marbles and Tom has 18. The ratio of Jim's marbles to Tom's marbles is 6:18. The marbles are sold in packages of six. In terms of packages of marbles, the ratio of Jim's to Tom's marbles is

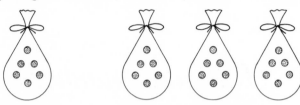

Jim's marbles   Tom's marbles

1:3. The packages sell for 5 cents each. Then in terms of cost the ratio is 5:15. These ratios 6:18, 1:3, and 5:15 are an illustration of *equivalent ratios.*

Before we define ratios we should decide what a ratio is. Suppose Sam has 24 marbles. The ratio of Jim's to Tom's to Sam's is 6:18:24. In terms of packages of marbles it is 1:3:4. A ratio does not necessarily consist of only two numbers. In the illustration we have used a ratio to indicate the relative measures of two sets, 6:18, then three sets, 6:18:24. We can compare in this way as many sets as we wish.

A ratio is an n-tuple of numbers

$$a_1 : a_2 : a_3 : \ldots : a_n$$

indicating n comparable measures.

We have said that 6:18, 1:3, and 5:15 were equivalent ratios. Each tells the same story by way of comparing the two sets, Jim's marbles and Tom's marbles. The three ratios are related such that each of the numbers in any ratio can be multiplied by some number k to produce any other of the ratios. For example, if we multiply the 1 and the 3 in the ratio 1:3 by 5 we get 5:15. If we multiply each of the members of 6:18 by $\frac{1}{6}$ we get 1:3. The same holds for the equivalent ratios 1:3:4 and 6:18:24, if each member of the first ratio is multiplied by 6 we get the second ratio.

Two ratios are equivalent,

$a_1 : a_2 : a_3 : a_4 : \ldots : a_n$ is equivalent to

$b_1 : b_2 : b_3 : b_4 : \ldots : b_n$ if and only if

$a_1 = kb_1 ; a_2 = kb_2 ; a_3 = kb_3 ; a_4 = kb_4 ; a_n = kb_n$ and $k \neq 0$.

In the definition of equivalent ratios no limitation is placed on the numbers except that k cannot be zero. For example, $\frac{1}{2}:\frac{3}{7}$ is a ratio and $\frac{1}{7} \times \frac{1}{2} : \frac{1}{7} \times \frac{3}{7}$ is a ratio equivalent to it.

The idea of equivalent ratios can be used to advantage in both the analysis and solution of many problems.

EXAMPLE. Mr. Jones, Mr. Smith, and Mr. Brown formed a partnership. Mr. Jones put up $10,000, Mr. Smith put up $15,000, and Mr. Brown operated the business. In dividing the profits it was agreed that Mr. Brown's contribution was to be evaluated at $25,000. Determine the share each should receive from a profit of $1200.

The ratio of investments of Jones: Smith: Brown: Total is 10,000 : 15,000 : 25,000 : 50,000. If we multiply each member of the ratio by 1/5000 we have the equivalent ratio 2:3:5:10. Or in general, $2k:3k:5k:10k$ is an equivalent ratio for any $k \neq 0$. We are required to find k such that we have $2k:3k:5k:1200$. That is, $10k = 1200$. Hence $k = 120$. Jones share is $2k = \$240$, Smith's share is $3k = \$360$, and Brown's share is $5k = \$600$.

Exercises

1 In each of the following fill the blanks so as to make the ratios equivalent.
(a) $3:\_, 5:8\frac{1}{3}, \_:15$
(b) $2:3:7, 4:\_:14, 6:\_:\_, \_:12\_:$
(c) $1:3:5, \_:\_:25, \_:12:\_, 4:\_:\_$

2 Which of the following sets have as elements equivalent ratios?
(a) $\{1:2, 2:3, 3:4, 4:5, 5:6\}$
(b) $\{2:3, 4:6, 5:15, 20:30\}$
(c) $\{3:5, 9:15, 6:10, 24:40\}$
(d) $\{4:8, 3:6:7, 9:18, 6:12:14:25\}$
(e) $\{9:6, 12:8, 30:20, 27:18\}$

3 For what values of k are each of the following pairs of ratios equivalent?
(a) $2:3:7$ and $2k:3k:21$
(b) $50:75:90$ and $10:5k:18$
(c) $6:7:9$ and $2k:21:3k$
(d) $2:3:5:10$ and $2k:3k:5k:25$

Use equivalent ratios to solve each of the following:

4 Mr. Brown made an automobile trip of 235 miles in 5 hours. At this same rate how far can he travel in 7 hours? How long will a trip of 530 miles require at this same rate?

5 Jim is paid $2 per hour, Tom is paid $3 per hour, and Bob is paid $5 per hour. If they work the same number of hours how much does each earn when their total earnings come to $150?

6 At the same time that a 6-foot fence post casts a shadow 8 feet long a flag pole casts a shadow 44 feet long. How high is the flag pole?

7 A fuel mixture requires 3 pounds of fuel A to 5 pounds of fuel B to 7 pounds of fuel C. How many pounds of each fuel are required to make 1500 pounds of the mixture?

8.2 EQUIVALENCE CLASSES

According to the definition of cardinal numbers on page 93, the cardinal number 2 is the set of all sets equivalent to $\{0, 1\}$. Since it is the set of *all* equivalent sets it is called an equivalence class. A somewhat different approach could have been used in defining negative numbers. We have seen that a negative number is actually an implied subtraction. Negative numbers can be defined as equivalence classes. If this approach were used -3 would be the class of all differences equivalent to $3 - 6$. There are an infinite number of such differences, so the equivalence class is an infinite set. But under what circumstances are such differences equivalent? We cannot find $3 - 6$ in the set of natural numbers. By definition, if a is less than b, the difference $a - b$ is equivalent to $c - d$ if and only if $b - a = d - c$. Using this approach

$$-3 = \{(1 - 4), (2 - 5), (3-6), (4-7), \cdots\}$$

where it is understood that the three dots imply not merely an endless set, but all such equivalent differences.

In Section 8.1 equivalent ratios were defined. The *class* of equivalent ratios $\{4k : 2k\}$ is the set of *all* ratios equivalent to the ratio $4:2$. Each possible value of k determines an element of the set of ratios.

If we confine our consideration to ratios of two numbers the notation a/b can be used instead of $a:b$. If we restrict ratios to ratios of integers we can now define rational numbers.

A rational number is an equivalence class of ratios of pairs of integers $\{ka/kb\}$, $b \neq 0$.

According to this definition, the equivalence class

$$\{\tfrac{1}{2}, \tfrac{2}{4}, \tfrac{3}{6}, \tfrac{4}{8}, \cdots, k/2k, \cdots\}$$

is a rational number. We need a more convenient way to indicate the number. We take as representative element of the set the simplest ratio $1/2$. Hence $1/2$ is both a ratio $1:2$ and a rational number. Any other element of the equivalence class can also be used to represent denominator b, meaning $a \div b$. It may also be interpreted as a ratio $a:b$. Finally, this may be interpreted as a symbol for a rational number. We must develop the properties of rational numbers in a manner consistent with this triple interpretation.

It is to this end that we exclude $b = 0$ from the rational number a/b. We *want* the rational number to mean an implied division, and division by zero is excluded as a possible operation. It is of interest to note here that the fraction $\frac{5}{0}$ is meaningless because a fraction is an implied division. But there is nothing wrong with the ratio $5:0$. The Yankees have scored 5 runs and the Giants no runs, what is the ratio of their scores? It is $5:0$. No inconsistency would result from the concept of a ratio $0:0$, but it is a rather useless concept. No other ratio is equivalent to it.

Exercises

1   Why is no other ratio equivalent to $0:0$?

2   What is the distinction, if any, between an equivalence class and an infinite set of equivalent elements?

3   If the elements of an equivalence class of ratios are considered implied divisions what is the simplest way to designate the equivalence class $\{\frac{8}{4}, \frac{16}{8}, \ldots, 2k/k, \ldots\}$?

4   In the light of Exercise 3 is 2 a rational number? Are all rational numbers fractions?

5   Give an example of a fraction that is not a rational number.

6   Give an example of a ratio that is not a rational number.

7   Is it possible for the ratio of two numbers, not necessarily integers, not to be a symbol for a rational number? Illustrate.

8   Write five elements of the equivalence class of which $\frac{2}{5}$ is representative element.

9   Is $12 \div 5$ a rational number? Discuss.

10   If 3 is a rational number what ratio is implied? The ratio implies what division? Why can we not then say that 3 is a fraction?

11   Interpreted as a fraction, what does $\frac{3}{4}$ mean? Interpreted as a ratio, what does it mean? Interpreted as a rational number, what does it mean?

8.3   OPERATIONS WITH RATIONAL NUMBERS

We wish to change our point of view slightly from the previous section. If a and b are integers and $b \neq 0$ we wish to say that by definition a/b is a rational number. This is simply more convenient than to say a/b is a symbol whereby we may identify the rational number (equivalence class of ratios) of which a/b is a member.

Furthermore, we may refer to two equal rational numbers when we have two ratios from the same equivalence class. Thus, $a/b = c/d$ if and only if $ad = bc$.

Next, we wish to determine how to multiply and add rational numbers. In doing so we shall be guided by these principles.

(1) The properties of the integers—the closure, associative, commutative, distributive, identity, and addition inverse properties—shall be preserved.

(2) Since we want closure for division by nonzero numbers we want the rational number a/b to mean $a \div b$.

(3) We want all nonzero rational numbers to have multiplication inverses. This will assure closure of rational numbers under division. Specifically, we want a times the inverse of b to mean a/b.

We shall follow the same procedure that was used in determining the rules of signs for addition and multiplication of integers. We shall not define addition and multiplication of rational numbers. We shall assume the properties listed above are satisfied by the rational numbers and derive the rules for addition and multiplication as a consequence of this assumption.

8.4 MULTIPLICATION OF RATIONAL NUMBERS

We have assumed the existence of a multiplication inverse for each nonzero integer. The inverse of the integer a is written $1/a$. Hence

$$a \times 1/a = 1$$

Note parenthetically that this is in keeping with our earliest contact with fractions. The child learns early in life that "one half of" means the same thing as "divided by two." Multiplying by $\frac{1}{2}$ has the same effect as dividing by 2, and $2 \times \frac{1}{2} = 1$.

Before proceeding to the general problem of multiplying two rational numbers let us investigate the product $1/b \times 1/d$. We know that $b \times 1/b = 1$, $d \times 1/d = 1$, and $(b \times d) \times 1/(b \times d) = 1$. This follows from the meaning of the multiplication inverse of an integer. But multiplying the first two equalities, we have

$$(b \times 1/b) \times (d \times 1/d) = 1 \times 1 = 1$$

and since the associative and commutative properties must hold for rational numbers

$$(b \times d) \times (1/b \times 1/d) = 1$$

We may conclude that both $1/(b \times d)$ and $(1/b \times 1/d)$ are the multiplication inverse of $b \times d$. That is, they are equal.

$$1/b \times 1/d = 1/(b \times d)$$

We wish to derive a rule for finding $a/b \times c/d$, the product of two rational numbers. Since a/b means $a \div b$ and c/d means $c \div d$ we have

$$a/b \times c/d = (a \div b) \times (c \div d) \tag{8.1}$$

But if we multiply by the inverse of b rather than divide by b, and similarly for d, we have

$$(a \div b) \times (c \div d) = (a \times 1/b) \times (c \times 1/d) \tag{8.2}$$

Since the associative and commutative properties must hold, we have

$$(a \times 1/b) \times (c \times 1/d) = (a \times c) \times (1/b \times 1/d) \tag{8.3}$$

or

$$(a \times 1/b) \times (c \times 1/d) = (a \times c) \times 1/(b \times d) \tag{8.4}$$

But this means

$$(a \times 1/b) \times (c \times 1/d) = (a \times c) \div (b \times d) = (a \times c)/(b \times d) \tag{8.5}$$

Combining Equations (8.1) through (8.5), we have the rule for multiplication of rational numbers.

If a, b, c, d are integers and neither b nor d is zero, the product of two rational numbers a/b and c/d is

$$a/b \times c/d = (a \times c)/(b \times d)$$

This is, of course, the usual rule for multiplication of fractions. The numerator of the product is the product of the numerators and the denominator of the product is the product of the denominators.

The question was raised in the exercises in Section 8.2 as to whether an integer is also a rational number. In the strict sense of the word it is not, whether we follow the definition in Section 8.2 or the alternate statement in the first paragraph of Section 8.3. From the point of view of an equivalence class of ratios, 5 cannot be the representative element of any such class simply because 5 is not a ratio. Similarly, if a rational number is a symbol a/b where a and b are integers and $b \neq 0$, 5 cannot qualify as a rational number.

On the other hand, we have said that a rational number must mean an implied division. There are infinitely many pairs of integers whose quotient is 5. If we interpret the elements of the equivalence class of ratios

$$\{5\!:\!1,\, 10\!:\!2,\, 15\!:\!3,\, \ldots,\, 5k\!:\!k,\, \ldots\}$$

as fractions each one of them will equal 5. The representative element of this equivalence class is $\frac{5}{1}$. Therefore we certainly can call $\frac{5}{1}$ a rational number. The question seems to reduce itself to this—Must the division which a rational number implies remain merely implied if we are to continue to call it a rational number?

Exactly the same kind of problem arises when integers are defined as implied subtractions of natural numbers. Since $5 - 2$ is an implied subtraction it defines an integer. Strictly speaking, the difference 3 is not an integer, it is a natural number. The difference $5 - 2$ defines the integer $+3$. But the positive integers and the natural numbers behave in a perfectly consistent manner. In the set of natural numbers $3 + 2 = 5$ and in the set of positive integers $(+3) + (+2) = (+5)$. Also, in the set of natural numbers $3 \times 2 = 6$ and in the set of positive integers $(+3) \times (+2) = (+6)$. For purposes of computation, we need make no distinction between the set of positive integers and the set of natural numbers. The principle exhibited here is called *isomorphism*. The set of natural numbers and the set of positive integers are *isomorphic*.

We wish to establish this same relationship between the set of rational numbers of the form $a/1$, where a is an integer, and the set of integers. Does the definition of multiplication preserve this relationship? Since $2 \times -3 = -6$ we should get the result $2/1 \times -3/1 = -6/1$ when we multiply the rational numbers $2/1$ and $-3/1$. This is precisely what the definition requires.

$$\frac{2}{1} \times \frac{-3}{1} = \frac{2 \times (-3)}{1 \times 1} = \frac{-6}{1}$$

This is true in the general case also. If a and b are integers and $a \times b = c$ then

$$\frac{a}{1} \times \frac{b}{1} = \frac{a \times b}{1 \times 1} = \frac{c}{1}$$

When we investigate the addition of rational numbers we shall see that this property also applies to addition. Then we need make no distinction between the integer a and the rational number $a/1$.

Do the rational numbers have a multiplication identity? That is, is there a rational number by which any rational number a/b may be multiplied such that the product is a/b? We would certainly expect the rational number equivalent to the multiplication identity for integers, namely 1, to be the multiplication identity.

$$\frac{a}{b} \times \frac{1}{1} = \frac{a}{b}$$

However, if c is any integer different from zero c/c is an element of the same equivalence class as $1/1$.

$$\frac{a}{b} \times \frac{c}{c} = \frac{a \times c}{b \times c}$$

Here we find the product is not a/b, but it is a member of the same equivalence class as a/b. That is $a/b = (a \times c)/(b \times c)$. We conclude that the multiplication identity is 1 in the sense that the integer c is the same as the rational number $c/1$. But the multiplication identity may appear as $\frac{3}{3}$, $\frac{5}{5}$, $\frac{9}{9}$, or any rational number c/c.

Exercises

1 Prove that the rational numbers are closed with respect to multiplication.

2 Demonstrate that multiplication of rational numbers is commutative by applying the rule for multiplication of rational numbers to each side of the following equalities.

(a) $\frac{5}{6} \times (\frac{2}{7} \times \frac{3}{5}) = (\frac{2}{7} \times \frac{3}{5}) \times \frac{5}{6}$
(b) $2/b \times c/5 = c/5 \times 2/b$
(c) $-3/7 \times 2/-5 = 2/-5 \times -3/7$
(d) $2x/y \times x/2y = x/2y \times 2x/y$

3 Demonstrate that multiplication of rational numbers is associative by applying the rule for multiplication of rational numbers to each of the following equalities.

(a) $(\frac{2}{3} \times \frac{5}{6}) \times a/2b = \frac{2}{3} \times (\frac{5}{6} \times a/2b)$
(b) $-3 \times (-\frac{2}{5} \times \frac{1}{7}) = (-3 \times -\frac{2}{5}) \times \frac{1}{7}$
(c) $(a/b \times \frac{4}{7}) \times b/a = a/b \times (\frac{4}{7} \times b/a)$
(d) $(\frac{6}{5} \times \frac{2}{3}) \times \frac{5}{6} = \frac{6}{5} \times (\frac{2}{3} \times \frac{5}{6})$

4 Prove that the following pairs of rational numbers are equal.

(a) $-a/b$; $a/-b$
(b) $-6/-2$; 3
(c) $1/-5$; $-\frac{1}{5}$
(d) $-7/-3$; $\frac{7}{3}$
(e) $\frac{0}{7}$; $\frac{0}{5}$

5 Prove that any two rational numbers whose numerator is zero are equal.

6 Justify "cancellation" in multiplication of fractions

$$\frac{\overset{1}{\cancel{3}}}{\underset{2}{\cancel{4}}} \times \frac{\overset{1}{\cancel{2}}}{\underset{3}{\cancel{9}}} = \frac{1}{6}$$

in terms of the development in this chapter.

7 Prove that the product of any rational number times a rational number whose numerator is zero is a rational number whose numerator is zero.

8.5 ADDITION OF RATIONAL NUMBERS

As we seek to establish the rule for addition of rational numbers, the usual rule for addition of fractions is, of course, our objective. We wish to show that this rule is a logical consequence of the properties of rational numbers.

The rule for multiplication emerges naturally because a rational number is an implied division, and division is the inverse of multiplication.

If we express the sum $a/b + c/d$ so as to indicate the division involved we have

$$\frac{a}{b} + \frac{c}{d} = (a \div b) + (c \div d)$$

And this can be changed to

$$\frac{a}{b} + \frac{c}{d} = a \times \frac{1}{b} + c \times \frac{1}{d}$$

by using the multiplication inverses of b and d. Here we have both addition and multiplication involved, which indicates the use of the distributive property. But in order that this can be done we must find equivalent forms for a/b and c/d such that they have a common factor.

$$\frac{a}{b} = \frac{a \times c}{b \times c} \quad \text{and} \quad \frac{c}{d} = \frac{a \times c}{a \times d}$$

Hence

$$\frac{a}{b} + \frac{c}{d} = \frac{a \times c}{b \times c} + \frac{a \times c}{a \times d} = (a \times c) \times \frac{1}{b \times c} + (a \times c) \times \frac{1}{a \times d}$$

$$= (a \times c)\left(\frac{1}{b \times c} + \frac{1}{a \times d}\right)$$

We have used the distributive property, yet we are still confronted with the necessity of adding two fractions. We can find equivalent fractions in yet another way.

$$\frac{a}{b} = \frac{a \times d}{b \times d} \quad \text{and} \quad \frac{c}{d} = \frac{b \times c}{b \times d}$$

Hence

$$\frac{a}{b} + \frac{c}{d} = \frac{a \times d}{b \times d} + \frac{b \times c}{b \times d} = (a \times d) \times \frac{1}{(b \times d)} + (b \times c) \times \frac{1}{(b \times d)}$$

which, by the commutative property, yields

$$\frac{a}{b} + \frac{c}{d} = \frac{1}{(b \times d)} \times (a \times d) + \frac{1}{(b \times d)} \times (b \times c)$$

and, employing the distributive property,

$$\frac{a}{b} + \frac{c}{d} = \frac{1}{b \times d} \times (a \times d + b \times c) = \frac{a \times d + b \times c}{b \times d}$$

Hence we have derived the rule for addition of rational numbers.

If a/b and c/d are any two rational numbers

$$\frac{a}{b} + \frac{c}{d} = \frac{a \times d + b \times c}{b \times d}$$

This should be recognized as the usual method for addition of fractions. To find $\frac{3}{4} + \frac{7}{5}$ we first reduce to a common denominator

$$\frac{3}{4} + \frac{7}{5} = \frac{15}{20} + \frac{28}{20}$$

then write the sum of the numerators over the common denominator.

$$\frac{15}{20} + \frac{28}{20} = \frac{43}{20}$$

But following the above rule, we do essentially the same thing.

$$\frac{3}{4} + \frac{7}{5} = \frac{3 \times 5 + 4 \times 7}{4 \times 5} = \frac{15 + 28}{20} = \frac{43}{20}$$

Are sums preserved when we identify the rational number $a/1$ with the integer a? Since $2 + 3 = 5$, we should have $\frac{2}{1} + \frac{3}{1} = \frac{5}{1}$. When we apply the definition of addition we have

$$\frac{2}{1} + \frac{3}{1} = \frac{1 \times 2 + 1 \times 3}{1 \times 1} = \frac{2 + 3}{1} = \frac{5}{1}$$

and in the general case

$$\frac{a}{1} + \frac{b}{1} = \frac{1 \times a + 1 \times b}{1 \times 1} = \frac{a + b}{1}$$

Since the rational numbers of the form $a/1$ behave precisely as the integers a, we shall make no distinction between them and consider any integer a as a rational number.

Accordingly, does the rational number 0 serve as the addition identity? That is, does $a/b + 0/1 = a/b$? Applying the definition, we have

$$\frac{a}{b} + \frac{0}{1} = \frac{1 \times a + 0 \times b}{b \times 1} = \frac{a}{b}$$

Exercises

1 Prove that the rational numbers are closed with respect to addition.

2 Verify that addition of rational numbers is commutative by evaluating independently each side of the following equations.

(a) $\frac{1}{3} + \frac{2}{5} = \frac{2}{5} + \frac{1}{3}$

(b) $-\frac{2}{7} + (\frac{1}{4} + \frac{5}{6}) = (\frac{1}{4} + \frac{5}{6}) + -\frac{2}{7}$

(c) $-a/5 + 3/2b = 3/2b + -a/5$

(d) $(\frac{1}{3} + 5) + \frac{1}{4} = \frac{1}{4} + (\frac{1}{3} + 5)$

3 Verify that addition of rational numbers is associative by evaluating independently each side of the following equations.

(a) $\frac{3}{4} + (\frac{1}{5} + -\frac{6}{2}) = (\frac{3}{4} + \frac{1}{5}) + -\frac{6}{2}$

(b) $-a/b + (\frac{1}{2} + a/b) = (-a/b + \frac{1}{2}) + a/b$

(c) $(-5 + -\frac{2}{3}) + \frac{2}{3} = -5 + (-\frac{2}{3} + \frac{2}{3})$

(d) $a/2b + (2/b + 2a/b) = (a/2b + 2/b) + 2a/b$

4 Verify that multiplication of rational numbers is distributive over addition by evaluating independently each side of the following equations.

(a) $\frac{2}{5} \times (\frac{1}{3} + \frac{1}{4}) = \frac{2}{5} \times \frac{1}{3} + \frac{2}{5} \times \frac{1}{4}$

(b) $a/b \times (1/c + d) = a/b \times 1/c + a/b \times d$

(c) $-4 \times (-\frac{2}{3} + -\frac{1}{6}) = -4 \times -\frac{2}{3} + -4 \times -\frac{1}{6}$

(d) $-1/a \times (2 + -1/b) = -1/a \times 2 + -1/a \times -1/b$

5 Prove that if addition of rational numbers were defined as $a/b + c/d = (a + c)/(b + d)$ addition would be associative and commutative.

6 Prove that if addition of rational numbers were defined as in Exercise 5 and multiplication were defined in the usual way multiplication would be distributive over addition.

7 In the light of Exercises 5 and 6 why is the definition in Exercise 5 not acceptable as a rule for addition of rational numbers?

8 The rule for addition of rational numbers given on page 282 does not require finding the lowest common denominator. Explain why the results are comparable to the lowest common denominator method.

8.6 THE INVERSE OPERATIONS

Negative integers were created in order that each integer a will have an addition inverse $-a$. Can this be extended to rational numbers? Either the numerator a or the denominator b of the rational number a/b may be negative. For that matter both may be negative. Without regard to the signs of a and b if $-a/b$ is the addition inverse of a/b then $a/b + -a/b = 0$. On the other hand, the rule for the addition of rational numbers gives

$$\frac{a}{b} + \frac{-a}{b} = \frac{a + (-a)}{b} = 0$$

Hence

$$-\frac{a}{b} = \frac{-a}{b}$$

Since subtraction of rational numbers is the inverse of addition, subtraction and addition of the addition inverse should give the same result.

$$\frac{a}{b} - \frac{c}{d} = \frac{a}{b} + \frac{-c}{d} = \frac{a \times d + b \times (-c)}{b \times d} = \frac{a \times d - b \times c}{b \times d}$$

If a/b and c/d are any two rational numbers

$$\frac{a}{b} - \frac{c}{d} = \frac{a \times d - b \times c}{b \times d}$$

This is consistent with the usual rule for subtraction of fractions. To find $\frac{5}{8} - \frac{1}{3}$ first change to a common denominator

$$\frac{5}{8} - \frac{1}{3} = \frac{15}{24} - \frac{8}{24}$$

then write the difference of the numerators over the common denominator.

$$\frac{15}{24} - \frac{8}{24} = \frac{7}{24}$$

The above rule requires essentially the same thing

$$\frac{5}{8} - \frac{1}{3} = \frac{5 \times 3 - 8 \times 1}{8 \times 3} = \frac{7}{24}$$

Every rational number a/b other than zero has a multiplication inverse b/a since

$$\frac{a}{b} \times \frac{b}{a} = \frac{a \times b}{b \times a}$$

But

$$\frac{a \times b}{b \times a} = \frac{a \times b}{a \times b}$$

is equivalent to the multiplication identity $1/1$.

Since division is the inverse of multiplication, division by the rational number c/d should give the same result as multiplication by the multiplication inverse d/c.

$$\frac{a}{b} \div \frac{c}{d} = \frac{a}{b} \times \frac{d}{c} = \frac{a \times d}{b \times c}$$

If a/b and c/d are rational numbers and $c/d \neq 0$

$$\frac{a}{b} \div \frac{c}{d} = \frac{a \times d}{b \times c}$$

Every rational number c/d other than zero has a multiplication inverse d/c. The definition of rational numbers excludes zero. The inverse of $0/a$ would be $a/0$, but since a rational number is an implied division this would mean division by zero.

The rule for division is consistent with the interpretation of a rational number as an implied division.

$$\frac{18}{3} \div \frac{4}{2} = (18 \div 3) \div (4 \div 2) = 6 \div 2 = 3$$

and by the rule for division

$$\frac{18}{3} \div \frac{4}{2} = \frac{18}{3} \times \frac{2}{4} = \frac{36}{12} = 3$$

In the general case, the rule can be established by using the division principle which permits multiplying both dividend and divisor by the same number without changing the quotient.

$$\frac{a}{b} \div \frac{c}{d} = \frac{a}{b} \times \frac{d}{c} \div \frac{c}{d} \times \frac{d}{c}$$

$$\frac{a}{b} \div \frac{c}{d} = \frac{a}{b} \times \frac{d}{c} \div 1$$

$$\frac{a}{b} \div \frac{c}{d} = \frac{a}{b} \times \frac{d}{c}$$

Exercises

1 Prove that the rational numbers are closed with respect to subtraction.

2 Prove the nonzero rational numbers are closed with respect to division.

3 Verify that subtraction of rational numbers is not commutative by evaluating the following pairs of expressions.

(a) $\frac{3}{5} - \frac{1}{2}$; $\frac{1}{2} - \frac{3}{5}$
(b) $(\frac{1}{4} + \frac{2}{3}) - \frac{5}{6}$; $\frac{5}{6} - (\frac{1}{4} + \frac{2}{3})$
(c) $a/b - 1/c$; $1/c - a/b$

4 Verify that subtraction of rational numbers is not associative by evaluating the following pairs of expressions.

(a) $\frac{1}{4} - (\frac{2}{3} - \frac{1}{6})$; $(\frac{1}{4} - \frac{2}{3}) - \frac{1}{6}$
(b) $2/a - (3/b - 1/(a \times b))$; $(2/a - 3/b) - 1/(a \times b)$
(c) $\frac{1}{5} - (-\frac{2}{3} - \frac{1}{4})$; $(\frac{1}{5} - -\frac{2}{3}) - \frac{1}{4}$

5 Verify that division of rational numbers is not commutative by evaluating the following pairs of expressions.

(a) $\frac{2}{5} \div \frac{3}{7}$; $\frac{3}{7} \div \frac{2}{5}$
(b) $1/a \div 1/b$; $1/b \div 1/a$
(c) $-\frac{2}{3} \div \frac{1}{6}$; $\frac{1}{6} \div -\frac{2}{3}$

6 Verify that division of rational numbers is not associative by evaluating the following pairs of expressions.

(a) $(\frac{2}{3} \div \frac{1}{5}) \div \frac{3}{4}$; $\frac{2}{3} \div (\frac{1}{5} \div \frac{3}{4})$
(b) $(a/1 \div 1/b) \div a/b$; $a/1 \div (1/b \div a/b)$
(c) $(-\frac{5}{6} \div 2/-3) \div \frac{1}{2}$; $-\frac{5}{6} \div (2/-3 \div \frac{1}{2})$

7 Evaluate each of the following pairs of expressions.

(a) $\frac{2}{5} \div \frac{3}{4}$; $(\frac{2}{5} \div \frac{1}{3}) \div (\frac{3}{4} \div \frac{1}{3})$
(b) $\frac{1}{7} \div \frac{2}{9}$; $(\frac{1}{7} \times \frac{9}{2}) \div (\frac{2}{9} \times \frac{9}{2})$
(c) $\frac{3}{8} \div \frac{2}{5}$; $(\frac{3}{8} \times \frac{5}{2}) \div (\frac{2}{5} \times \frac{5}{2})$

What generalization does this suggest?

8 The following are written in base eight. Compute in base eight.

(a) $\frac{2}{5} + \frac{2}{11}$
(b) $\frac{5}{14} \times \frac{1}{10}$
(c) $\frac{11}{12} \div \frac{3}{24}$
(d) $\frac{5}{11} - \frac{2}{3}$

9 Convert each of the parts of Exercise 8 to base ten and evaluate. Convert the answers obtained in Exercise 8 to base ten and compare with the answers obtained here.

10 Are there any integers a and b for which $1/a + 1/b = 1/(a + b)$? If so, what are they?

11 Find the addition inverse and the multiplication inverse of each of the following.

(a) $-\frac{3}{4}$ (b) $- -\frac{3}{5}$ (c) $\frac{2}{5}$ (d) $a/2b$ (e) $-b/2a$

12 Is there a rational number whose addition inverse is its multiplication inverse? If so what is it, if not why not?

8.7 COMPARING RATIONAL NUMBERS

In Section 8.2 we saw that "fraction" has to do with the form of a number. A fraction has a numerator and denominator and is an implied division, numerator divided by denominator. If the numerator and denominator are both integers the fraction is a *simple fraction*. If numerator or denominator, or both, are themselves fractions it is a *complex fraction*. If the numerator is smaller than the denominator the fraction is called a *proper fraction*. If the numerator is equal to or greater than the denominator the fraction is an *improper fraction*.

EXAMPLES. $\frac{2}{3}, \frac{7}{4}, \frac{5}{5}$ are simple fractions, but not all of them are proper fractions.

$\frac{\frac{1}{2}}{\frac{2}{5}}, \frac{1}{\frac{4}{7}}, \frac{\frac{3}{8}}{5}$ are complex fractions, but not all of them are improper fractions.

$\frac{3}{4}, \frac{\frac{1}{2}}{5}, \frac{2}{7}$ are proper fractions, but not all of them are simple fractions.

$\frac{5}{5}, \frac{\frac{1}{2}}{\frac{2}{5}}, \frac{3}{\frac{3}{4}}$ are improper fractions, but not all of them are complex.

An improper fraction may always be reduced to an integer or a *mixed number* by carrying out the implied division.

EXAMPLES. $\frac{28}{7} = 4$ because $28 \div 7 = 4$

$\frac{30}{7} = 4\frac{2}{7}$ because $30 = 4 \times 7 + 2$

A mixed number, such as $4\frac{2}{7}$, is actually an integer plus a proper fraction; $4\frac{2}{7}$ means $4 + \frac{2}{7}$.

What is the relationship between rational numbers and fractions? Every rational number can be expressed as a simple fraction, either proper or improper. If a complex fraction has numerator and denominator which are obtained by adding, subtracting, and multiplying simple fractions then it may be considered a fraction with simple fractions as numerator and denominator. This is because rational numbers are closed with respect to addition, subtraction, and multiplication. Since such a complex fraction is an implied division it also represents a rational number if the denominator is not zero. We know this because, except for division by zero, the rational numbers are also closed with respect to division. Hence, with this one exception of division by zero, any fraction consisting exclusively of integers, added, subtracted, multiplied, and divided, represents a rational number.

All rational numbers can be represented on the number line. If the rational number is a proper fraction it is represented on the number line as a point between 0 and 1. If it is an improper fraction, expressed as a mixed number as a plus a proper fraction, the point on the number line is found between a and $a + 1$ just as the same proper fraction is found between 0 and 1.

EXAMPLE. Find on the number line points corresponding to $\frac{2}{5}$ and $\frac{23}{7}$.

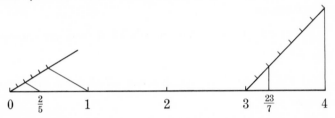

Any convenient line is drawn through the point 0. On this line 5 equal segments are marked off. Join the end of the fifth segment and the point 1. At the end of the second segment draw a parallel to this line. The parallel will cut the number line at the required point $\frac{2}{5}$.

To find $\frac{23}{7}$ change to the corresponding mixed number $3\frac{2}{7}$. We now proceed as before except that we begin at the point 3 and use 7 equal segments rather than 5.

The generality of the method used in the example is evident. To locate the point on the number line corresponding to the proper fraction a/b we lay off b equal segments and draw the parallel at the end of the ath segment.

The integer a is greater than the integer b if a is represented on the number line to the right of b. The symbol $>$ is read "greater than." Thus, $5 > 3, 12 > 1, 2 > 0$. However, any positive number is greater than any negative number, $10 > -10, 5 > -1, 1 > -100$.

The same criterion can be used to determine which of two rational numbers is the greater. However, we can determine this without the aid of the number line, assuming we know which of any two integers is the greater. If the denominators of both numbers are equal and positive, the one with the greater numerator is the greater. We can assure that the denominators are positive by multiplying both numerator and denominator by the denominator.

EXAMPLE. $\dfrac{5}{-3} = \dfrac{5 \times -3}{-3 \times -3} = \dfrac{-15}{9}$

$\dfrac{a}{b} = \dfrac{a \times b}{b \times b}$ and the denominator $b \times b$ is positive whether b is positive or negative.

We wish to compare the two rational numbers a/b and c/d.

$$\frac{a}{b} = \frac{a \times b}{b \times b} \quad \text{and} \quad \frac{c}{d} = \frac{c \times d}{d \times d}$$

Both denominators are now positive. Next, find a common denominator

$$\frac{a \times b}{b \times b} = \frac{a \times b \times d \times d}{b \times b \times d \times d} \quad \text{and} \quad \frac{c \times d}{d \times d} = \frac{c \times d \times b \times b}{d \times d \times b \times b}$$

Now the fraction with the greater numerator is the greater. Hence

$$a/b > c/d \quad \text{if and only if} \quad a \times b \times d \times d > c \times d \times b \times b$$

EXAMPLE.   Determine which is the greater $-5/6$ or $-2/-7$

$$-5 \times 6 \times -7 \times -7 = -1470$$
$$-2 \times -7 \times 6 \times 6 = 504$$

Since $504 > -1470$ it follows that $-2/-7 > -5/6$

Exercises

1   Classify each of the following as simple or complex and as proper or improper.

(a) $\frac{7}{6}$ (b) $\dfrac{\frac{1}{2}}{5}$ (c) $\dfrac{2}{\frac{2}{3}}$ (d) $\frac{4}{9}$

2   Express each of the following as a simple fraction.

(a) $\dfrac{\frac{1}{2} + \frac{1}{3}}{\frac{1}{4}}$ (b) $\dfrac{\frac{2}{5} \times \frac{3}{4}}{\frac{1}{2} - \frac{2}{3}}$

3   Find on the number line.

(a) $-3/-5$ (b) $\frac{32}{6}$ (c) $-\frac{3}{4}$ (d) $-\frac{25}{6}$

4   Prove that if a, b, c, and d are positive

$$a/b > c/d \quad \text{if and only if} \quad a \times d > b \times c$$

5   Prove that if two positive fractions have the same positive numerator the one with the smaller denominator is the greater. That is, $a/b > a/d$ if and only if $d > b$.

6 Arrange the following from smallest to largest

$$\frac{2}{3}, \frac{20}{31}, \frac{21}{30}, \frac{21}{31}, \frac{3}{5}, \frac{5}{7}.$$

7 Find a rational number between $\frac{3}{7}$ and $\frac{2}{5}$, that is, larger than the smaller of the two and smaller than the larger of the two.

8 Evaluate the following, all numbers written in base eight:

(a) $\frac{1}{2} + \frac{10}{12}$ (c) $\frac{11}{3} \times \frac{30}{22}$

(b) $\frac{2}{3} \times [\frac{1}{2} - \frac{2}{5}]$ (d) $\frac{1}{5} \div \frac{16}{12}$

Suggested Supplementary Readings

Banks, J. Houston, *Elements of Mathematics* Second Edition. Boston: Allyn and Bacon, Inc., 1961. Chap. V.

Cooley, Hollis R., David Gans, Morris Kline, and Howard E. Wahlat, *Introduction to Mathematics*. Boston: Houghton Mifflin Co., 1949. Pp. 20–34.

Jones, Burton W., *Elementary Concepts of Mathematics*. New York: The Macmillan Company, 1947. Chap. III.

Richardson, Moses, *Fundamentals of Mathematics*. New York: The Macmillan Company, 1941. Pp. 88–100.

The Teaching
of Fractions

THE NAME "FRACTION" IS INDICATIVE of the cultural struggle which preceded its invention. *Fraction* is derived from *fractio*, a breaking. Fractions were first considered "broken numbers," a fraction thought of as a piece of a number.

Many mathematical advances, in fact most of them, have come about as the result of intellectual curiosity. Most of the extensions of number are the result of the mathematician's desire for completeness. An awareness of their practical value was not the motivation for their creation. This is however not true in the case of fractions. A need for them greatly antedates their creation.

The reason for this state of affairs is not too difficult to imagine. Man's need for counting numbers, both cardinal and ordinal, stemmed from a need to keep track of his possessions. As need for division arose, measurement division and partitioning, the inadequacy of the whole numbers became apparent. The division was not always exact. School practice relative to the development of number parallels its historical development rather than the logical development we have followed in constructing the rational numbers. Man's need for fractions antedates his need for negative numbers. In fact, various devices were used to avoid the general fraction, its consideration as *a number*. By contrast, negative numbers were invented a long time before their practical utility was discovered.

9.1 EARLY USE OF FRACTIONS

Attempts to avoid general fractions have taken three forms. The one which seems most odd to us is the Egyptian usage. The Egyptians seem to have been able to conceive of the reciprocal of a whole number, as $\frac{1}{4}$ or $\frac{1}{7}$, but not multiples of the reciprocals, as $\frac{3}{4}$ or $\frac{5}{7}$. This usage is known as the use of *unit fractions*, because *one* was the only numerator they used. There was one exception to this rule: they used the fraction $\frac{2}{3}$. Any fraction can be expressed as the sum of unit fractions. For example, $\frac{37}{63} = \frac{1}{3} + \frac{1}{7} + \frac{1}{9}$. The Egyptians apparently knew how to express any desired fractional part in this way, and thus avoided general fractions.

The most obvious unit fractions to use to express $\frac{2}{7}$ are $\frac{1}{7}$ and $\frac{1}{7}$. For some strange reason the Egyptians did not consider this appropriate. No repetitions were used. Instead of $\frac{1}{7} + \frac{1}{7}$ such unit fractions as $\frac{1}{4} + \frac{1}{28}$ were used to express $\frac{2}{7}$.

The Babylonians used a scheme which is the equivalent of our own decimal fractions. They would use any whole number for numerator but denominators were restricted to powers of 60. When you recall that the base of their number system was 60 it becomes evident that the same principle is involved as when we write a fraction decimally. When we express $\dfrac{7}{400} = .0175$ we actually have $\dfrac{7}{400} = \dfrac{1}{10^2} + \dfrac{7}{10^3} + \dfrac{5}{10^4}$. Substituting our own notation, the Babylonians would write the same number as $\dfrac{1}{60} + \dfrac{3}{60^2}$. One might conclude that this showed a great deal of insight on their part. We use decimal fractions, not to avoid the concept of a general fraction, but for convenience of notation and computation. Although their number system was positional, with 60 as base, it did not lend itself to computational algorithms. Their motive for this kind of fraction seems to have stemmed from inability to conceive of a fraction as *a number*. We realize that .0175 is a single number, which is equivalent to the sum, $\frac{1}{10^2} + \frac{7}{10^3} + \frac{5}{10^4}$. The Babylonians thought of $\frac{1}{60} + \frac{3}{60^2}$ as two numbers added together.

Since the need for fractions arose from problems requiring division, units of measure were involved. The Romans were noted for a third means of avoiding fractions, the creation of new units of measure. If the result of a measurement is $2\frac{3}{4}$ bushels we can avoid the fraction by creating a smaller unit, we can express the result as 2 bushels 3 pecks. The frequent occurrence of 12 in our system of weights and measures—12 inches per foot, 12 ounces per troy pound, 12 units per dozen, have their origins in Roman practice.

9.2 EXTENDING THE NUMBER CONCEPT TO FRACTIONS

Although formal work with fractions is deferred until the middle grades, development of the fraction concept should begin much earlier. Children constantly hear references to halves and fourths or quarters: half an hour, quarter of an hour, half-time score, third-quarter score, half dollar, quarter mile, half-horsepower motor, and so on.

The young child's idea of half is vague and unprecise. "His half is bigger than mine" is an often-heard complaint which indicates that half means a piece or, at best, one of two pieces. Throughout the development of the meaning of fractions the division concept should be uppermost. "One half of" should be synonymous with "divided by two." From the standpoint of partitive division this means separating a set into two *equal* parts. The set may be a set of one. Thus the child should come to the understanding of "half" or "one half" as one of the two equal parts into which a unit or a collection of units may be separated. Extensions of this basic concept include these notions: there are two halves in a whole (unit or group); halves of the same thing are the same size; a half taken from a whole leaves a half; two halves and two halves make two wholes; three halves is a whole and a half. From the standpoint of measurement division, $\frac{1}{2}$ means one out of every two. Thus $12 \div 2 = 6$, interpreted as a partition, means 12 is separated into 2 equal parts, 6 to the part. Then $\frac{1}{2}$ of 12 means one of the two equal parts into which 12 is divided. But $12 \div 2 = 6$, interpreted as measurement, means there are six 2s in 12. Then $\frac{1}{2}$ of 12 ("of" connotes partition) means there are as many ones in six as there are twos in twelve.

Spencer and Brydegaard[1] propose that we should use *dividend* and *divisor* respectively rather than numerator and denominator. There is merit to the proposal in that a fraction *is* a division, the numerator is the dividend and the denominator is the divisor. However, it is more than a division; it is a *number* designating quantity. *Numerator* (how many) and *denominator* (how large) are helpful terms for conveying the quantitative aspect of the *rational number*.

There are many opportunities in the primary grades for developing the concept of one half. The following are typical "one half" situations: Half the class is on each team for a game. Each child gets half a cookie. We have half a pint of milk for lunch. Fold the sheet of paper in half. Fill the aquarium half full of water. Tom and Jim each take half the clocks. Mary gave half her apple to Betty. We have half an hour for rest.

Before work on the fundamental operations with fractions is attempted children should have acquired well developed meanings for fractions such as $\frac{1}{2}, \frac{1}{3}, \frac{1}{4}, \frac{1}{5}, \frac{1}{6}, \frac{1}{8}, \frac{1}{10}, \frac{2}{3}, \frac{4}{5}, \frac{5}{8}$, and so on. These meanings should grow out of situations which require them. Children are not apt to learn what $\frac{5}{6}$ means if their only motive is to learn later to add and multiply such numbers. Many such situations can be utilized. The following are typical: fractions designating the content of packages; fractions in recipes; such fractional measures as a fourth of a mile, half a dozen, a third of a yard; fractions used in designating clothing sizes; fractional comparisons such as one third as long, three fourths as much; time measure, $9\frac{8}{10}$ seconds, $2\frac{1}{2}$ years, $\frac{1}{2}$ a month.

There are many meanings relative to the fraction concept which the child must learn. The name of the fraction (unit fraction), such as *half, third, fifth*, tells how many equal parts the whole is divided into. Half implies two equal parts, third, three equal parts, fifth, five equal

[1] Peter L. Spencer, and Marguerite Brydegaard, *Building Mathematical Concepts in the Elementary School* (New York: Henry Holt and Company, 1952), p. 216.

parts. The greater the number of equal parts the smaller the part, thus a sixth is less than a fifth but more than a seventh. Two thirds is the same as a third taken twice, three fourths is the same as a fourth taken three times. The *namer* of the fraction, telling the number of parts into which the whole is divided, is called the *denominator*. The *numberer* of these parts is called the *numerator*. The denominator is written below the line and the numerator above the line. The relative sizes of the simpler fractions should be learned. One half is less than two thirds, which is less than three fourths. One half is the same as three sixths and therefore less than four sixths, but more than two sixths. Fractions are used to designate the *size* of a quantity—half a pound, four and a half feet, three fourths of an hour, half pint. Fractions are used to indicate *division*; one third of a quantity is found by dividing by three, one fifth by dividing by five. Fractions are used to make *comparisons*. If Jim has three times as many marbles as Bill then Bill has one third as many as Jim.

Learning devices which aid in fixing the above ideas include circle cut-outs. They may be used quite well on flannel board. Circles of the same size cut into halves, thirds, fourths, and sixths should be available.

Counting materials, pint and quart containers, foot rules and yard sticks are other useful materials.

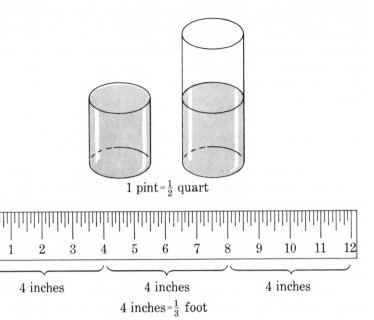

1 pint = $\frac{1}{2}$ quart

4 inches   4 inches   4 inches

4 inches = $\frac{1}{3}$ foot

9.3 EQUIVALENT FRACTIONS

Viewed from the standpoint of the mechanics of the operations, multiplication of fractions is much easier than addition. Many early writers advocated this order.[2] However, if we want the child to know *why* he proceeds as he does, not merely that he understands *how* to proceed, addition should come first.

This being the case, the child must learn to convert fractions to equivalent forms without the aid of multiplication. This should precede addition or at the latest be taught as soon as the addition of fractions with like denominators is studied. Attempts to add fractions with unlike denominators is excellent motivation for this. This is not to imply that the child need not ever visualize the reduction of fractions as multiplying (or dividing) by one.

In the study of division the principle should be developed which permits the multiplication (or division) of both dividend and divisor by the same number without changing the quotient. Then with the concept of a fraction as an indicated division we can proceed immediately to the reduction of a fraction by multiplying (or dividing) both numerator and denominator by the same number. However,

[2] D. E. Smith, *History of Mathematics* (Boston: Ginn and Company, 1925), Vol. II, p. 222.

there will be many children who cannot follow this abstraction. In such cases a return to the earlier concept building program is indicated. Equivalencies should be reviewed. The children should be helped to discover that as we increase the denominator the whole is divided into more equal parts and therefore each part must be smaller. If we

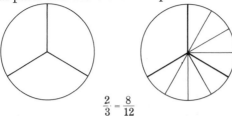

$$\frac{2}{3} = \frac{8}{12}$$

double the denominator the whole is divided into twice as many parts, hence each part is half as large. Multiply the denominator by three and there are three times as many parts to make a whole, so parts are one third as large. After the rule for making the reductions has been formulated, the children should be encouraged to diagram their reductions until the idea is well fixed.

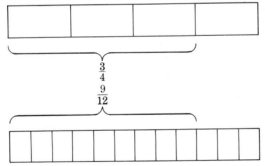

$$\frac{3}{4}$$
$$\frac{9}{12}$$

Although the term *reduction* is applied both to changing to higher terms and to lower terms the important point is for the child to realize that he is merely finding an equivalent fraction expressed in different form. Our motivation for changing the form is to get a common denominator in order to add. Here we are "reducing" up. The process may be reversed and we can reduce down to lowest terms. Why bother to do that? A child's work should not be labeled as incorrect when he has not reduced his answer to lowest terms unless that is specified as part of the problem. The question "How should the answer be left?" is often asked. The only correct answer is "That depends on how it is to be used." $\frac{1}{4} + \frac{1}{12}$ does equal $\frac{4}{12}$ and that may be a better way to leave the answer than $\frac{1}{3}$. Children should realize that we usually reduce to lowest terms as a matter of convenience. It is much easier to visualize $\frac{2}{3}$ than $\frac{34}{51}$.

When we are dealing with approximate numbers the indiscriminate reduction of fractions is not justified. We cannot change $\frac{4}{8}$ inch to $\frac{1}{2}$ inch unless we want to indicate a result correct to the nearest $\frac{1}{2}$ inch rather than the nearest $\frac{1}{8}$ inch. In this case we have rounded off the answer. We would never be justified in changing the approximate $\frac{1}{2}$ to $\frac{4}{8}$, for this would imply greater accuracy than that implied by the original $\frac{1}{2}$.

In no other phase of arithmetic is the tendency to "follow the rule" more prevalent than with fractions. The statement of the rule is often the point of departure in the study of a new topic. This should not be done, the formulation of the rule should be the culmination of investigation and discovery by the children. A rule thus obtained carries more meaning for the child than one which is first stated, then explained.

Fractions less than one are called *proper fractions*, such as $\frac{1}{5}$, $\frac{7}{8}$. Fractions greater than one are called *improper fractions*, such as $\frac{15}{2}$, $\frac{9}{8}$. This is an unfortunate choice of names. There is nothing wrong or inappropriate about an improper fraction. The same observations as those directed toward fractions not in lowest terms may be applied to improper fractions. It is not wrong to leave the answer to $\frac{3}{4} + \frac{5}{6}$ as $\frac{19}{12}$ unless specific instructions have been given to reduce all improper fractions to mixed numbers. A *mixed number* is merely an indicated sum of an integer plus a proper fraction. There is need for both changing a mixed number to an improper fraction and changing an improper fraction to a mixed number. There are situations where each form is the more convenient. The rule for changing a mixed number to a fraction, "The denominator times the whole number plus the numerator over the denominator," should not be taught as some mysterious procedure which gives the right answer. It should be thought of as a short cut to the longer, more meaningful procedure. It should not be used even as a short cut until and unless the child understands what the short cut actually accomplishes. When we convert $4\frac{2}{3}$ to a fraction we simply perform the indicated addition $4 + \frac{2}{3}$. This requires the common denominator 3; then we have $\frac{12}{3} + \frac{2}{3} = \frac{14}{3}$.

We may justify the inverse process as performing the indicated division. Since $\frac{14}{3}$ means $14 \div 3$, we divide to obtain the whole number 4 and remainder 2. But we can *indicate* the division of 2 by 3 as $\frac{2}{3}$. When we write the quotient as $4\frac{2}{3}$ we have completed the division. It is incorrect to refer to the fraction $\frac{2}{3}$ as the remainder, it is a part of the quotient.

We may approach the reduction of an improper fraction to a mixed number in a somewhat different manner. We know that $\frac{14}{3}$ is more than a whole or $\frac{3}{3}$. Then we wish to find how many groups of 3 thirds we can get from 14 thirds. This requires that we divide 14 by 3, giving 4 groups of 3 thirds. The remainder, 2, is the same kind of number as the dividend, 14, namely thirds. Then we get 4 wholes (sets of 3 thirds) and 2 thirds from 14 thirds.

Exercises

1 Why is the concept of a fraction as a "broken number" inadequate?

2 Express $\frac{3}{5}$ as the sum of unit fractions.

3 How would the Babylonians have expressed $\frac{3}{5}$?

4 What is the significance of the names "numerator" and "denominator"?

5 List and illustrate all interpretations which may on occasion be given to $\frac{3}{5}$.

6 Explain the difference between "a fraction is a part of a group" and "a fraction is a part of a whole."

7 Outline a procedure for developing the meaning of equivalent fractions.

8 What prerequisite skills and concepts are necessary before the finding of equivalent fractions can be viewed as multiplying (or dividing) by one?

9 Distinguish between the concept of a fraction as a number and the concept of a fraction as an implied division.

10 Can the meaning of a mixed number be developed before the child understands the addition of fractions? Discuss.

9.4 ADDITION OF FRACTIONS

Types of addition problems should be studied in the following sequence:

(1) Fractions and mixed numbers with like denominators.

(2) Fractions and mixed numbers whose denominators are factors of the largest denominator.

(3) Fractions and mixed numbers whose denominators are not factors of the largest denominator.

The class should be led to discover the rules for the operations and the best algorithms. The children will already have added fractions with like denominators. They know that two halves equal one whole, that a third and a third equal 2 thirds. It is when formal algorithms are adopted that the denominators are apt to cause trouble. In the addition of whole numbers we add ones to ones, tens to tens, and so on. We add *like* numbers. This idea can be carried over to fractions, but in common fraction form the *kind* of thing added is indicated by the denominator rather than the position of the digit. Four *eighths* plus 3 *eighths* equals 7 *eighths* just as 4 *apples* plus 3 *apples* equals 7 *apples*, 4 *tens* plus 3 *tens* equals 7 *tens*. Problems of this

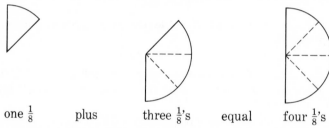

one $\frac{1}{8}$ plus   three $\frac{1}{8}$'s   equal   four $\frac{1}{8}$'s

sort should first be solved by employing diagrams or cut-outs. Then after some practice the class should be asked to state a rule for adding fractions with the same denominator. If the correct rule "add the numerators and write their sum over the denominator" is not forthcoming there is good evidence that the significance of the fraction notation is not understood. Since 2 tens plus 3 tens does not give 5 twenties we should not expect 2 eighths plus 3 eighths to give 5 sixteenths. The denominators, which tell what *kind* of things are added, should be the same in the sum as in each addend.

The vertical form

$$\begin{array}{r} \frac{1}{5} \\ +\frac{3}{5} \\ \hline \frac{4}{5} \end{array}$$

has the advantage of similarity to vertical addition of integers. It is certainly the more convenient form when adding mixed numbers. However, since numerators and denominators are all in a column, there is a greater tendency to add the denominators, or even add denominators to numerators, than is the case with the horizontal form $\frac{1}{5} + \frac{3}{5} = \frac{4}{5}$. In any event the child should ultimately feel at ease with either.

Problems involving mixed numbers with like fractions should be approached in a manner similar to the above. The class should first solve the problem pictorially. A typical solution to $4\frac{1}{3} + 2\frac{1}{3}$ follows.

We combine the wholes and combine the parts. Another approach might be $4\frac{1}{3} + 1 = 5\frac{1}{3}$, $5\frac{1}{3} + 1 = 6\frac{1}{3}$, $6\frac{1}{3} + \frac{1}{3} = 6\frac{2}{3}$. Although the latter is correct, class discussion should lead to the observation that it is more convenient to add the whole numbers together and add the fractions together.

Two ideas should be stressed in adding mixed numbers. First, a mixed number is a sum, whole number plus fraction. Secondly, we can only combine like numbers. The similarity between $23 + 45$ and $2\frac{3}{9} + 4\frac{5}{9}$ should be stressed. In the first case the 2 and the 4 each stand for tens, and the 3 and 5 stand for ones. In the latter case the 2 and 4 stand for ones and the 3 and 5 each stand for ninths. Then, when confronted with a problem like $2\frac{5}{8} + 3\frac{7}{8}$ we have a perfect analogy to carrying when adding whole numbers. The correct sum is $5 + \frac{12}{8}$, but we do not leave an improper fraction in a mixed number. We can have no more than 7 in the eighths position. We carry 8 of the eighths to the ones position as a 1, giving the answer $6\frac{4}{8}$. It is worth noting in this connection that our system of notation makes it impossible to have more than 9 ones in the ones position, but it is merely a matter of good form which prevents the writing of $7\frac{1}{8}$ as $6\frac{9}{8}$.

Fractions with the same denominator are called *similar* or *like* fractions. Types (2) and (3) in the sequence suggested above are *dissimilar* or *unlike* fractions. Type (2) is suggested as a type merely as a preliminary to the more general situation in Type (3). Children should not be taught to solve problems by types. We merely suggest this sequence of steps to the most general case. For that matter, when the child has learned to add like fractions he has learned all he is going to about adding fractions, since they are the only kind that can be added. This point should be stressed. We add only like fractions. If the fractions to be added are not like we must first make them so.

Many children will have no difficulty with Type (2) problems such as $\frac{1}{2} + \frac{1}{4}$, $\frac{1}{6} + \frac{1}{3}$. They will be able to obtain the result orally: "1 half is 2 fourths, so 1 half and 1 fourth make 3 fourths." More difficult problems of this type can be solved by diagrams similar to the following:

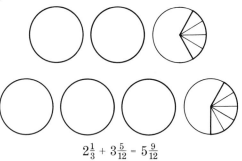

$$2\tfrac{1}{3} + 3\tfrac{5}{12} = 5\tfrac{9}{12}$$

A number of such problems should be solved by the various means available to the children. Then they should be led to the realization that they have actually changed the fractions to like fractions by expressing the one with the smaller denominator as an equivalent fraction with the larger denominator.

In Type (2) problems the form of only one fraction must be changed. We multiply its numerator and denominator by the quotient of the two denominators. When the class is confronted with the general case, one denominator not an integral multiple of the other, they may again resort to pictorial solutions. For example, we add $\tfrac{5}{6} + \tfrac{3}{8}$:

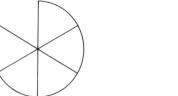

The sixths are subdivided into twelfths, smaller than the eighths. But we cannot divide the eighths into twelfths. If the sixths are divided into eighteenths we still cannot split the eighths so as to match them. Then we divide the sixths into twenty-fourths and the eighths can also be divided into twenty-fourths.

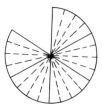

Then we have $\frac{5}{6} = \frac{20}{24}$ and $\frac{3}{8} = \frac{9}{24}$, so we may add $\frac{20}{24} + \frac{9}{24} = \frac{29}{24}$. Members of the class will doubtless attempt other divisions, sixths to twelfths to twenty-fourths and eighths to sixteenths to thirty-seconds, a process which will never yield a solution. Some may divide each sixth into 8 equal parts and each eighth into 6 equal parts. This will yield a solution, but not the simplest one.

The first point to be made from this experimental approach is the fact that the forms of both fractions must be changed. Secondly, the smaller denominator must be changed so that it becomes a multiple of the larger.

We then can extend the procedure which was adopted for Type (2) fractions. Divide the smaller denominator into the larger. If it does not go an even number of times, divide into twice the larger. If it still does not go an even number of times divide into three times the larger. Continue until we find a multiple of the larger which does divide evenly. Then we change the fraction with the smaller denominator into an equivalent one by multiplying numerator and denominator by the quotient we obtained. We change the other fraction by multiplying numerator and denominator by the required multiplier of the larger. The numerical solution to $\frac{5}{6} + \frac{3}{8}$ would be as follows:

Since $8 \div 6$ is not an integer we try $2 \times 8 \div 6$. Since $2 \times 8 \div 6$ is not an integer we try $3 \times 8 \div 6$. $3 \times 8 \div 6 = 4$. Then

$$\frac{5}{6} = \frac{4 \times 5}{4 \times 6} = \frac{20}{24} \quad \text{and} \quad \frac{3}{8} = \frac{3 \times 3}{3 \times 8} = \frac{9}{24}.$$

Hence,
$$\frac{5}{6} + \frac{3}{8} = \frac{20}{24} + \frac{9}{24} = \frac{29}{24}.$$

The procedure indicated above is recommended as the method to be taught for finding the least common denominator. However, children should be encouraged to devise their own short cuts, to take advantage of their knowledge of the factors of the denominators. For example, since 6 is 2×3 and 8 is 2×4 we have a common denominator in $2 \times 3 \times 4$.

When a common denominator other than the lowest is found the child should not be made to feel that his is wrong. He simply has taken the long way home. It is much better to use a more awkward though *understood* and mathematically correct method than to blindly follow the rule for the most direct solution.

The algorithm

$$\frac{5}{6} + \frac{3}{8} = \frac{20 + 9}{24} = \frac{29}{24}$$

should not be used if it is based on an arbitrary rule requiring "6 into 24 goes 4 times, $4 \times 5 = 20$, 8 into 24 goes 3 times, $3 \times 3 = 9$." Such short cuts should be used only if they rest on a foundation of clear understanding of what really takes place. A much better form, one which emphasizes the fact that we change the fractions to like fractions then add, is

$$\frac{5}{6} + \frac{3}{8} = \frac{4 \times 5}{4 \times 6} + \frac{3 \times 3}{3 \times 8} = \frac{20}{24} + \frac{9}{24} = \frac{29}{24}$$

The second step should not be eliminated too quickly.

9.5 SUBTRACTION OF FRACTIONS

Although some texts do not follow the plan, subtraction may well be taught along with addition. The concepts and techniques involved are so similar there seems to be no particular reason for separating them. We can subtract only like numbers. The problem of finding the lowest common denominator is exactly the same.

That method of subtraction of whole numbers which is taught should of course be used when subtracting fractions. The subtraction of mixed numbers offers about the only new difficulty which is not encountered in addition. When the fractional part of the subtrahend exceeds that of the minuend a situation comparable to borrowing in the subtraction of whole numbers is present. For example:

$$\begin{array}{r} 14\frac{1}{3} \\ -7\frac{5}{6} \end{array}$$

If the take-away–decomposition method is used, the solution consists of changing $14\frac{1}{3} = 14\frac{2}{6}$ to $13\frac{8}{6}$. Then we subtract in the usual way

$$\begin{array}{r} 14\frac{1}{3} = 13\frac{8}{6} \\ 7\frac{5}{6} = 7\frac{5}{6} \\ \hline 6\frac{3}{6} \end{array}$$

One frequently sees the algorithm written

$$14\frac{1}{3} = \frac{8}{6}$$
$$\underline{-7\frac{5}{6} = \frac{5}{6}}$$
$$6\frac{3}{6}$$

This is an example of a habit which should not be permitted. Children should be taught to respect the equality mark for what it is. If we add $5 + 6 + 8$ in horizontal form the child should not be allowed to write $5 + 6 = 11 + 8 = 19$. The equality mark should never be used unless the quantities on each side are equivalent. Although it is longer we should insist on the form $5 + 6 = 11$, $11 + 8 = 19$.

If the class has learned to subtract by the take-away–equal additions method, the correct procedure follows:

$$14\frac{1}{3} - - - - 14\frac{4}{3} = \;\;14\frac{8}{6}$$
$$\underline{-7\frac{5}{6} - - - - \;\;8\frac{5}{6} = -8\frac{5}{6}}$$
$$6\frac{3}{6}$$

Note that we have *not* said $14\frac{1}{3} = 14\frac{4}{3}$. We have written a second total problem which is equivalent to the first.

Exercises

1 Which of the following is illustrative of the type of problem that should be introduced first in teaching the addition of fractions?

(a) $5\frac{3}{4} + 1\frac{7}{8}$ (b) $\frac{1}{4} + \frac{1}{4}$
(c) $2\frac{1}{2} + 4$ (d) $\frac{1}{3} + \frac{3}{4}$

2 How would you explain to a child that he is wrong if he adds fractions thus: $\frac{3}{4} + \frac{5}{6} = \frac{8}{10}$

3 List advantages and disadvantages of teaching multiplication of fractions before addition.

4 In what respect must the meaning of addition be extended when we learn the meaning of addition of fractions?

5 Outline a program for teaching how to obtain the common denominator in adding unlike fractions.

6 Why is it necessary to reduce fractions to a common denominator in order to add them?

7 In adding $\frac{5}{6} + \frac{7}{9}$ if the child uses 36 for common denominator has he made a mistake? What would your attitude be toward a situation like this?

8 What added problem in "carrying" and "borrowing" is present in adding and subtracting mixed numbers?

9 Is the child wrong if he obtains the following answers? Discuss.

(a) $\frac{7}{8} + \frac{3}{4} = \frac{13}{8}$ (b) $\frac{1}{6} + \frac{1}{2} = \frac{8}{12}$ (c) $2\frac{2}{3} + 4\frac{1}{2} = 6\frac{7}{6}$

9.6 MULTIPLICATION OF FRACTIONS

If the multiplication of fractions is to be mastered in a meaningful way a far greater task is presented than that presented by addition and subtraction. The concept of multiplication must be extended. The earlier concept as applied to whole numbers is inadequate. In addition and subtraction the notion of a fraction as a part of a unit is adequate. This is not true of all cases of multiplication. Although the terminology of Chapter Eight is not advocated for elementary school children the ideas of a fraction as an implied division of two integers and of the fraction being the multiplication inverse of its reciprocal are highly desirable. That is not to say we should expect fourth-grade pupils to grasp such ideas immediately. However, they are objectives toward which we should strive.

Multiplication problems involving fractions may be classified as follows:

(1) A proper fraction times a proper fraction, as $\frac{3}{4} \times \frac{2}{9}$

(2) An integer times a proper fraction, as $4 \times \frac{2}{5}$

(3) A proper fraction times an integer, as $\frac{3}{4} \times 6$

(4) A mixed number or improper fraction times an integer, as $2\frac{3}{4} \times 6$

(5) An integer times an improper fraction or mixed number, as $5 \times 1\frac{5}{8}$

(6) A mixed number or improper fraction times a proper fraction, as $4\frac{1}{3} \times \frac{1}{5}$

(7) A proper fraction times a mixed number or improper fraction, as $\frac{1}{3} \times 2\frac{2}{3}$

(8) A mixed number or improper fraction times a mixed number or improper fraction, as $2\frac{2}{3} \times 1\frac{3}{4}$

We can see at once that (2) and (3), (4) and (5), and (6) and (7) are applications of commutativity. The child can convince himself of the appropriateness of commutativity as applied to whole numbers. Although this and the other properties of whole numbers apply also to fractions, the fact is not so obvious. We cannot verify commutativity by showing $4 \times \frac{2}{5} = \frac{2}{5} + \frac{2}{5} + \frac{2}{5} + \frac{2}{5}$ is equivalent to $\frac{2}{5} \times 4$ since we cannot take 4 as an addend $\frac{2}{5}$ times.

If our objective were the mechanical mastery of a rule, Type (1) should be the first kind of multiplication situation to consider. The rule is simple; furthermore, all of the other types can be converted to it when we consider an integer as a fraction with 1 as denominator. However, if this procedure is followed it should come as no surprise when the child is confused by the fact that the product is less than the multiplicand when we multiply $\frac{2}{3} \times 12$, or for that matter, the product is smaller than either factor when two proper fractions are multiplied. This is in direct contradiction with the previously learned idea that multiplication is an *increasing* operation.

We should begin with the type of problem which can be interpreted in the same way as the multiplication of whole numbers. This implies Type (2), an integer times a proper fraction. If the class is asked to find, any way they can, $4 \times \frac{2}{5}$, this is interpreted four $\frac{2}{5}$s added together. Either a pictorial solution such as

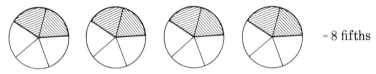

= 8 fifths

or a solution by addition

$$\tfrac{2}{5} + \tfrac{2}{5} = \tfrac{4}{5}, \tfrac{4}{5} + \tfrac{2}{5} = \tfrac{6}{5}, \tfrac{6}{5} + \tfrac{2}{5} = \tfrac{8}{5}$$

is the logical procedure for the child to follow. Or if the fraction is interpreted as it was in addition, the child may reason 4 × 2 fifths = 8 fifths, just as 4 × 2 apples = 8 apples. Problems should be included which yield reducible answers, as $15 \times \frac{5}{6}$ or $8 \times \frac{3}{4}$. After some experience with problems of this type the class should be led to formulate the rule: *When multiplying a fraction by a whole number multiply the whole number by the numerator and divide the result by the denominator.* In those cases where the answer is not reducible the latter part of the rule helps to emphasize that a fraction is an *implied* division.

The problem situations which lead to the multiplication of a fraction by a whole number suggest the above procedure. For example: It takes $\frac{3}{8}$ yards of material to make a paper hat. If 16 children are to be at the party how many yards of material are needed? This suggests 16 $\frac{3}{8}$s added together.

Multiplying a fraction by a whole number, as $\frac{3}{4} \times 6$, is illustrative of an entirely different kind of problem situation. For example: If Jack spent $\frac{3}{4}$ of his \$6 for a baseball glove, how much did the glove cost? This involves finding a part of a number, not $\frac{3}{4}$ taken 6 times.

The child may be willing to take for granted that $6 \times \frac{3}{4}$ and $\frac{3}{4} \times 6$ are equivalent, but he should not. There should be a reason for the acceptance of the equivalence of 6×3 and 3×6. We interpret the meaning of each, $3 + 3 + 3 + 3 + 3 + 3$, and $6 + 6 + 6$, and find the results to be identical. Similarly, there should be a justification for $6 \times \frac{3}{4} = \frac{3}{4} \times 6$ before it is accepted. Commutativity is not an immutable law of nature. It is only after we give an acceptable interpretation of the meaning of this kind of multiplication, under which we arrive at the same rule as before, that we may say the commutative property holds.

We must use the notion of a unit fraction as the multiplication inverse of an integer. Finding $\frac{1}{2}$ of a number is the same as dividing the number by 2. Finding $\frac{1}{4}$ of a number is the same as dividing by 4. Since $\frac{3}{4}$ of 6 is 3 times as large as $\frac{1}{4}$ of 6 we can find $\frac{3}{4}$ of 6 by dividing 6 by 4 and multiplying the result by 3. We are led to precisely the same rule as before: *We multiply the whole number by the numerator and divide by the denominator.* When the child is convinced that—although entirely different situations are involved—the numerical solution is identical, we can then generalize to the commutative property. The difference between the two situations, $6 \times \frac{3}{4}$ and $\frac{3}{4} \times 6$, can be shown pictorially:

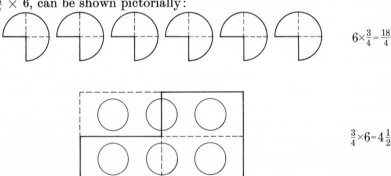

$$6 \times \frac{3}{4} = \frac{18}{4}$$

$$\frac{3}{4} \times 6 = 4\frac{1}{2}$$

There is almost universal agreement that the child should be taught that with a fractional multiplier "of" means "times." Rigid uncritical adherence to this word cue results in many mistakes. Children will infer that "of" is invariably a signal to multiply provided a pair of numbers are available. The reading of a problem becomes a search for "of." We may expect the answer 48 to the question: If 4 of the 12 boys went swimming how many stayed behind? We could more properly say that "of" means partitioning, division by the denominator. We say that $\frac{3}{4}$ of 6 means $\frac{3}{4} \times 6$ because it is the numerical equivalent of $6 \times \frac{3}{4}$. In the expression "three-fourths of 6" "of" is in reality a signal to *divide* by 4.

Still another approach may be used. Since $a \times b$ means $b + b + \ldots$ until b is used as an addend a times, we may think of $\frac{3}{4} \times 6$ as meaning 6 used as an addend less than one time, $\frac{3}{4}$ of a time. And here again we get the implication to divide by 4 and multiply by 3 since we want 3 of the 4 equal parts into which 6 is divided.

The rationale for the product of two fractions is the same. If we are to find $\frac{1}{2} \times \frac{1}{3}$ this means $\frac{1}{2}$ of $\frac{1}{3}$, or we are to find one of the two equal parts into which $\frac{1}{3}$ is divided. The pictorial solution appears as

$$\frac{1}{2} \times \frac{1}{3}$$

We cannot very well justify the multiplication of fractions in terms of division, $\frac{1}{3} \div 2$, since division is usually a later topic. However, as the pictorial solution suggests, we actually change the thirds to sixths. Our 1 third becomes 2 sixths. We wish to divide the 2 sixths by 2. Then the actual division is $2 \div 2$ or 2 sixths $\div 2 = 1$ sixth.

We may approach more complicated problems in the same manner. To find $\frac{2}{3} \times \frac{5}{8}$

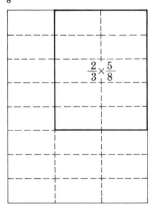

$$\frac{2}{3} \times \frac{5}{8}$$

we change $\frac{5}{8}$ to $\frac{15}{24}$ and take 2 out of 3, or 10 of them.

A number of such graphic solutions should lead to the generalization that if the multiplicand is changed to a fraction whose denominator is the product of the two original denominators we then divide by the denominator and multiply by the numerator of the multiplier. When it is observed that this rule requires that the numerator be both multiplied and divided by the same number the rule can be shortened to the usual rule for multiplication of two fractions: multiply the numerators for the numerator of the product and multiply the denominators for the denominator of the product. Under the longer rule we have

$$\frac{2}{3} \times \frac{5}{8} = \frac{2}{3} \times \frac{3 \times 5}{3 \times 8} = \frac{3 \times 5 \div 3 \times 2}{3 \times 8}$$

instead of the usual

$$\frac{2}{3} \times \frac{5}{8} = \frac{2 \times 5}{3 \times 8}$$

Once the rule for the product of two fractions is well established it should be generalized so as to include the first two cases. The idea of a fraction as an implied division is important here. We may say that 4 is the same as $\frac{4}{1}$ because $\frac{4}{1}$ means $4 \div 1 = 4$. Then if we express the whole number as a fraction the one rule—multiply numerators for the numerator of the answer and multiply denominators for the denominator of the answer—will suffice for all three cases:

$$6 \times \frac{3}{4} = \frac{6}{1} \times \frac{3}{4} = \frac{6 \times 3}{1 \times 4}$$

$$\frac{3}{4} \times 6 = \frac{3}{4} \times \frac{6}{1} = \frac{3 \times 6}{4 \times 1}$$

$$\frac{2}{3} \times \frac{5}{8} = \frac{2 \times 5}{3 \times 8}$$

If mixed numbers are first reduced to improper fractions they will offer no new difficulties. However, there are times when it is better to leave them as mixed numbers. In that case the distributive principle should be stressed. When we find $\frac{3}{4} \times 4\frac{1}{2}$ we are to find $(\frac{3}{4} \times 4) + (\frac{3}{4} \times \frac{1}{2})$.

If the problem requires the multiplication of mixed numbers it is usually much better to change them to improper fractions. We can of course use the distributive principle here, but it is much more difficult for the child. He will probably proceed by rule of thumb. When we multiply $2\frac{1}{2} \times 3\frac{1}{3}$ application of the distributive principle will give

$(2 + \frac{1}{2}) \times (3 + \frac{1}{3}) = (2 + \frac{1}{2}) \times 3 + (2 + \frac{1}{2}) \times \frac{1}{3} = 2 \times 3 + \frac{1}{2} \times 3 + 2 \times \frac{1}{3} + \frac{1}{2} \times \frac{1}{3}$. A much simpler approach is available through improper fractions:

$$2\frac{1}{2} \times 3\frac{1}{3} = \frac{5}{2} \times \frac{10}{3}$$

9.7 DIVISION OF FRACTIONS

Division of a fraction by an integer may be solved pictorially quite easily as partition division. For example: If two children share $\frac{3}{4}$ of an apple what part does each get? To find $\frac{3}{4} \div 2$, each of the

fourths is divided by 2, giving 3 eighths. To find $\frac{1}{4} \div 3$, the fourth is

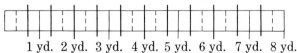

$\frac{1}{4} \div 3$

cut into 3 equal parts, one of which is $\frac{1}{12}$. From such examples the class will formulate the rule: *To divide a fraction by a whole number multiply the denominator by the whole number.* It should be apparent to the class that $\frac{3}{4} \div 2$ is equivalent to $\frac{1}{2} \times \frac{3}{4}$. This should cause no confusion if we have stressed from the outset that "$\frac{1}{2}$ of" means "divided by 2," "$\frac{1}{3}$ of" means "divided by 3," and so on.

Division of a whole number by a fraction is best visualized as measurement division. For example: How many ribbons $\frac{2}{3}$ yards long can be cut from 8 yards of ribbon? This can be solved by successive subtraction:

$8 - \frac{2}{3} = 7\frac{1}{3}, 7\frac{1}{3} - \frac{2}{3} = 6\frac{2}{3}, 6\frac{2}{3} - \frac{2}{3} = 6, 6 - \frac{2}{3} = 5\frac{1}{3},$
$5\frac{1}{3} - \frac{2}{3} = 4\frac{2}{3}, 4\frac{2}{3} - \frac{2}{3} = 4, 4 - \frac{2}{3} = 3\frac{1}{3}, 3\frac{1}{3} - \frac{2}{3} = 2\frac{2}{3},$
$2\frac{2}{3} - \frac{2}{3} = 2, 2 - \frac{2}{3} = 1\frac{1}{3}, 1\frac{1}{3} - \frac{2}{3} = \frac{2}{3}, \frac{2}{3} - \frac{2}{3} = 0.$ We succeed in subtracting $\frac{2}{3}$ from 8 twelve times.

The same problem may be solved pictorially:

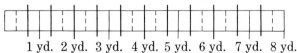

1 yd. 2 yd. 3 yd. 4 yd. 5 yd. 6 yd. 7 yd. 8 yd.

Here, we change the 8 yards to 24 $\frac{1}{3}$-yard strips. Then we are actually concerned with finding 24 thirds $\div$ 2 thirds $= 12$. This is the common-denominator method for division:

$$8 \div \tfrac{2}{3} = \tfrac{24}{3} \div \tfrac{2}{3} = 12$$

The two most commonly used methods for division of fractions are the common denominator method and the inversion method. By the common denominator method, the two fractions are reduced to a common denominator and the quotient is the quotient of the numerators.

$$a/b \div c/b = a \div c$$

$$\tfrac{2}{3} \div \tfrac{4}{7} = \tfrac{14}{21} \div \tfrac{12}{21} = \tfrac{14}{12}$$

By the inversion method, we invert the divisor and multiply.

$$a/b \div c/d = a/b \times d/c = ad/bc$$

$$\tfrac{2}{3} \div \tfrac{4}{7} = \tfrac{2}{3} \times \tfrac{7}{4} = \tfrac{14}{12}$$

It is advisable not to introduce the inversion method when dividing a whole number by a fraction. Although division of a fraction by a whole number as indicated at the first of this section is actually an inversion method it is a special case of inversion, the inversion of an integer. The children will not think of it as inversion, but as an application of the basic meaning of a fractional part. One fifth of a quantity is one of the five equal parts into which it can be divided. The common denominator method should be used to introduce the division of a fraction by a fraction. This method should receive considerable emphasis, both for its own sake and as a basis for rationalizing the inversion method. We can then generalize the result, showing that inversion of the divisor and then multiplying is equivalent to the process we have used with all cases.

Problems involving the division of a fraction by a fraction which are meaningful to children are not plentiful. However, the development of any new process should be the outgrowth of solution of problems. The following is an example of such a problem:

The label on the can of fruit juice states the contents to be $\tfrac{2}{5}$ gallons. How many 6-ounce servings are there per can if 6 ounces equal $\tfrac{3}{64}$ gallon? The problem requires that we find $\tfrac{2}{5} \div \tfrac{3}{64}$, that is, how many $\tfrac{3}{64}$ there are in $\tfrac{2}{5}$. Using the common-denominator method we get $\tfrac{2}{5} \div \tfrac{3}{64} = \tfrac{128}{320} \div \tfrac{15}{320} = 128 \div 15 = 8\tfrac{8}{15}$ servings.

The complete numerical representation of the solution is more apt to cause confusion than 128 *three-hundred twentieths* ÷ 15 *three-hundred twentieths*. When the denominator is written out we emphasize that we are dividing 128 things by 15 of the same things; the denominator tells us what the things are.

The common-denominator method, being measurement division, requires the dividend and divisor to be the same kind of concrete number while the quotient is an abstract number. For example, 15 feet ÷ 5 feet = 3, an abstract number—not feet. We should recall that the dividend and divisor must agree in measurement division but the dividend and quotient agree in partition division. In multiplication this dual interpretation is not possible. The multiplicand and product must agree. The multiplier is an abstract number. This idea is essential to understanding division of fractions by the common denominator method. Otherwise the child may reason "If $\frac{4}{8} \div \frac{2}{8} = 2$, why not $\frac{4}{8} \times \frac{2}{8} = 8$?"

On the other hand, we can make a correct analogy to multiplication of fractions. In multiplication of fractions we *multiply* numerators to find the numerator of the product and *multiply* the denominators to find the denominator of the product. When we divide by the common-denominator method we may properly say that we *divide* the numerators for the numerator of the quotient and *divide* the denominators for the denominator of the quotient:

$$\frac{4}{8} \times \frac{2}{8} = \frac{4 \times 2}{8 \times 8} = \frac{8}{64} \quad \text{and} \quad \frac{4}{8} \div \frac{2}{8} = \frac{4 \div 2}{8 \div 8} = \frac{2}{1} = 2$$

Since the denominators are the same their quotient will always be 1.

Another caution which the teacher should keep in mind when using the common-denominator method relates to the earlier use of common denominators. The child is familiar with the process. It is used in addition and subtraction of fractions. Unless underlying reasons for the processes are understood, children are apt to decide that whenever we use a common denominator it is also common to the answer:

Since $\frac{6}{5} + \frac{3}{5} = \frac{9}{5}$ why not $\frac{6}{5} \div \frac{3}{5} = \frac{2}{5}$?

The occurrence of this type of mistake, if not due to carelessness, indicates a need for reteaching *why* we add as we do in contrast to *why* we divide as we do.

The rule for division—Divide numerators for the quotient

numerator and divide denominators for the quotient denominator—
is not dependent upon the presence of common denominators:

$$\frac{8}{15} \div \frac{2}{5} = \frac{8 \div 2}{15 \div 5} = \frac{4}{3}$$

However, it is not advisable to present this as a general rule since it
leads to complex fractions unless both numerator and denominator
of the divisor are factors of the numerator and denominator respectively of the dividend:

$$\frac{3}{4} \div \frac{5}{9} = \frac{\frac{3}{5}}{\frac{4}{9}}$$

The common-denominator method is a "rule that always works,"
though it is sometimes inefficient. The ease with which it can be
rationalized justifies its emphasis as a working method rather than
merely an exploratory step toward the rule. However, the ultimate
objective should be the establishment of the inversion method as a
general rule for dividing fractions. It can be developed as an outgrowth of the common-denominator method.

Consider $\frac{3}{4} \div \frac{2}{5}$. When reduced to a common denominator we
have changed the problem to $\frac{15}{20} \div \frac{8}{20} = 15 \div 8 = \frac{15}{8}$. The numerator of the result, 15, is obtained by multiplying the numerator of the
dividend, 3, by the denominator of the divisor, 5. The denominator of
the result, 8, is obtained by multiplying the denominator of the
dividend, 4, by the numerator of the divisor, 2. Then in effect we have
multiplied $\frac{3}{4}$ by 5 and divided by 2, which is equivalent to multiplying
by $\frac{5}{2}$, the reciprocal of the divisor.

If we consider an integer as a fraction with denominator 1,
division of both a fraction by a whole number and a whole number by
a fraction may easily be included in the generalization of division by
multiplication by the inverse of the divisor.

If we write $\frac{3}{4} \div 2$ as $\frac{3}{4} \div \frac{2}{1}$, then apply inversion to get $\frac{3}{4} \times \frac{1}{2}$,
we will in effect be doing precisely as required by the former rule—to
divide a fraction by a whole number multiply the denominator by the
whole number.

When we divide a whole number by a fraction by the common-
denominator method this can be extended to the inversion concept in
the same manner as with division of a fraction by a fraction. When
we find $8 \div \frac{2}{3}$ by changing to $\frac{24}{3} \div \frac{2}{3} = 24 \div 2 = 12$ we have
actually multiplied the whole number 8 by 3 to get 24, then divided
by 2. But this is equivalent to multiplying by $\frac{3}{2}$, the reciprocal of the
divisor, $\frac{2}{3}$.

9.8 OTHER ASPECTS OF FRACTIONS

Although the four fundamental operations with fractions are given intensive treatment in the middle grades, fractions should continue to receive major attention in Grades 7 and 8. The basic ideas will need frequent reteaching. For the sake of those who merely need review more advanced applications should be used where possible. More emphasis should be given to mixed numbers and improper fractions.

Cancellation is a useful and efficient technique but it should not be taught until after the four fundamental operations are thoroughly understood. It should never be taught merely as a mechanical short cut which leads to the answer. It is best left untaught unless the child sees the justification for what he is doing. Cancellation should not be thought of as *a mathematical operation*. As the name implies, cancellation is the utilization of the fact that two operations nullify each other. When we find the product $\frac{9}{16} \times \frac{4}{3}$ by cancellation,

$$\frac{\overset{3}{\cancel{9}}}{\underset{4}{\cancel{16}}} \times \frac{\cancel{4}}{\cancel{3}} = \frac{3}{4},$$

we recognize that multiplying by 4 in the numerator and the use of the factor 4 in the denominator, which is equivalent to dividing by 4, nullify each other. Similarly for the factor 3 in numerator and denominator. When cancellation is first introduced it is well to write the terms of the fraction in factored form before canceling:

$$\frac{9}{16} \times \frac{4}{3} = \frac{3 \times \cancel{3} \times \cancel{4}}{4 \times \cancel{4} \times \cancel{3}} = \frac{3}{4}$$

Two points should be made clear: (1) Since we are concerned with multiplication, only *factors*, multipliers, are canceled. Even though

$$\frac{1\cancel{6}}{\cancel{6}4} = \frac{1}{4}$$

yields the correct answer this kind of cancellation is usually fatal. Nor can we cancel addends as

$$\frac{1 + \overset{2}{\cancel{4}}}{\cancel{3} \times 2} \times \frac{\cancel{3} + 5}{\cancel{2}}.$$

Neither can we cancel *factors* unless we are multiplying the fractions.

For example, $\frac{3}{4} + \frac{2}{3}$ does not equal $\frac{1}{2}$. (2) A multiplier in the denominator is equivalent to a divisor of the number. In the above example the canceled factors in the numerator and denominator signify that we have recognized that to multiply by 3×4 and to divide by 3×4 nullify each other. The idea that inverse operations with the same number leave us where we started is not restricted to cancellation in multiplying fractions. We employ cancellation when we recognize that to add and to subtract the same number nullify each other:

$$17 + 25 - 8 - 25 = 17 - 8 = 9$$

or that to multiply and to divide by the same number nullify each other

$$23\tfrac{1}{5} \times 36 \div 36 = 23\tfrac{1}{5}$$

or that to both square and extract the square root of a positive number nullify each other:

$$(\sqrt{16\tfrac{3}{4}})^2 = 16\tfrac{3}{4}$$

We may also rationalize the cancellation process from the standpoint of a fraction as an indicated division. We have learned one of the properties of the division process which permits the division of dividend and divisor by the same nonzero number without changing the quotient:

$$125 \div 25 = 5 \div 1$$

Then, when we think of the fraction as an indicated division, cancellation becomes *dividing* both dividend (numerator) and divisor (denominator) by the canceled factors.

Still another approach depends upon the notion of a number times its reciprocal being equal to 1. From this point of view

$\dfrac{9}{16} \times \dfrac{4}{3} = \dfrac{3}{4}$ may be considered

$$\frac{3 \times 3}{4 \times 4} \times \frac{4}{3} = \frac{(3 \times 3)}{(4 \times 4)} \times \frac{4}{3} = \frac{3}{4} \times \frac{(3 \times 4)}{(4 \times 3)} = \frac{3}{4} \times 1 = \frac{3}{4}$$

This notion may also be used to develop the rule for division of fractions by the inversion method. This approach can be used to advantage in the upper grades when review of the process is desired. Suppose we wish to divide $\frac{3}{8} \div \frac{2}{5}$. If both dividend and divisor are multiplied by the reciprocal of the divisor we get $\frac{3}{8} \div \frac{2}{5} = (\frac{3}{8} \times \frac{5}{2}) \div (\frac{2}{5} \times \frac{5}{2}) = \frac{3}{8} \times \frac{5}{2} \div 1 = \frac{3}{8} \times \frac{5}{2}$.

The concept of a fraction as a ratio has many applications. Batting averages and team standings illustrate the idea of a ratio as a fraction (written decimally). The batting average is the ratio of the number of hits to the times at bat. If it were written as a common fraction the number of hits would be the numerator and the times at bat the denominator. Team standings are given as the ratio of games won to games played. In baseball standings tie games are considered no contest. An interesting problem for upper-grade boys presents itself when a team is "no games behind" (won one more game and lost one more) and yet in second place.

When two quantities are compared in a "how many times as large" or "what part of" way the comparison is the ratio of the two quantities. The denominator of the ratio is the basis for the comparison. If brand A baseballs cost $1.25 and brand B cost $1.75, brand B costs how many times as much as A? Here the cost of brand A is the basis for comparison, we are to express B in terms of A. Then the denominator of the ratio is the cost of A. B costs $\dfrac{1.75}{1.25}$ times as much. The comparison can be made either way. The cost of A is what part of B? Here B is the basis for comparison, the ratio is $\dfrac{1.25}{1.75}$.

A problem involving two quantities and their ratio may require any one of the three numbers, given the other two:

(1) A baseball costs $1.50. A glove costs $6.00. The cost of the ball is what part of the cost of the glove? Or a glove costs how many times as much as a ball? Here the ratio is required.

(2) A baseball costs $1.50. A glove costs 4 times as much. What does a glove cost? Here the ratio and the basis for comparison are given. Since the ratio is the cost of the glove divided by the cost of the ball, the ratio times the cost of the ball (basis for comparison) gives the cost of the glove.

(3) A $6.00 glove costs 4 times as much as a baseball. What is the cost of the ball? The basis for comparison is now required. Since $6.00 is 4 times the basis for comparison the latter is $6.00 ÷ 4.

The same reasoning will apply even though the quantities compared and the ratio are all fractions.

(1) A $1\frac{3}{4}$-horsepower gasoline mower is how many times as powerful as a $\frac{3}{4}$-horsepower electric mower? Since $\frac{3}{4}$ is the basis for comparison it is the divisor. The ratio is $\frac{7}{4} \div \frac{3}{4} = \frac{7}{3}$.

(2) What is the horsepower of a gasoline mower if it is $\frac{7}{3}$ times as powerful as a $\frac{3}{4}$-horsepower electric mower? Since the ratio $\frac{7}{3}$ is the horsepower of the gasoline mower divided by $\frac{3}{4}$, the horsepower of the gasoline mower is $\frac{7}{3} \times \frac{3}{4} = \frac{7}{4}$.

(3) A $1\frac{3}{4}$-horsepower gasoline mower is $\frac{7}{3}$ times as powerful as an electric mower. Find the horsepower of the electric mower. Since $1\frac{3}{4}$ horsepower is $\frac{7}{3}$ times the power of the electric mower, the power of the electric mower is $1\frac{3}{4} \div \frac{7}{3} = \frac{7}{4} \div \frac{7}{3} = \frac{7}{4} \times \frac{3}{7} = \frac{3}{4}$.

Exercises

1 In teaching multiplication of fractions why is $3 \times \frac{1}{2}$ recommended for initial study rather than $\frac{1}{2} \times 3$?

2 In situations where a fraction has to be divided by a whole number, which type of division (measurement or partitioning) occurs more frequently?

3 What feature of the common denominator method of dividing fractions makes this method easy for children to master?

4 Devise drawings and accompanying explanations whereby you would make the following meaningful to pupils.
$\frac{7}{8}$ of a pie divided by $\frac{2}{5}$
$\frac{2}{3}$ of a square multiplied by $\frac{4}{5}$
$\frac{2}{10}$ of a line subtracted from $\frac{5}{8}$ of the line
$\frac{6}{8}$ of a rectangle added to $\frac{4}{5}$ of a rectangle

5 Which method of division of fractions do you think should be taught? Why?

6 When and how should cancellation be taught in connection with work in fractions?

7 What effect does it have on a fraction if
(a) The denominator is multiplied by 3?
(b) The numerator is divided by 5?
(c) The numerator is multiplied by zero?
(d) The denominator is multiplied by zero?
(e) The numerator is increased by 6?
(f) The denominator is increased by 1?
(g) The numerator is multiplied by 4?

8 Compare addition and multiplication of fractions from the standpoint of difficulty of mechanics and from the standpoint of interpretation of meaning.

9 Explain the common-denominator method for dividing fractions.

10 How would you answer a seventh-grade pupil who asked why, to divide by a fraction, we invert and multiply?

11 What is "cancellation" as applied to fractions? What are some cautions one should keep in mind in teaching this?

12 The following exercise is written in base-eight notation. Find the answer without converting to base ten:

(a) $\frac{1}{2} + \frac{3}{12}$

(b) $\frac{5}{6} \times \frac{14}{17}$

13 If we reduce $\frac{16}{64}$ by canceling 6s, $\frac{1\cancel{6}}{\cancel{6}4} = \frac{1}{4}$, we get the correct result. Find other fractions which have this property.

14 How would you explain to a fifth-grade pupil that the property illustrated in Exercise 13 is not general?

Suggested Supplementary Readings

Brueckner, Leo J., and Foster C. Grossnickle, *How to Make Arithmetic Meaningful*. Philadelphia: The John C. Winston Company, 1947. Pp. 294–348.

Buckingham, B. R., *Elementary Arithmetic: Its Meaning and Practice*. Boston: Ginn and Company, 1947. Chap. IX.

Clark, John R., and Laura K. Eads, *Guiding Arithmetic Learning*. Yonkers-on-Hudson, N.Y.: World Book Company, 1954. Chap. VI.

Spencer, Peter L., and Marguerite Brydegaard, *Building Mathematical Concepts in the Elementary School*. New York: Henry Holt and Company, 1952. Chap. VII.

Spitzer, Herbert F., *The Teaching of Arithmetic*, Third Edition. Boston: Houghton Mifflin Company, 1961. Chap. VII.

More About
Rational Numbers

CHAPTER TEN

A RATIONAL NUMBER IS AN IMPLIED division of two integers. Yet it is a *single* number. The number 27 is a single number in spite of the fact that three numbers are used to express it—2, 7, and by implication 10. The digits of a whole number indicate how many ones, tens, hundreds, and so on there are in the number. In like fashion, fractions consist of a given number of halves, thirds, or fourths, and so on. The basic difference between integers and fractions, insofar as notation is concerned, lies in the fact that the value of each digit of the integer depends upon its position but the value of each of the units expressed by the numerator of a fraction is explicitly stated by the denominator.

We know that in some cases a common fraction may be expressed exactly in the same manner as that of an integer, that is, as sums of powers of ten. For example $\frac{3}{4}$ (3 fourths) = .75 (7 tenths plus

5 hundredths). But in other cases we cannot get an exact equivalent. We know that $\frac{1}{3}$ is not exactly equal to .3 or .33 or .333 and so on for any number of 3s. However, we do know that the sequence .3, .33, .333, . . . continues to approach closer and closer to $\frac{1}{3}$. If it is agreed that the sequence of 3s is endless we can show the endless decimal does equal $\frac{1}{3}$.

10.1   REPEATING DECIMALS

The rational number $\frac{3}{4}$ is an endless decimal in the sense that .75 may be followed by an endless succession of zeros, .75000 . . . . [The three dots are used to indicate that the fraction continues endlessly.]

Since the rational number is an indicated division we may convert it to decimal form by carrying out the indicated division. If the division terminates, as in the case of $\frac{3}{4}$, then we agree that the terminating decimal is to be considered a repeating decimal with an endless sequence of zeros as its repeating cycle.

Not all rational numbers have a single digit as their repeating cycle:

$$\tfrac{1}{11} = .090909 \ldots$$

Here the two-digit cycle 09 repeats endlessly. Nor does the repeating cycle always begin with the decimal point:

$$\tfrac{1}{6} = .1666 \ldots$$

The cycle consists of the single digit 6 and begins at the second digit to the right of the decimal point.

A rational number, which incidentally may be greater than one, may have any finite number of digits preceding its repeating cycle. The cycle may begin before or after the decimal point:

$$42\tfrac{14}{33} = 42.42 \ldots$$

The repeating cycle is 42. But

$$42\tfrac{19}{45} = 42.422 \ldots$$

The cycle is in the single digit 2.

To show that every rational number, when expressed in decimal form, either repeats or terminates we first examine an example. To convert $\frac{3}{7}$ to decimal form we divide

$$
\begin{array}{r}
.428571 \\
7\,\overline{\smash{)}\,3.000000} \\
28 \\
\hline
\textcircled{2}0 \\
1\,4 \\
\hline
\textcircled{6}0 \\
5\,6 \\
\hline
\textcircled{4}0 \\
3\,5 \\
\hline
\textcircled{5}0 \\
4\,9 \\
\hline
\textcircled{1}0 \\
7 \\
\hline
\textcircled{3}
\end{array}
$$

For emphasis we have circled the remainders which were obtained each time a quotient digit times divisor product was subtracted. If a remainder zero were ever obtained after all nonzero digits of the quotient had been used this would mean the division terminates. And, under the earlier interpretation of repeating zeros, we then have a repeating decimal. In the above illustration it is possible to have only six different nonzero remainders, namely the numbers 1 through 6. Otherwise we have made a mistake. Since the divisor is 7, each remainder must be an integer less than 7. Then after not more than 6 steps have been completed we must be faced with some dividend figure for the second time. In this particular case the maximum number of steps was required. Every possible remainder appeared in the order 2, 6, 4, 5, 1, 3. Since the first step required $30 \div 7$ it is evident that the same sequence of remainders, and consequently the same sequence of digits in the quotient, will appear again and again endlessly:

$$\tfrac{3}{7} = .428571428571 \ldots$$

As we shall see presently, every repeating decimal is also a rational number. For example, .428571717171 . . . is also a rational number, the repeating cycle being the two-digit cycle 71. It is the rational number 212143/495000. The three dots after the number indicate that the number does not terminate, but we need a means of identifying what the sequence of digits is that is to repeat. This may be done by drawing a bar over the repeating cycle. Thus we write:

$$\tfrac{3}{7} = .\overline{428571} \ldots$$

$$\tfrac{1}{6} = .1\overline{6} \ldots$$

$$\tfrac{1}{5} = .2\overline{0} \ldots$$

$$\tfrac{1}{11} = .\overline{09} \ldots$$

We return to the proposition that every rational number when expressed decimally either terminates or repeats. If after the digits of the dividend have been used we obtain a remainder zero the decimal terminates. Otherwise, after a sequence of steps not more in number than one less than the divisor we must obtain some remainder for a second time. The digits of the quotient which were obtained between the first and second occurrence of this remainder will repeat endlessly.

EXAMPLE. Represent $\tfrac{61}{13}$ decimally. The digits of 61 will be used in the first step. We know that from that point on we can have not more than 12 different nonzero remainders. The repeating cycle *may have* as many as 12 digits.

$$
\begin{array}{r}
4.692307 \\
13 \,\overline{\big)\, 61.000000} \\
52 \\
\overline{} \\
\textcircled{9}0 \\
7\,8 \\
\overline{} \\
\textcircled{1}\textcircled{2}0 \\
1\,1\,7 \\
\overline{} \\
\textcircled{3}0 \\
2\,6 \\
\overline{} \\
\textcircled{4}0 \\
3\,9 \\
\overline{} \\
\textcircled{1}\textcircled{0}0 \\
9\,1 \\
\overline{} \\
\textcircled{9}
\end{array}
$$

The first remainder after the digits of 61 were used (subsequent dividends will then merely be the remainder with zeros attached) was 9. After six steps the remainder 9 reappeared. Then the digits of the quotient, 6, 9, 2, 3, 0, 7, will repeat because the remainders 9, 12, 3, 4, 1, 10 will also repeat:

$$\tfrac{61}{13} = 4.\overline{692307} \ldots$$

It does not follow that every repeating decimal is a rational number simply because every rational number is a repeating decimal. It is nonetheless true.

First let us consider the decimal whose repeating cycle is zero, in other words a terminating decimal. It is evident that this is a rational number since it is the ratio of the integer indicated by the digits to the power of ten indicated by their position. For example, $.175 = \frac{175}{1000}$. The fact that this can be reduced to lower terms has no bearing on its being a rational number. Sometimes the result cannot be reduced to lower terms. $.33$ does not equal $\frac{1}{3}$ but it does equal $\frac{33}{100}$, which cannot be reduced. We have said that $\frac{1}{3} = .3\overline{3}\ldots$. We discover this to be true by carrying through the division implied by $\frac{1}{3}$. Now let us show that $.3\overline{3}\ldots = \frac{1}{3}$. If we designate the number $.3\overline{3}\ldots$ as N we get

$$N = .3\overline{3}\ldots$$

and multiplying by 10

$$10N = 3.\overline{3}\ldots$$

Then, if we subtract the top equation from the bottom, we get

$$10N - N = 3.33\overline{3}\ldots - .33\overline{3}\ldots$$

or

$$9N = 3$$

$$N = \tfrac{3}{9} = \tfrac{1}{3}$$

It is evident that the repeating decimal $2.00\ldots$ is equal to the rational number $\frac{2}{1}$. Let us inquire what rational number $1.9\overline{9}\ldots$ equals.

$$\text{Let } N = 1.9\overline{9}\ldots$$

$$\text{then } 10N = 19.\overline{9}\ldots$$

$$\text{and } 10N - N = 19.9\overline{9}\ldots - 1.9\overline{9}\ldots$$

$$9N = 18$$

$$N = 2$$

Since they both equal 2 we may say

$$2.00\overline{0}\ldots = 1.99\overline{9}\ldots$$

(Of course, for any *finite* number of 9s, 1.999 does not quite equal 2.)

The two different decimal representations of 2 should cause no surprise. We have already seen a variety of ways to write 2, such as $5 - 3$, $1 + 1$, $\frac{4}{2}$, 2×1. However, the fact that $2 = 1.\overline{9}\ldots$ suggests the possibility of expressing a rational number which terminates decimally as a repeating decimal without the necessity of a repeating cycle of zeros.

We found $\frac{3}{4} = .75\bar{0}\ldots$. Let us find what rational number $.74\bar{9}\ldots$ equals:

$$\text{Let } N = .749\bar{9}\ldots$$
$$\text{Then } 100N = 74.9\bar{9}\ldots$$
$$\text{and } 1000N = 749.\bar{9}\ldots$$

Subtracting, $1000N - 100N = 749.\bar{9}\ldots - 74.\bar{9}\ldots$

$$900N = 675$$
$$N = \tfrac{675}{900} = \tfrac{3}{4}$$

Any terminating decimal is equivalent to the repeating decimal obtained from the former by reducing the last digit of the former by one, then adding an endless sequence of 9s:

$$17.35 = 17.34\bar{9}\ldots$$

This follows at once from the fact that

$$1.\bar{0}\ldots = .\bar{9}\ldots$$
$$\text{Let } .9\bar{9}\ldots = N$$
$$\text{then } 9.9\bar{9}\ldots = 10N$$
$$\text{and subtracting,} 9 = 9N \text{ or } N = 1$$

Let us find $.45\overline{23}\ldots$ as the ratio of two integers

$$\text{Let } N = .45\overline{23}\ldots$$
$$\text{then } 100N = 45.\overline{23}\ldots$$
$$\text{and } 10000N = 4523.\overline{23}\ldots$$
$$\text{Subtracting, } 9900N = 4478$$
$$N = \tfrac{4478}{9900} = \tfrac{2239}{4950}$$

This example illustrates the general procedure. First, if the cycle does not begin with the decimal point multiply by the necessary power of ten to bring the decimal point immediately to the left of the cycle. In the above example this was accomplished when we multiplied by 100

$$100N = 45.\overline{23}\ldots$$

Next we multiply by the power of ten corresponding to the number of digits in the repeating cycle. In the example the cycle has two digits, so we multiply by 10^2 or 100 giving

$$10000N = 4523.\overline{23}\ldots$$

These two steps will always yield two numbers, each greater than one, which have the same repeating cycle for fractional part. Then if we subtract these two numbers we get an integer for difference. But this integer must be an integral multiple of the original number, N. Therefore N is the ratio of these two integers.

10.2 DECIMALS

The fact that all rational numbers are either terminating or repeating decimals does not in and of itself make decimal notation either a time-saver or a convenience. There would not be much profit in converting a common fraction to decimal form even though it terminates—after 175 digits. If the fraction is a repeating decimal we must use a terminating approximation to it for purposes of computation. We frequently use for $\frac{1}{3}$ the decimal approximation .33 and for $\frac{2}{3}$ the decimal approximation .67.

We have seen that a repeating decimal will have not more than one less digit in its repeating cycle than the denominator of the corresponding common fraction. There were six digits in the cycle of $\frac{3}{7}$. There can be no more than 22 digits in the cycle of $\frac{6}{23}$. There can be no more than 20 digits in the cycle of $\frac{7}{21}$. However, we can place a further restriction. The above criterion applies to the common fraction when reduced to lowest terms. There can be no more than two digits in the cycle of $\frac{7}{21}$ since it is equal to $\frac{1}{3}$. Of course, we know there is only one digit in its cycle, but the denominator 3 tells us there can be no more than two.

We now consider the question "Under what condition will a common fraction terminate when expressed decimally?" Again let us consider the common fraction in lowest form. All factors common to numerator and denominator have been canceled. Although we think of decimal fractions in terms of a new kind of notation, far more significant is the fact that it is a fraction whose denominator is an integral power of 10. Then if a common fraction is to be a terminating decimal it must be possible to write it as the ratio of an integer to an integral power of 10.

Consider the fraction $\frac{4}{15}$. It is in lowest terms, we may write it in factored form as $\frac{2 \times 2}{3 \times 5}$. The only factors of 10 are 2 and 5. Therefore we must get rid of the factor 3 in the denominator. If we divide the denominator by 3 we must also divide the numerator by 3. But the numerator does not have the factor 3. We may conclude from this that if the denominator contains any factor other than 2 or 5 it is not a terminating decimal. On the other hand, if the denominator consists of 2s and/or 5s exclusively we can always multiply the numerator and denominator by the power of 2 or 5 which is necessary in order that the 2 and 5 be raised to the same power. This will mean that the denominator is that power of 10. For example, $\dfrac{11}{80} = \dfrac{11}{2^4 \times 5}$. If we multiply numerator and denominator by 5^3 we get $\dfrac{11 \times 5^3}{2^4 \times 5^4} = \dfrac{11 \times 5^3}{10^4} = \dfrac{1375}{10000} = .1375$. Then, in answer to our question, a common fraction in lowest terms will terminate if and only if the factors of its denominator consist exclusively of 2s and 5s.

Whether or not a common fraction terminates as a decimal is not a property of the number alone. It is also a function of the system of notation. *Twelve* has *four* as a factor. This is a property of the number. It is independent of the system of notation employed. But the statement "a number has four for a factor if and only if the ones digit is a multiple of four" is true or false depending on the system of notation. It is false if ten is base and true if eight is base. The denominator of the fraction must consist exclusively of 2s and 5s because 2 and 5 are the factors of the base 10.

In Chapter Two we observed that a fraction may terminate in one base and repeat in another, terminate in both, or repeat in both. We can generalize the foregoing discussion. Regardless of the base in which we write, a fraction in lowest terms will terminate when written as a positional fraction if and only if all prime factors of the denominator are prime factors of the base of notation. It is for this reason that a fraction will either terminate in both base-eight and base-two notation or will repeat in both. Since two is the only prime factor of eight the fraction will terminate in either base only when its denominator is an integral power of two.

EXAMPLE.   Convert $\frac{1}{5}$ to a positional fraction in base two and in base eight.

We express $\frac{1}{5}$ decimally as .2. To convert it to base two we multiply by 2. The integer of the product is the first digit of the fraction. The process is then repeated with the fractional part of the product. See page 52.

.2	.4	.8	.6	.2	.4	.8	.6
2	2	2	2	2	2	2	2
0.4	0.8	1.6	1.2	0.4	0.8	1.6	1.2

$$\therefore \quad .2_{ten} = .0011\overline{0011}\ldots._{two}$$

We may verify this result by using the same technique used in base ten.

$$\text{Let } N = .0011\overline{0011}\ldots$$
$$\text{then } 10000N = 11.\overline{0011} \quad (10000N = \text{sixteen } N)$$
$$\text{Subtracting, } 1111N = 11$$

$$N = \tfrac{11}{1111}$$

But $11_{two} = 3_{ten}$ and $1111_{two} = 15_{ten}$

$$\therefore \quad (\tfrac{11}{1111})_{two} = (\tfrac{3}{15})_{ten} = (\tfrac{1}{5})_{ten}$$

To express $\tfrac{1}{5}$ in base eight we proceed as before.

.2	.6	.8	.4	.2
8	8	8	8	8 ...
1.6	4.8	6.4	3.2	1.6

$$\therefore \quad .2_{ten} = (.\overline{1463}\ldots)_{eight}$$

We may verify the correctness of the result by employing the principle developed on page 53. The sum of the first three binary digits gives the first octonal digit, the sum of the second three binary digits gives the second octonal digit, and so on.

$$001_{two} = 1_{eight}, \quad 100_{two} = 4_{eight}, \quad 110_{two} = 6_{eight}, \quad 011_{two} = 3_{eight}$$
$$\therefore \quad (.001 \quad 100 \quad 110 \quad 011)_{two} = (.1463)_{eight}$$

Note that the repeating cycle .0011 in base two was needed three times in order to establish the cycle in base eight. We can convert from base two to base eight in the above manner because eight is two to the third power. We say that $.111_{two} = .7_{eight}$. This is evident if we write the expression in base ten: $.111_{two} = \tfrac{1}{2} + \tfrac{1}{4} + \tfrac{1}{8} = \tfrac{4}{8} + \tfrac{2}{8} + \tfrac{1}{8} = \tfrac{7}{8}$. The numerators 4, 2, and 1 are expressed in base two as 100, 10, and 1. Or when we add the numerators $4 + 2 + 1$ the sum, written in base two, is 111. Then if the base-two digits are added in groups of three we obtain the base-eight digits.

A fraction will terminate in both of two bases only if the prime factor of its denominator are prime factors of both bases. From this it follows that no fraction can terminate in each of two bases which are relatively prime. For example, no fraction can terminate in both base five and base six. The factors of the denominator of $\frac{1}{30}$ include the factors of both bases but it has factors not found in each. Therefore it will not terminate in either base. Since it does not terminate in base ten we must convert it to the new base and divide in order to find its cycle. We first convert to base five, $(\frac{1}{30})_{\text{ten}} = (\frac{1}{110})_{\text{five}}$.

The following division is done in base five:

$$
\begin{array}{r}
.00404 \\
110\overline{)1.0000} \\
440 \\
\hline
1000 \\
440 \\
\hline
10
\end{array}
$$

Therefore $(\frac{1}{30})_{\text{ten}} = (.00\overline{404}\ldots)_{\text{five}}$

Next, we convert to base six, $(\frac{1}{30})_{\text{ten}} = (\frac{1}{50})_{\text{six}}$. The division is now in base six:

$$
\begin{array}{r}
.011 \\
50\overline{)1.00} \\
50 \\
\hline
100 \\
50 \\
\hline
10
\end{array}
$$

Therefore $(\frac{1}{30})_{\text{ten}} = (.0\overline{1}\ldots)_{\text{six}}$.

By contrast $\frac{1}{18}$, which does not terminate in base ten, does in base six and base twelve.

$$(\tfrac{1}{18})_{\text{ten}} = (\tfrac{1}{30})_{\text{six}} = (\tfrac{1}{16})_{\text{twelve}}.$$

Dividing in base six, we get

$$
\begin{array}{r}
.02 \\
30\overline{)1.00} \\
1\ 00 \\
\hline
\end{array}
$$

Hence $(\frac{1}{30})_{\text{six}} = .02_{\text{six}}$

$$(\tfrac{1}{18})_{\text{ten}} = (\tfrac{1}{16})_{\text{twelve}}$$

Dividing in base twelve, we get

$$
\begin{array}{r}
.08 \\
16\overline{)1.00} \\
1\ 00 \\
\hline
\end{array}
$$

Hence $(\frac{1}{16})_{\text{twelve}} = .08_{\text{twelve}}$

We may check the correctness of each of the above by observing that

$$.02_{six} = \tfrac{2}{36}\text{ten}, \quad .08_{twelve} = \tfrac{8}{144}\text{ten}, \quad \text{and}$$

$$\tfrac{2}{36} = \tfrac{8}{144} = \tfrac{1}{18}.$$

Exercises

1 Show that the terminating decimal .25 is equivalent to the repeating decimal .24$\bar{9}$ . . . .

2 Find the common fraction to which .123 is equal. Find the common fraction to which .$\overline{123}$ . . . is equal.

3 Show that .$\overline{123}$ . . . = .1$\overline{231}$ . . . .

4 Find the repeating cycle of the fraction $\tfrac{1}{7}$.

5 Multiply the result of Exercise 4 by 3 and compare your answer with the repeating cycle of $\tfrac{3}{7}$ on page 323.

6 The number 142,857 is called a revolving number because, if it is multiplied by any integer 2 through 6, the same cyclic arrangement of digits is obtained. Verify this.

7 Attempt to determine, without actually multiplying out, 142857 × 7. Verify your answer by multiplication. Explain the result.

8 Find the repeating cycle of $\tfrac{1}{81}$. Multiply by 45. Explain the result.

9 Which of the following will terminate when written decimally: $\tfrac{1}{16}$, $\tfrac{3}{17}$, $\tfrac{9}{40}$, $\tfrac{1}{9}$, $\tfrac{10}{128}$?

10 Which of the above will terminate when written as a positional fraction in base twelve? base five?

11 Convert .39453125$_{ten}$ to base eight.

12 Convert the answer to Exercise 11 to base two.

13 If a fraction is a terminating decimal, how can one determine in advance of the division the number of digits in its decimal expansion?

14 If 5.00$\bar{0}$ . . . = 4.99$\bar{9}$ . . . does 4.88$\bar{8}$ . . . = 4.77$\bar{7}$ . . . ? Prove your answer.

15 Will the following fractions terminate or repeat when reduced to decimals: $\tfrac{4}{7}$; $\tfrac{2}{5}$; $\tfrac{5}{6}$.

16 Select a base greater than ten in which each of the fractions in Exercise 15 will terminate.

17 Find the repeating cycle for each of the following: $\tfrac{1}{7}$; $\tfrac{1}{13}$; $\tfrac{1}{11}$; $\tfrac{1}{17}$.

18 How does the number of digits in the cycle compare with the denominator in each case in Exercise 17? Which of these cycles represents a "cyclic number"? The cycle for $\tfrac{1}{13}$ is called "partially cyclic." Why?

19 Will any of the following terminate in base 7 or base 9? If so expand them, if not find the cycle. $\frac{1}{6}$; $\frac{3}{5}$; $\frac{2}{3}$.

20 Write the following as base ten common fractions.

(a) $.111_{two}$ (b) 1.10101_{two} (c) $.666_{seven}$ (d) 32.13_{five}

21 Prove that $.45 = .44999 \ldots$.

10.3 DECIMALS THAT ARE NOT RATIONAL

If it is possible for a decimal not to be a rational number we know from Section 10.1 that it does not terminate or continue after some point as a repeating cycle. We cannot tell from an examination of any finite number of digits whether such is possible. We might examine a million digits without the appearance of a repeating cycle. Yet this first million digits might be the cycle. For that matter, if we know nothing beyond our million digits we have no way of knowing whether it terminates. On the other hand, even though a decimal consists of a million repetitions of 1, 2, 3, that alone gives us no assurance what the 3-million-and-first digit is. If we write .1763 we have written a terminating decimal whether we meant to or not. If we write .1763 . . . we have indicated that the decimal is endless but we have not indicated what its repeating cycle is, or for that matter whether it has one. If we write .1763 . . . we have indicated an endless decimal and further we have shown how to continue it as far as we please, by repeating the last two digits 6, 3 over and over.

If we can describe the manner of extending an endless decimal in such manner that there will be no repeating cycle we will have exhibited an endless decimal which is not a rational number. This can be done in many ways. Consider the following: .10 110 1110 . . . . The rule of formation is obvious—a *one* followed by zero, followed by 2 *ones* followed by zero, followed by 3 *ones* followed by zero, and so on, continuing to increase the number of *ones* by one each time. Another decimal which is not a rational number is

.1 12 123 1234 12345 123456 1234567 12345678 123456789

12345678910   1234567891011   123456789101112

The spacing is employed to indicate the manner of forming the sequence. At each interval we repeat the previous one and extend it one more number. Not one more digit after we get past 9, but one more number in the sense that we are adjoining the integers $1, 2, 3 \ldots$.

What are such sequences? Are they mere freaks of nature or do they have the properties of number? We shall not attempt to establish this here but it can be shown that all endless decimals, both those that repeat and those that do not, have all the properties of the rational numbers. See page 277. We shall, however, approach the question intuitively.

10.4 SQUARE ROOT OF TWO

If you remember the square root algorithm you will recall that it can be continued indefinitely so long as an exact result is not reached. There are other ways to find square roots. For example, we may find $\sqrt{2}$ as follows: $1^2 = 1$, $2^2 = 4$; then $\sqrt{2}$ lies between 1 and 2. By trial we may discover that $1.4^2 = 1.96$, $1.5^2 = 2.25$; then $\sqrt{2}$ lies between 1.4 and 1.5. Continuing, $1.41^2 = 1.9881$, $1.42^2 = 2.0164$; then $\sqrt{2}$ is between 1.41 and 1.42. We can continue this process until we find the exact square root of 2 if it has one or until we get as many digits as we like. If we carry the process one more step we get 1.414. If this suggests the repeating cycle 14 disappointment is the reward for finding the next digit. Assuming the process does not terminate, how are we to know whether the sequence repeats?

It cannot repeat because if it did $\sqrt{2}$ would be a rational number. We can prove $\sqrt{2}$ is not a rational number. Incidentally, in so doing we shall not be concerned with any of the digits of the sequence. Let us assume $\sqrt{2}$ is the ratio of two integers. It the ratio exists we can further stipulate that it has been reduced to lowest terms. Symbolically we are asserting

$$\sqrt{2} = \frac{a}{b} \quad (a, b \text{ have no common factors.})$$

From this assumption it follows by squaring on both sides

$$2 = \frac{a^2}{b^2}$$

$$\text{or} \quad 2b^2 = a^2$$

The fundamental theorem of arithmetic, page 205, requires that $2b^2$ and a^2 have the same prime factors. Furthermore, each b in b^2 must have the same prime factors and each a in a^2 must also have the same prime factors. Specifically, the factor 2 must appear an even number of times on the right side of the equation because each a in a^2 must have the factor 2 the same number of times. Similarly, b^2 must have 2 as a factor an even number of times. Hence the left side of the equation, $2b^2$, must have the factor 2 an odd number of times. Hence the two sides of the equation cannot have the same prime factors. That is, $2b^2$ cannot equal a^2. This contradiction forces us to conclude that there are no two integers whose ratio is $\sqrt{2}$. There is no rational number whose square is 2.

We have seen that on a directed line there is a point corresponding to every rational number. If we take the distance from 0 to 1 as

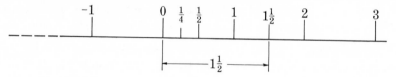

our unit of measure the distance from 0 to any other point has the numerical value of that point.

There is a line whose distance is $\sqrt{2}$. According to the Theorem of Pythagoras the square of the hypotenuse of a right triangle is equal to the sum of the squares of its legs. If we construct a square whose side is 1, application of this theorem establishes the diagonal as a line whose square is 2, that is, the diagonal is $\sqrt{2}$ times as long as the side. Then if we lay off this distance from the origin of a directed

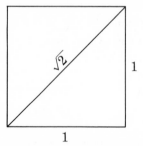

line which has the side of the square as unit length, it will not terminate on a rational point. Although there is a point to correspond to each rational number there is not a rational number to correspond to each point. There are other points on the line and therefore there are distances which cannot be expressed as rational numbers.

If we wish these distances or, what is the same thing, endless nonrepeating decimals to be numbers we are in the same predicament as when we attempt to subtract the natural number 7 from the natural number 4 or when we attempt to divide the integer 5 by the integer 2; we must create a new kind of number. We *define* an endless decimal (remember that a terminating decimal is followed by an endless succession of zeros) as a *real number*. If the decimal repeats it is a rational number. If a real number is not rational it is *irrational*.

10.5 IRRATIONAL NUMBERS IN ELEMENTARY ARITHMETIC

It may come as a surprise to learn that there are infinitely more irrational numbers than rational. For that matter, nature abounds with irrational magnitudes. In spite of this there is only slight need for irrational numbers in elementary arithmetic. Since all measurements are approximations, even though we were measuring an irrational magnitude we would never discover it. The result of the measurement would be a rational approximation to the irrational magnitude. If it were possible to construct an exact unit square and we measured its diagonal we would get 1.4 or 1.41 or 1.414 units, depending on the accuracy with which we measure.

We obtained an irrational number by attempting to find the square root of 2. The result is irrational if we take the square root of any nonperfect square such as 3, 5, 1.4 but not 4, 9, 144. The same applies to other roots; $\sqrt[3]{5}$ is irrational but $\sqrt[3]{64}$ is not.

However, the extraction of roots is by no means the only way irrationals arise. Perhaps the most familiar irrational of the other sort is π, the ratio of the circumference to the diameter of a circle. This ratio is not $3\frac{1}{7}$ nor is it 3.1416. These are merely two approximations which have found a great amount of popular favor. That both of these cannot be π may be demonstrated by converting $3\frac{1}{7}$ to decimal form. One of a number of rules for finding the digits of π is

$$\pi = 4 \times \left(1 - \frac{1}{3} + \frac{1}{5} - \frac{1}{7} + \frac{1}{9} - \ldots \pm \frac{1}{2n-1} \ldots\right)$$

When we use the decimal form of fractions for the purpose of computation we must use a terminating approximation to each repeating decimal involved. We can of course use as close an approximation as we wish. For $\frac{1}{3}$ we can use .3, .33, .333 or as many digits as we wish. The same is true of irrational numbers. Successively refined decimal approximations to π are 3, 3.1, 3.14, 3.142, 3.1416, ...

The elementary-school pupil need not be concerned with the theory of irrational numbers. But it is important for him to realize that he is using approximations to exact quantities which cannot be expressed by a finite number of digits. It is important that he realize the same situation exists relative to many of the decimal fractions he uses.

Exercises

1 Devise a rule for writing an endless nonrepeating decimal other than the examples in the text.

2 Explain the difference between 17.3, 17.3 . . . , and 17.$\bar{3}$ . . . .

3 Use the argument of Section 10.4 to show that $\sqrt{3}$ is irrational.

4 Follow the argument of Section 10.4, using $\sqrt{4}$. Show where the argument breaks down.

5 Adapt the argument of Section 10.4 to show $\sqrt[3]{2}$ irrational. Indicate where the arguments differ.

6 Show $\sqrt[3]{4}$ irrational.

7 Describe a method for constructing a line $\sqrt{3}$ units long.

8 Apply the rule on page 335 for finding the decimal expansion of π and find the first ten approximations by using one, then two, and so on, terms.

9 If we use $\sqrt{2} = 1.4$, is the error an excess or a deficiency?

10 Which is the closer approximation to $\frac{2}{3}$, .66 or .67?

11 Using the fact that every rational number either repeats or terminates when expressed decimally, prove that there is a rational number between any two rational numbers.

12 Prove that there is an irrational number between any two rational numbers.

13 Prove there is a rational number between any two irrational numbers.

14 Prove there is an irrational number between any two irrational numbers.

15 Do Exercise 11 through 14 justify the contention that there are the same number of rational numbers and irrational numbers? If not, why not?

Suggested Supplementary Readings

Banks, J. Houston, *Elements of Mathematics, Second Edition*. Boston: Allyn and Bacon, Inc., 1961. Pp. 205–231.

Bell, Clifford, Clela D. Hammond, and Robert B. Herrera, *Fundamentals of Arithmetic for Teachers*. New York: John Wiley and Sons, Inc., 1962. Pp. 193–194; 302–311.

Dutton, Wilbur H., and L. J. Adams, *Arithmetic for Teachers*. Englewood Cliffs, N.J.: Prentice-Hall, Inc., 1961. Ch. X.

Osborn, Roger, M. Vere DeVault, Claude C. Boyd, W. Robert Houston, *Extending Mathematics Understanding*. Columbus, Ohio: Charles E. Merrill Books, Inc., 1961. Pp. 94–95.

Swain, Robert L., *Understanding Arithmetic*. New York: Rinehart and Company, Inc., 1957. Pp. 182–191.

Decimals and Percent

CHAPTER ELEVEN

A DECIMAL FRACTION IS A FRACTION whose denominator is a positive integral power of 10, 10^1, 10^2, 10^3, ... Decimal fractions are therefore merely a special kind of common fractions. Every terminal decimal fraction is a common fraction, but not every common fraction is a terminating decimal. We usually think of decimal fractions in terms of notation, .5, .076. However $\frac{5}{10}$, $\frac{76}{100}$ are also decimal fractions. If we contend that the former are decimal fractions and the latter common fractions, the two being mutually exclusive, then we are referring to the form of notation. But one sixth is not a decimal fraction and six tenths is, regardless of the symbol we use to write them.

It would of course become burdensome to insist on "a fraction in decimal form" rather than "decimal fraction." This would be contrary to accepted usage.

However, throughout instruction in decimal fractions the idea should be stressed that they are merely a special kind of fractions *written in a special way*.

11.1 READING DECIMALS

Before systematic instruction in decimals is begun the child will already have made contact with them. The most obvious contact is probably our method of writing monetary values, as $3.69. Automobile odometers are another common occurrence, the tenths wheel having white numerals on black background in contrast to the others having black numerals on white background. Baseball standings, track records, metric equivalents, and weather reports are a few other situations involving decimals with which the fifth-grader is apt to be familiar. The teacher should always begin instruction on a new topic within the context of a familiar setting and/or as an approach to a meaningful problem, a problem which is real to the children.

Essentially, the reading of decimals requires the extension of our system of notation to quantities less than unity. Common fraction form need not be a hindrance in making the extension; in fact it can be an aid. All numbers derive their value from *one*. Thus a magnitude is assigned the number 12 to indicate that it is 12 times as large as our unit or basis for comparison. We assign the number $\frac{1}{3}$ to a magnitude to indicate that it is 3 times as small as unity. The whole numbers are multiples of unity and the fractions are multiples of equal parts of unity. We employ a ten grouping in expressing the multiples of unity.

thousands (1000 ones)
hundreds (100 ones)
tens (10 ones)
ones

Each grouping may be used from zero to nine times. There is a constant proportionality relationship between the values of successive groupings. Each is *ten times* as great as the one to its right.

The same scheme is employed in indicating the multiples of the equal parts of unity (numerators). But the number of parts (denominators) do not increase tenfold from one grouping to the next. They increase by one.

	2 equal parts of a unit	3 equal parts of a unit	4 equal parts of a unit
units	halves	thirds	fourths

When we consider proper fractions, or more appropriately mixed numbers, there is a further restriction placed on the numerators. The numerator can be not more than one less than the denominator. A number may contain as many as 9 sets of 100, or sets of 10 or of any other size sets of *multiples* of unity, but it can contain not more than 6 sevenths and not more than 5 sixths but as many as 10 elevenths. The whole number may require any number of kinds of sets, such as sets of thousands, sets of tens, and sets of ones. But the fraction requires only one kind of set, halves or fourths but not both. We do not write $56\frac{3}{4}$ as $56\frac{1}{2}\frac{1}{4}$. (This is essentially what the Egyptians did when they used unit fractions.)

As a preliminary to decimal notation the child should come to look upon a mixed number not merely as an indicated sum of a whole number plus a fraction but as *a number*. On the number line $2\frac{3}{4}$ is indicated by a point just as integers are. The point indicates one end of a segment whose other end is zero and whose length is $2\frac{3}{4}$. But it also indicates 2 units plus $\frac{3}{4}$ of a unit.

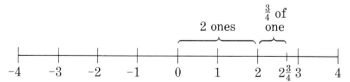

The integral part should be viewed as a multiple of unity and the fractional part as a part of unity. The idea of the number being a sum of sets should be stressed. The digits of the whole number as well as the numerator of the fraction tell us how many of each set are present. For example, $16\frac{5}{8}$ means 1 set of ten units plus 6 sets of one unit plus 5 sets of an eighth of a unit. The size of each set in the whole number is determined by the position of the digit but the size of the fraction set (part of unity rather than multiple of unity) is determined by the denominator.

We should stress the fact that the value of each size set in the whole number is determined by *multiplication*. In 567 the value of the set of which there are 5 is 1 *times* 100, the value of the set of which there are 6 is 1 *times* 10. On the other hand, the value of the set size in the fraction is determined by *division*. Thus in $\frac{3}{4}$ the size of the set of which there are 3 is 1 *divided by* 4, in $\frac{5}{19}$ the size of the set of which there are 5 is 1 *divided by* 19.

A further preliminary to decimal representation of fractions should include the fact that it is theoretically possible to represent a fraction as the sum of more than one size set, as is done with whole numbers. For example, in the mixed number $45\frac{7}{8}$ we express 45 as 4 tens plus 5 ones. We *could theoretically* express $\frac{7}{8}$ as 1 half plus 1 fourth plus 1 eighth. We can express $\frac{13}{14}$ as 1 half plus 3 sevenths. If we then restrict ourselves to those parts of unity which are obtained by division by 10, 100, 1000, and so on, just as we have restricted the integral set sizes to those obtainable by multiplying unity by 10, 100, 1000, and so on, we have decimal fractions. For example, $13\frac{1}{4}$ may be thought of as 1 ten plus 3 ones plus 2 tenths plus 5 hundredths. The class can verify that $\frac{1}{4} = \frac{2}{10} + \frac{5}{100}$ by adding in common fraction form and reducing the answer to lowest terms.

In this developmental work the simpler common fractions which terminate decimally should be used. If some bright youngster objects "What about $\frac{1}{3}$ or $\frac{1}{7}$?" we should face the issue squarely. We have not said *all* fractions can be expressed exactly this way. Although to raise the point at this time would confuse most of the pupils, at the proper time they should be made well aware that $\frac{2}{3}$ does not equal .67 exactly. The final step consists of incorporating fractions of the form $\frac{2}{10} + \frac{5}{100}$ into decimal notation. Just as 520 means $5 \times 100 + 2 \times 10$, so 0.25 means $2 \div 10 + 5 \div 100$.

With this background we are ready to study the decimal structure of the notation system as extended to fractional parts of unity.

The decimal point is not the center of the number. It has no digit position. It is a separator, separating the whole number from the fraction. *The center of the number is the ones digit.* The value of each digit position to the left of the ones digit is obtained by multiplying by 10, 10 × 10, 10 × 10 × 10, and so on. The value of each digit position to the right of the ones digit is obtained by dividing by 10, 10 × 10, 10 × 10 × 10, and so on. The children's previous contacts with decimals should be utilized fully at this point. For example, $1.56 means 1 dollar

thousands	hundreds	tens	ones	tenths	hundredths	thousandths
1 × 10 × 10 × 10	1 × 10 × 10	1 × 10		1 ÷ 10	1 ÷ 10 ÷ 10	1 ÷ 10 ÷ 10 ÷ 10

plus 5 tenths of a dollar (dimes) plus 6 hundredths of a dollar (cents). If a boy ran the hundred yard dash in 11.3 seconds the time was 1 × 10 seconds + 1 second + 3 ÷ 10 seconds.

In reading decimals pure (0.56) or mixed (15.63), two forms have received wide acceptance. We may read 0.56 as "fifty-six hundredths" or "zero point five six." The mixed number 15.63 may be read "fifteen *and* sixty-three hundredths" or "fifteen point six three." The "point" terminology has advantages; it is easier, faster, and less conducive to mistakes. However, it is recommended that this terminology be postponed until considerable facility with decimals is obtained. The "and" form is more conducive to understanding of the symbolism. In reading a number, "and" is correctly reserved to serve only as a separator of the integer from the fraction. This rule of mathematical grammar is, however, consistently broken. One constantly hears "one hundred and fifty" for 150. There is no ambiguity here, but the misuse of "and" can be so. Does "one hundred and fifty thousandths" mean 100.050 or 0.150? Children should be taught the correct use of "and" in reading a number.

Incidentally, in writing 0.56 there is no logical necessity for the zero. But it is well to use the form in the developmental program since it emphasizes the all-important ones position.

How do we read a decimal? We are reading a mixed number. The whole number should be read in the usual way; the decimal point should be read "and." The digits to the right of the decimal point are the numerator of the fraction. They should be read as a whole number, *disregarding initial zeros*. We determine the denominator of the fraction by counting the digits to the right from unity as "tenths," "hundredths," "thousandths," . . . until the last digit is reached. The name of the last-digit position, which is the denominator of the fraction, is then read. Here we should point out the analogy to reading a whole number. We must count "ten," "hundred," "thousand," . . . from unity to the *left* until we reach the first digit in order to get the name of the highest ordered digit in the whole number. For example, we read four *thousand* three hundred seven *and* thirty-four *thousandths*.

$$4 \quad 3 \quad 0 \quad 7 \quad .0 \quad 3 \quad 4$$

thousands	hundreds	tens	ones	tenths	hundredths	thousandths

We read 135.135 one *hundred* thirty-five *and* one hundred thirty-five *thousandths*. We do not count to the left and right of the decimal point, but from the ones digit.

11.2 DECIMAL EQUIVALENTS

Ours is not a completely decimalized society. There are those who feel that it should be. The point is debatable. Thirds, sixths, and twelfths are of common occurrence. Yet they have no exact decimal equivalent in the sense of a terminating decimal. However, in its practical application this deficiency of decimals is not too serious. We frequently have need for such numbers as $\frac{1}{3}$. For example, in the formula for the volume of a cone, $V = \frac{1}{3}\pi r^2 h$, all numbers are exact. But when we put it to use we must measure the radius and the height, and our measurements are never exact. We have lost no accuracy in our result if $\frac{1}{3}$ and π are approximated to conform to the accuracy with which we measure the radius and height. For that matter, common fractions have a similar deficiency; we cannot express all quantities exactly by means of common fractions. In the above formula π cannot be expressed exactly as either a common fraction or a decimal.

There is however no denying the utility of decimals as aids to computation. They have done for fractions what the Hindu–Arabic system did for computation with integers. The decimal equivalents of the more simple and most frequently used common fractions should be committed to memory just as the basic addition and multiplication facts are.

Table of Decimal Equivalents

Common fraction	Decimal equivalent	Common fraction	Decimal equivalent
$\frac{1}{2}$	.5	$\frac{1}{8}$	.125
$\frac{1}{3}$	.33$\frac{1}{3}$	$\frac{3}{8}$	.375
$\frac{2}{3}$	.66$\frac{2}{3}$	$\frac{5}{8}$	.625
$\frac{1}{4}$	.25	$\frac{7}{8}$	.875
$\frac{3}{4}$	.75	$\frac{1}{10}$	.1
$\frac{1}{5}$	.20	$\frac{1}{12}$	.08$\frac{1}{3}$
$\frac{2}{5}$	.40	$\frac{1}{20}$	.05
$\frac{3}{5}$	.60	$\frac{1}{25}$	.04
$\frac{4}{5}$	.80	$\frac{1}{50}$	.02
$\frac{1}{6}$	.16$\frac{2}{3}$		

The derivation of decimal equivalents is essentially a problem involving division of decimals. There is need for a knowledge of the frequently used equivalents prior to the study of division. The child should ultimately know how to make the conversion of any common fraction to decimal form, but the development of an equivalence chart need not await this.

The terminating decimals may be derived as follows: Write $\frac{1}{2}$ as a fraction with denominator 10. $\frac{1}{2} = ?/10$. This is a familiar problem in reduction of common fractions. $\frac{1}{4} = ?/100$, $\frac{1}{8} = ?/1000$. The conversion of these results to decimal form will provide practice in and added insight into the above described program of development of the extension of the decimal system of notation to fractions. The nonterminating decimals may be derived in the same way. $\frac{1}{3} = ?/100$. We must multiply the denominator by $33\frac{1}{3}$, therefore we must multiply the numerator by $33\frac{1}{3}$. The form $.33\frac{1}{3}$ is an acceptable one but it requires an extension of the basic idea of a mixed number. When we write $125\frac{1}{2}$ the $\frac{1}{2}$ indicates a part of the preceding digit value, $\frac{1}{2}$ of 1 in this case. Similarly in $.33\frac{1}{3}$ the $\frac{1}{3}$ indicates $\frac{1}{3}$ of the preceding digit value, $\frac{1}{3}$ of $\frac{1}{100}$. This usage is sometimes employed with integers. A house quoted at $17\frac{1}{2}$ or 17.5 does not sell for $17.50, it sells for $17\frac{1}{2}$ thousands of dollars. The $\frac{1}{2}$ is used to indicate $\frac{1}{2}$ of 1000. One frequently sees on an equivalence chart $\frac{1}{3} = .33$. This should not be done because it is not true. It should be done only if it is clearly understood that we mean one third equals thirty-three hundredths *to the nearest hundredth.*

11.3 ADDITION AND SUBTRACTION OF DECIMALS

The addition and subtraction of decimals is deceptively simple. Children can learn these operations in a mechanical way with ease. But the very simplicity of the process may well prove a difficulty when multiplication and division are encountered. The teacher should exercise special care to insure that the process is meaningful for the child. In this instance we cannot rely on written responses which merely show mechanical proficiency.

Instruction should begin with problems involving tenths. For example: If Bill lives 3.2 miles from school and Tom lives 0.7 miles in the opposite direction, how far is it from Bill's home to Tom's? The problem may first be solved by converting to common fraction notation, then converting the answer to decimal notation. It should take few such problems to elicit the correct process from the children. Points which should be emphasized are:

(1) We still are restricted to the addition of *like groups*, tens with tens, ones with ones, tenths with tenths.

(2) When we add the digits which are in tenths place we are actually adding the numerators of fractions that already have a common denominator, 10.

(3) The sum of the digits in tenths place is the numerator of the sum of the fractions they represent, and should therefore be written in tenths place.

(4) If the sum of the digits is 10 or more we have an improper fraction, but since there are 10 tenths to a unit we can convert the improper fraction to a mixed number by "carrying" as in adding whole numbers.

These points should be stressed so that the children will know *why* the decimal points should be in a column, the columns are added columnwise as with whole numbers, and the decimal point of the sum falls in the column of the decimal points of the addends.

With a background of understanding of addition of tenths the extension to decimals of any order offers no difficulties. The "carry" process works from any digit to the next, not just from tenths to ones, because of the constant relationship: any position value is ten times as great as the one to its right.

The objection which some writers raise to the addition of so called "ragged" decimals is not entirely appropriate. The term "ragged decimal" refers to decimals with a varying number of digits, for example $1.5 + .073 + 15$. If we are dealing with exact numbers there is no difference between 1.5 and 1.500. It is not at all inappropriate to know measures of differing degrees of refinement in the same problem. If a rectangle is approximately 100 feet by 5 feet it is not at all unlikely to measure the long dimension to the nearest foot and the short one to the nearest tenth of a foot. If our concern is with area this ought to be done. It is of course true that the added precision of the short dimension will be of no value in finding the perimeter. However, not all rules for approximate computation require each addend of a sum to be rounded off. A little more confidence can be placed in the sum if only the sum is rounded off to the precision of the least precise addend. There is nothing wrong with the admonition to fill in the vacant spaces with zeros as an aid in keeping digit positions straight. However, if the problem situation involves approximate numbers the allowable precision of the result should be determined in advance of the filling in process. The child certainly should not be allowed to think that 15 and 15.000 convey the same meaning if they are approximate numbers.

The subtraction of decimals offers little in the way of new difficulties if the subtraction of integers and the addition of decimals have been mastered. "Borrowing," if the decomposition method is used, or "borrowing and paying back" if the equal-additions method is followed with integers, is performed precisely as before. When we borrow a *one* we actually decompose a unit into 10 tenths of a unit. The one new difficulty encountered in subtraction stems from "ragged" decimals. It is not at all uncommon to encounter problems like $10 - 3.87$. If we follow the precautions indicated relative to addition in situations of this sort then certainly we should fill in with zeros. If the problem is written

$$\begin{array}{r} 10 \\ -3.87 \\ \hline \end{array}$$

from what is the child to attempt to subtract 7 as the first step? We have insisted that in teaching the addition facts involving zero, such as $5 + 0$, the child should consider this as combining a set of 5 with an empty set. It should not be thought of as not adding anything to the 5. The above problem illustrates one reason for this point of view. If the additive method of subtraction is taught this situation poses the question "What must be added to 7 so that the result is 'not adding anything'?" Such an interpretation might make sense when there is a void over the 7, but it will not help the child learn how to subtract in the above situation.

Problems involving money frequently result in the above type of subtraction. For example: John paid $3.87 for a baseball glove. If he gave the clerk a $10 bill how much change should he get?

Grant that the child knows that ten dollars may be written $10.00 without necessarily having the corresponding insight into its significance relative to decimal notation. We may still utilize this familiarity in developing the scheme for handling the general type problem, such as: If we saw a 6.5-foot piece from a 10-foot plank how long is the other piece?

We note in passing that in the above usage $10 is exact; we are not assuming added precision when we express it as $10.00. If the 10-foot plank was bought in the lumber yard as a 10-foot plank the length is still an approximate number, but we have every right to assume from the context that it is precise to less than the nearest foot. When we express it as 10.0 feet we have not assumed added precision. The correct answer to the problem is 3.5 feet.

If the minuend in a "ragged" subtraction problem is an approximate number with its precision correctly indicated by its digits we may still adjoin the necessary zeros with the proviso that the difference may be no more precise than the minuend. In this situation it is a better procedure to round off the subtrahend before subtracting.

EXAMPLE. Ann said her aunt lives 125 miles away. The last time she visited her aunt they stopped on the way for lunch. The odometer indicated they had travelled 73.7 miles. How much further did they have to go?

If we solve as below

$$\begin{array}{r} 125.0 \\ -73.7 \\ \hline 51.3 \end{array}$$

we must realize that 125.0 is more precise than the known total distance. It was known only to the nearest mile, therefore we can obtain the answer only to the nearest mile. The correct answer is 51 miles *to the closest mile.* We can also avoid the ragged decimal by rounding off the distance travelled so as to agree in precision with the total distance. To the nearest mile the distance travelled is 74 miles. Then

$$\begin{array}{r} 125 \\ -74 \\ \hline 51 \end{array}$$

gives the remaining distance *to the nearest mile.*

11.4 MULTIPLICATION OF DECIMALS

The only new source of difficulty in multiplying decimals consists of learning how to place the decimal point in the product.

Instruction in multiplication and division of decimals in general should be preceded by multiplication and division by powers of ten. If decimal notation is understood, the children will not find it difficult to understand the process. The teacher should guard against the child's learning to apply the rule by rote. If the rule is given first this is apt to occur. It can be avoided if the children are helped to discover the rule for themselves. If we write on the chalk board

tens	ones	tenths	hundreds
2	5	6	3

and ask the class to read the number, the correct response should come without hesitation. The names of the digit positions are then erased and the class again asked to read the number. It should now be read as an integer. The digits names are then replaced

hundreds	tens	ones	tenths
2	5	6	3

and the class again reads the number. The whole procedure should then be repeated with the decimal point rather than the names indicating the digit positions. The idea here is to emphasize the fact that the decimal point locates the ones position and all other positions are located relative to it. Then each time we shift the decimal point one place to the right the digit which was tenths becomes ones, ten times as great. Similarly for every digit, therefore the number is 10 times as great. Correspondingly, each shift of the decimal point to the left makes each digit value, and the number, ten times as small.

There should be included in this development situations requiring the adjoining of zeros, both on the right and left:

$$1.6 \times 100 = 1.6 \times 10 \times 10 = 160.$$
$$1.6 \div 100 = 1.6 \div 10 \div 10 = .016$$

It is possible by addition to solve a problem involving the multiplication of a decimal by an integer. The correct method of placing the decimal point can be inferred from the solution of problems in this manner. However, this approach has two serious limitations. First, we cannot extend the method to the multiplication of decimal by decimal. A more serious limitation lies in the fact that the children can discover *what* to do much more readily than *why* the rule is correct. It is a much better approach to suggest the possibility of solving the problem by first converting the fractions to common notation.

Suppose the introductory problem requires finding $7 \times .3$. Writing $.3$ as $\frac{3}{10}$ reduces the problem to a familiar one, $7 \times \frac{3}{10} = \frac{21}{10} = 2\frac{1}{10}$. But the result can be converted to decimal form, 2.1. (It is better to select numbers which will not lead to cancellation or reduction to lowest terms. For example, if we use $15 \times .4$ we will get

$$15 \times \tfrac{4}{10} = 1\overset{3}{\cancel{5}} \times 2/\cancel{5} = 6,$$ and the significance of the result 6.0 is

lost.) After a few problems of this sort the children will generalize that the answer always contains tenths. This is a plausible inference, we are finding so many sets of so many tenths (in the illustration 7 sets of 3 tenths). But the matter should not rest here. We are multiplying two fractions whose denominators are 1 and 10 when we find $7 \times \frac{3}{10} = \frac{7}{1} \times \frac{3}{10}$, then the product must have the denominator $1 \times 10 = 10$. This means the decimal fraction must contain one digit.

Rationalization of the general procedure for multiplying decimals may follow this same approach. Suppose we wish to multiply 6.2×1.25. If this is written in common fraction form we get

$$\frac{62}{10} \times \frac{125}{10 \times 10} = \frac{62 \times 125}{10 \times 10 \times 10}$$

In this form it becomes evident that the numerator of the product is obtained by multiplying the numbers without regard to decimal points. The product is always a decimal fraction since the denominator is of the form $10 \times 10 \times 10 \times \ldots$. But since each factor 10 in the denominator implies one digit in the decimal fraction we know the number of digits in the product must be the same as the number of factors 10 it contains. But this is simply the sum of the factors 10 in each of the denominators of the original fractions, which is also the sum of the digits of the fractions in decimal form. Since 6.2 has one digit in its fraction it has one factor 10 in its denominator, since 1.25 has two digits in its fraction it has two 10 factors in its denominator. Then the product has three 10 factors in its denominator and thus 3 digits in its decimal fraction.

A similar approach may be used which depends upon the concept of multiplying (dividing) by ten by shifting the decimal point one place to the right (left). Under this approach we employ the idea of inverse operations. We multiply each factor by whatever is necessary to make it an integer, and apply the inverse operations to the product of the integers. The work may be arranged thus

$$6.2 \times 10 = 62$$

$$1.25 \times 100 = 125$$

$$62 \times 125 = 7750$$

$$7750 \div 100 = 77.50$$

$$77.50 \div 10 = 7.750$$

After a few problems of this sort the children should be able to generalize that to "undo" the shifting of the decimal points of the factors the decimal point of the product must be shifted in the opposite direction the sum of the places it was shifted in the factors.

Special attention should be given to problems requiring annexing or prefixing zeros. Many children's mistakes are of this nature. In this connection, the habit of approximating the answer is particularly helpful both as a check and as an alternative means of placing the decimal point in the answer:

EXAMPLES.

3.82 16 ――― 2292 382 ――― 6112	Since 3.82 is almost 4 and $4 \times 16 = 64$ the answer could not possibly be .6112, or 6.112; they are too small. Also 611.2 is too large. The correct answer must be 61.12.

.215 .12 ――― 430 215 ――― 2580	Since .12 is about $\frac{1}{10}$ and .215 is about $\frac{2}{10}$ the answer should be about $\frac{2}{100}$. Even .2580 is too large so we must prefix a zero, .02580, which is about $\frac{2}{100}$.

8.2 200 ――― 16400	Since 8.2 is nearly 10 and $10 \times 200 = 2000$ the answer is nearly 2000. We need one of the two annexed zeros, the answer is 1640.

11.5 DIVISION OF DECIMALS

Of the four fundamental operations with decimals division accounts for far the greatest number of mistakes.[1] This is undoubtedly due to the all-too-prevalent practice of teaching a mechanical rule for pointing off the quotient without supplying a background of understanding. Meaningless rules are easily forgotten. One is much more apt to become confused in applying a rule if the reason for its application is not understood.

[1] See Leo J. Brueckner and Guy L. Bond, *The Diagnosis and Treatment of Learning Difficulties* (New York: Appleton-Century-Crofts, Inc., 1955), p. 232.

There are four cases to consider: (1) a fraction divided by an integer, (2) an integer divided by an integer which is not an integral factor of the dividend, (3) an integer divided by a fraction, and (4) a fraction divided by a fraction. Instruction in division should begin with the first type. The other three types may be reduced to it.

Placing of the decimal point is the only new difficulty involved. In solving the introductory problems the division can be done as if the dividend were also an integer. The decimal point should be placed by approximation or by solving the problem in common fraction form and converting the answer to decimal form. In either event the answer should be checked by multiplication. Care should be exercised to select for initial work division situations which do not require the annexing of zeros in the dividend. The procedure is illustrated below.

PROBLEM: Jim is raising chickens for the market. He found that in one week they ate 40.6 pounds of feed. How much did they eat per day?

The solution requires $7 \overline{)40.6}$. The class is instructed to perform the division without regard to the decimal point.

$$\begin{array}{r} 58 \\ 7 \overline{)40.6} \end{array}$$

Then they are to determine in any way they can where to place the decimal point. The answer cannot be 58 pounds. By approximation we know that 40 is nearly 7×6 so the answer should be nearly 6; we place the decimal after the 5, 5.8. Other children may reduce to common fractions

$$40.6 \div 7 = \tfrac{406}{10} \div 7 = \tfrac{406}{10} \times \tfrac{1}{7} = \tfrac{406}{70} = 5\tfrac{56}{70}$$

Therefore we must point off the answer so as to have as whole number 5, 5.8. Each child should verify his result by multiplication, $5.8 \times 7 = 40.6$.

A number of such problems should be solved in this way and a record kept of the results. The class is then asked to examine the results and see if they can make a rule to determine where the decimal point belongs in the answer. The illustrations should include a number of variations, such as more-than-one-digit divisors and pure decimal divisors including those with initial zeros. This will make the desired generalization, "The decimal point goes directly over the decimal point in the dividend," stand out more clearly.

Once this generalization has been suggested the teacher should then raise the question "How can we be sure this will always be true?" Although no one should expect a formal proof, the dangers of incomplete induction should not be ignored.

Insistence upon the check by multiplication may provide an answer. Since the divisor has no decimal places the dividend and quotient must have the same number if the check is to work. Another rationalization may be—If the dividend has tenths, hundredths, and so on, so must the quotient since we are finding a part of the dividend.

Although the latter rationalization is perhaps a little less neat, logically it has an advantage in that it is an aid when considering the next type of problem. This type, an integer divided by an integer, is essentially the problem of reducing a common fraction to decimal form. It is also essentially the problem of completing the division when the divisor is not an integral factor of the dividend. Both types of situation should be utilized in introducing the topic.

We should begin by utilizing decimal equivalents which are already known:

PROBLEM: Four boys decided to pool their resources and buy a motor scooter. They found a second-hand one for $65. What is each boy's share of the cost?

Some members of the class may solve this as

$$
\begin{array}{r}
\$16\frac{1}{4} \\
4\,\overline{\smash{)}\,\$65} \\
\underline{4} \\
25 \\
\underline{24} \\
1
\end{array}
$$

However there will probably be those with sufficient experience in dividing dollars and cents to give the solution

$$
\begin{array}{r}
\$16.25 \\
4\,\overline{\smash{)}\,\$65.00} \\
\underline{4} \\
25 \\
\underline{24} \\
10 \\
\underline{8} \\
20 \\
\underline{20}
\end{array}
$$

In any event the equivalence of the two results will be apparent. The important point, the only new idea present, is the fact that we can add as many terminal zeros as we please to a decimal (if it is exact). With the incorporation of this idea the problem reduces itself to the first type.

Most of the difficulty with decimal division, as well as most of the disagreement as to the best way to proceed, stems from situations involving fractional divisors. The third and fourth types listed on page 353 may well be treated together.

The cardinal principle that a rule should follow, not precede, its meaningful development holds with equal force here. But in this case it is probably more expedient to lead the children to the rule than to guide them to discovering it for themselves.

As a preliminary to this case there should be intensive review of the principle of division which allows us to multiply dividend and divisor by the same number without changing the quotient. It is well to relate this to the fact that a fraction is an implied division. This is precisely what we do when we reduce to a common denominator. When the division is viewed as a fraction

$$0.3 \overline{\smash{\big)}\ 9.24} = \frac{9.24}{0.3}$$

the justification of the procedure is apparent from the fact that 1 is the multiplication identity.

$$\frac{9.24}{0.3} \times 1 = \frac{9.24}{0.3} \times \frac{10}{10} = \frac{92.4}{3}$$

In summarizing the earlier cases it should be emphasized that we now can divide *if the divisor is a whole number*. The teacher should then suggest that we make the divisor a whole number by multiplication by shifting the decimal point. But the above principle requires that we do the same to the dividend. We should emphasize that we obtain the answer to our problem by working a different one. The problem should be rewritten:

$$.46 \overline{\smash{\big)}\ 93.058} = 46 \overline{\smash{\big)}\ 9305.8}$$

The use of carets is a popular textbook device:

$$.46_\wedge \overline{\smash{\big)}\ 93.65_\wedge 8}$$

If used in the developmental stage, these become a rule-of-thumb crutch. We have actually introduced a new symbol without defining it. It should not be used until the child has developed insight into what is taking place. Afterwards it is not needed. If such a device is to be used one more suggestive of what really happens is

$$\overset{\curvearrowleft}{.46}. \overline{\smash{)}93\underset{\curvearrowright}{.}05.8}$$

The practice of rewriting the problem should not be dropped too soon. Only after the child clearly sees the nature of the situation should we formulate a rule for pointing off the quotient. Even then it should be proposed as a short cut which alleviates the necessity of rewriting the problem.

In checking by multiplication the check should be applied to the original problem, not the one substituted for it:

$$.46\,\overline{\smash{)}93.058} \;=\; \overset{202.3}{46\,\overline{\smash{)}9305.8}}$$

CHECK: $202.3 \times .46 = 93.058.$

11.6 TEACHING THE MEANING OF PERCENT

"Percent," derived from the Latin *per centum*, literally means "per hundred." Arithmetic texts usually say it therefore means hundredth or hundredths—6 percent means 6 hundredths ($\frac{6}{100}$). There are advantages to adherence to the literal meaning, 6 percent means 6 *per* hundred, 6 out of each 100, which is of course $\frac{6}{100}$ of the total. The modern-day conception of percent is a further specialization of fractions—just as decimals are special kinds of fractions with their special symbolism so percent is a special kind of decimal which has its special symbolism.

Historically, percent was an outgrowth of general practice in expressing the rate of toll. Taxes, interest, commission and brokerage, and rate of profit or loss were expressed as one per twenty, three per hundred, and so on. Real estate tax rates are sometimes stated as so many dollars per $100 of assessed valuation. Thus if the rate is $3.15 this means a tax of $3.15 is levied on each $100 of assessed valuations, which is equivalent to a rate of 3.15 percent. Taxes are sometimes stated in mils. The tax rate here is 31.5 mils. This means a tax of 31.5 mils or 3.15 cents is levied against each $1 of assessed valuation. We can consider this an application of *permilage* as opposed to *percentage*. The emergence of percent was simply the acceptance of 100 as the base amount upon which the toll was stated. It is well to include the notion of *per hundred* rather than merely hundredths as we develop the meaning of percent. Such troublesome forms as 200 percent then mean 200 per 100 or 2 to 1 or twice as much; 0.5 percent means $\frac{1}{2}$ per 100, or 1 in 200 as well as the fraction .005.

The term *percentage* has a dual usage which sometimes causes confusion. Percentage is used in a broad sense to describe the topic of percent. The word is also used to designate the toll itself as opposed to the rate of toll. The interest on $200 at 6 percent is $12. The base is $200, the rate is 6 percent, and $12 is the percentage. It is the lender's toll, his "take," or his margin. Confusion over the use of the word arises when the toll is stated in terms of rate of toll instead of the absolute amount. What is the house percentage on a bet if the odds are 6 to 5 in favor of the house? The house advantage is $\frac{1}{11}$ or $9\frac{1}{11}$ percent. We may correctly say the house percentage is $9\frac{1}{11}$ percent, but not $9\frac{1}{11}$. On the other hand, on a $11 bet the house percentage is $1, but not 1 percent. Nor is the rate of margin $1, it is $1 per $11.

The recent trend to postpone the study of percentage to the seventh and eighth grades is in keeping with the general trend of postponement of topics of arithmetic. One cannot quarrel with the philosophy of postponement to insure sufficient maturity and to provide opportunity for readiness activities. Logically, the topic of percents must await the development of the theory of decimals. However, percentage is so widely used the child will normally come in contact with percents as early as, or earlier than, he will decimal notation, except in the case of dollars-and-cents notation. It would therefore seem wise to incorporate the development of the meaning of the notation as a part of the work with decimals.

To this end the percent sign, %, can be utilized. Since 6 % means 6 per 100 we can determine what fractional part the 6 is by dividing by 100. The two zeros in the percent sign may be taken to be synonymous with $\frac{1}{100}$. But division by 100 is accomplished by shifting the decimal point 2 places to the left.

Motivation for the interpretation of percents is readily available. The children are asked to bring to class uses of percents which they have encountered. Their sources will include their textbooks, news items, advertisements, store signs, and many others.

The most commonly found percents will be two-digit integers. "Sale, 20 % discount"; "The relative humidity was 84 % today"; "The Christian Democrats had 50 % of the total vote"; "Automobile production was 16 % under the same period last year." Examples of this sort cause least difficulty in interpretation and conversion to fraction form. Percents which are greater than 100 or which contain fractions, such as 250 %, $1\frac{1}{2}$ %, .03 % are more difficult for children to understand. Such mistakes as 250 % = .25, $1\frac{1}{2}$ % = .15, .03 % = .03 are not uncommon. They indicate a lack of grasp of the meaning of percent. The child may reason: "All the numbers have been changed to hundredths and percent means hundredths." Confusion may arise from inability to appreciate the possibility of having more than 100 hundredths or less than 1 hundredth. In any event mistakes of this sort call for careful reteaching of both the meaning of percent and the mechanics of converting to decimal form.

11.7 APPLICATIONS OF PERCENT

Although percent merely means hundredths insofar as numerical value is concerned, in its application a comparison is implied. Percentage problems involve quantities to be compared and a percent which compares them ratiowise. One of the two quantities constitutes the basis for comparison: it is the one compared to. It is commonly referred to as the *base*. The quantity which is compared to the base is the *percentage*. The percent, which states the ratio of percentage to base, is called the *rate*. Hence we have an application of the idea of equivalent ratios. The percent is a ratio, 16 % means 16:100. The ratio, *percentage:base*, is equivalent to the rate ratio. If we wish to find 16 % of 125 we have one ratio 16:100 and one of the terms of the equivalent ratio. We must find the percentage p such that 16:100 and p:125 are equivalent. We must multiply the second term, 100, by 125/100 in order to obtain the second term in the other ratio, 125. Hence the first term, 16, must be multiplied by 125/100 also in order to have an equivalent ratio. The percentage p is 16 × 125/100, but this is the same result as 125 × .16.

If we recall that the rate is a ratio, the equivalent ratios can be expressed as

$$\text{rate} = \frac{\text{percentage}}{\text{base}} \qquad \text{or}$$

$$\text{base} \times \text{rate} = \text{percentage}$$

This is the basic relationship governing all problems in percentage.

It is a common practice among textbook writers to approach percentage problems by cases: Case I, finding a given percent of a number; Case II, finding what percent one number is of another; Case III, finding a number when a given percent of it is known. The case approach is good or bad, depending upon how it is done. If the children are taught a rule of procedure to go along with each case— Case I, express the percent as a decimal and multiply; Case II, divide the first number by the second and change the answer to percent; Case III, divide the number by the percent expressed as a decimal— then the method is merely a mechanical rule of thumb. It is an attempt to avoid the necessity of insight into the nature of the relationships involved. The child's memory is taxed not only to remember the three cases and the three rules but to keep the correct rule associated with its case. Confusion in the mind of the child is almost inevitable.

On the other hand, if the approach is used to emphasize the basic nature of the situation, the fact that three quantities are involved and we may find any one if we know the other two, then the method has merit. Under this approach the rules will come about as generalizations of results which have been reached from careful analysis of the relationships existing in the problems. The teacher should not make a fetish of applying the rule. A rule which is understood is a convenient short cut. If it is temporarily forgotten it can easily be reestablished. We are enslaved by a rule learned and applied by rote. We are unaware of incorrect use. If the rule is forgotten we are lost.

Whether the case method is employed or not, the first step in the solution of the problem consists of correctly identifying what is compared, what it is compared to, and how it compares. The following problem analyses are illustrative of the application of this all-important first step:

> PROBLEM: A given concrete mix requires 16% cement. How many 70-pound bags of cement are required to make a ton of concrete?

Case I is the easiest of the three to analyze. The comparison here is cement compared to concrete. We know the rate—cement is 16% of concrete. The desired amount of concrete, the basis for comparison, is known. We are required to find the amount of cement or 16% of a ton.

PROBLEM: Mr. Brown bought half of a baby beef for storage in his freezer. It weighed 170 pounds. If beef loses 36% in dressing what was the weight of the live beef?

Just as in the previous problem a percent is given and a weight is known. Another weight is to be found. Before we can determine whether the problem is of the same type we must identify the basis for comparison and what is compared. The rate, 36%, does not compare the animal's dressed weight to its live weight. It compares loss of weight to live weight. But we know the dressed weight, since $\frac{1}{2}$ of it is given, and by inference the ratio of dressed weight to live weight, 100%–36%. Since 64% of the live weight is dressed or .64 × live weight = dressed weight, we may find the live weight by dividing dressed weight by .64.

A two-step analysis is sometimes used here. Since 64% of live weight = 340 pounds, 1% = $\frac{1}{64}$ of 340 pounds, and 100% = 100 × $\frac{1}{64}$ × 340.

PROBLEM: There are 17 boys and 21 girls in the class. What percent of the class are girls?

This is the easiest type to identify. It is the only case of the three which requires the finding of a percent. The crucial point is again to determine what is compared to what. Not boys to girls or girls to boys, but girls to the total. Then we are to change $\frac{21}{38}$ to percent.

From the standpoint of social utility there is no denying the importance of the topics of *interest* and *discount*. However, the assumption that seventh- and eighth-grade children are vitally interested in these and such allied topics as installment buying, insurance, and taxation is open to question. A part of children's difficulty with such topics may stem not from a lack of prerequisite mathematical skills and concepts but from a lack of interest in and appreciation of the importance of such topics to adult consumers.

No new mathematics beyond that required for percent is necessary for handling problems of simple interest and discount. The only new idea introduced in interest problems is the time element. The money on which interest is paid, the principal, is the *base*; the interest is the *percentage*; the interest rate is the *rate*. Rate of interest is stated in percent *per year*. When we solve an interest problem in which the interest is required we find the interest for one year, then multiply by the number of years. The same three cases of percent are possible with interest problems. Case I, we know the principal and rate and are to find the amount of interest. Case II, we know the annual interest and the principal and are to find the rate of interest. Case III, we know the annual interest and rate of interest and are to find the principal.

The same situation holds for discount problems. The original amount, the list price is the *base*; the amount deducted, the discount, is the *percentage*; and the rate of discount is the *rate*.

In the interest of consumer education certain business practices relative to interest and discount should be studied critically. Interest is an amount added on, discount is a deduction. The banking practice of discounting notes is a case in point. If the bank makes a loan and discounts the note at 6 % the rate of interest is more than 6 %. The argument that the borrower is merely paying the interest in advance is a spurious one. Suppose we sign a note for $100 and the bank discounts it at 6 %. We receive $94; we have not paid $6 interest, we have paid nothing. At the end of the year we must pay the $100 face of the note. We have repaid the principal, which is $94—not $100—and we have paid $6 interest. The rate of interest is $\frac{9}{64}$, which is just under 6.4 %.

The quoted rate of interest on an installment purchase is far more deceptive. It is common practice to charge interest on the total unpaid balance until it is completely repaid. Let us say the unpaid balance is $100 and 10 % interest is charged. If the debt is to be paid in 12 equal installments we must pay $\frac{1}{12}$ of $110 or $9.17 per month. The interest on $100 at 10 % for 1 month is 83¢. Then $8.34 of the first monthly payment is applied to the unpaid balance. During the second month the debtor owes only $101.66. Each subsequent payment further reduces the unpaid balance until the final payment reduces it to zero. Yet we pay interest on the total $100 for the entire year. The actual rate of interest is not 10 %. We can approximate the actual rate by assuming the average unpaid monthly balance to be $50. (It was $100 at the beginning of the first month and $0 at the end of the twelfth.) If $10 interest is paid in one year on an average indebtedness of $50 the rate is $\frac{10}{50}$ or 20 %.

When dealing with percents we should remember that a percent is a ratio. One occasionally sees percents averaged. Although we can average any set of numbers, it is meaningless to find the average of a set of percents unless the bases are the same or very nearly so. We shall illustrate the point with a simple problem:

PROBLEM: Mr. Brown made two real estate sales. He gained 10% on the first transaction and 20% on the second. What was his average gain?

As stated, the problem cannot be solved. The average gain was not 15 % unless the cost of the two pieces of property was the same. We know the average gain was more than 10 % and less than 20 %. We must know the costs before anything more definite can be determined. To take an extreme case, suppose the 10 % gain was made on a piece of property which cost Mr. Brown $100,000 and the 20 % gain was on property costing $2000. The total gain is $10,400, the total cost $102,000. Then the average gain is $\frac{10400}{102000} = 10.19\%$, approximately.

Exercises

1 What determines the denominator of a decimal fraction?

2 Is it more important for the child to know that the decimal point separates the whole number from the fraction or that it marks the position of the ones digit? Why?

3 Are there ways other than by using the decimal point to write decimal fractions? If so, what are they?

4 When we multiply a number by 100 by annexing two zeros, have we moved the decimal point to the right or the original digits to the left?

5 Demonstrate, using powers of 10, the significance of the statement that the ones digit is the center of a number.

6 How would you explain to an eighth-grade pupil the rule for placing the decimal in a product? How would you develop the rule with a fifth-grade class?

7 Illustrate how to place the decimal point in a quotient by approximation.

8 Is the fact that not all common fractions can be reduced to terminating decimals a serious limitation? Can all decimal fractions be expressed exactly as common fractions?

9 What background is essential if in division all divisors are to be reduced to integers?

10 If we find the average of a number of percents, what assumption must be made in order for the average to have any significance?

11 Are baseball "batting averages" really averages? If so, what kind? Are they percents?

12 Why is it not feasible to "invert and multiply" when we divide by a decimal fraction? Can it be done?

13 Give arguments for and against solving percentage problems by type.

14 List the more common types of mistake encountered in working with percents.

15 Will the check of nines work with decimal fractions in the same way it does with integers? Will it check the placing of the decimal point in the answer? Will the check work with common fractions?

16 Give two reasons for teaching common fractions before decimals.

17 Some persons advocate the complete abandonment of common fractions. Discuss this from the standpoint of mathematics and from the standpoint of practicality.

18 Is it easier to compare the size of two common fractions or two decimal fractions? Why?

19 In multiplying decimals how would you lead children to derive the rule for pointing off the product?

20 Which of the following divisions of decimals is the most difficult for children to grasp?

(a) $4 \div .2$
(b) $.2 \div 4$
(c) $2.4 \div 1.2$
(d) $.4 \div .2$

How would you explain each?

Suggested Supplementary Readings

Buckingham, B. R., *Elementary Arithmetic: Its Meaning and Practice.* Boston: Ginn and Company, 1947. Chaps. X, XI.

Larsen, Harold D., *Arithmetic for Colleges.* New York: The Macmillan Company, 1950. Chaps. VIII, IX.

Morton, Robert L., *Teaching Children Arithmetic.* New York: Silver Burdett Company, 1953. Pp. 319–388.

Spencer, Peter L., and Marguerite Brydegaard, *Building Mathematical Concepts in the Elementary School.* New York: Henry Holt and Company, 1952. Chap. VI.

Spitzer, Herbert E., *The Teaching of Arithmetic*, Third Edition. Boston: Houghton Mifflin Co., 1961. Chap. VIII.

Swain, Robert L., *Understanding Arithmetic.* New York: Rinehart and Company, Inc., 1957. Chap. IX.

Measurement and
Approximate Computation

CHAPTER TWELVE

A WORLD WITHOUT MEASUREMENT IS almost inconceivable. The houses we live in, the automobiles we ride in, the clocks we go to work by, most of the jobs we do, all involve measurement. The story of the development of systems of measurement and units of measure is a fascinating one.

All measurements are of necessity approximations. Consequently, computations involving measurements must be done with approximate numbers. Yet many persons have implicit faith in the exactness of all numbers. At the other extreme, it is possible to implement the theoretical aspects of computation with approximate numbers to an impractical and unrealistic degree.

Here we shall develop common sense working rules which yield satisfactory and practical results which are consistent with the inherent nature of measurement.

12.1 APPROXIMATE NUMBERS

When we refer to approximate numbers this is not a reference to a kind of number, it is a reference to the use to which the numbers are put. Just as .67 may be used as an approximation of $\frac{2}{3}$ we may also on occasion use $\frac{2}{3}$ as the approximate value of .67 or possibly .7. It is quite possible to use irrational numbers as approximate values of rationals or other irrationals. A very good approximation to π is $\sqrt{10}$. Verify this by finding decimal approximations for each of them.

We use rational approximations of irrational numbers as an aid to computation. It is possible to express the area of a circle exactly, assuming we know the exact radius, but the result will have to be in terms of π. A circle whose radius is exactly 2 inches has an exact area of 4π square inches. But the result is usually more useful if it is expressed as $\frac{88}{7}$ square inches. Although many uses of approximate numbers are a matter of convenience, many others are unavoidable.

Every measurement is an approximation. A measurement is a comparison with a standard. We measure a room as 12 feet wide. This means that it is 12 times as wide as the length of a foot rule. The room may be exactly 12 feet wide but we can never establish the fact by measurement. We must place the rule end to end and count the number of one-foot intervals. We may get exactly 12 intervals but we cannot be certain that each interval starts exactly where the preceding one ended. We cannot be certain whether the last interval exactly completes the width of the room. Nor can we be certain the rule is exactly one foot long. If a random collection of half-a-dozen yardsticks (the give-away variety) are compared, the results may be surprising. Our measuring instruments are copies of the legal standard and we can never be certain that they are perfect. We are limited both by the extent to which the measuring instrument agrees with the standard and by its precision. A yardstick is usually subdivided into eighths of an inch. This means that we can obtain a measurement which is correct to the nearest eighth of an inch. We can usually go a step further. We can usually determine the measurement to the nearest sixteenth of an inch. If we attempt to go beyond this point we are in the realm of guessing. Limitations of the instrument itself and human limitations make it impossible for a measurement to be exact.

Most enumerations are exact. We can count the number of people in a room and know exactly how many there are but we could never determine exactly what they weigh. Sometimes even enumerations are not exact. The taking of the census is an enumeration, but births and deaths which occur while the count is in progress, as well as people who are missed, make the final result only approximately correct.

12.2 PRECISION AND ACCURACY

If it is impossible to make an exact measurement we must have some means of evaluating the appropriateness of our approximation. How far from the true value is the measurement? How much variation from the true value is permissible?

Let us assume that the measuring instrument is perfect in the sense that it is an exact duplicate of the standard and that it is perfectly subdivided. For example, assume we have a yardstick that is exactly a yard long and is perfectly subdivided into eighths of an inch. Let us further assume that we make no mistakes in using it. We align the zero end perfectly with one end of the distance to be measured. We read correctly the marking on the rule which corresponds to the other end. The assumptions are impossible to obtain in practice; deviations from the ideal are unavoidable *errors*. Suppose the end of the measured distance coincides with a point on the yardstick which lies between $23\frac{5}{8}$ inches and $23\frac{3}{4}$ inches. The user of the instrument must exercise judgment at this point in deciding whether the point if nearer $23\frac{5}{8}$ or $23\frac{3}{4}$. If the point is very near the center of the interval it is quite possible for an error of judgment to enter. The same measurement might appear nearer $23\frac{5}{8}$ to some observers and nearer $23\frac{3}{4}$ to others. In a case of this sort we could with assurance report the distance as $23\frac{11}{16}$ inches, but not exactly. Is it closer to $23\frac{21}{32}$, $23\frac{22}{32}$, or $23\frac{23}{32}$? The process could go on endlessly.

Let us suppose the end of the distance measured is definitely nearer $23\frac{5}{8}$ inches and we make no attempt to read sixteenths. We then record the distance as $23\frac{5}{8}$ inches. If another distance is measured and found to be between $23\frac{1}{2}$ and $23\frac{5}{8}$ inches, but nearer the latter, it too is recorded $23\frac{5}{8}$ inches. All measurements which are recorded as $23\frac{5}{8}$ inches are presumed to be measures of distances which are nearer $23\frac{5}{8}$ inches than $23\frac{1}{2}$ or $23\frac{3}{4}$. Then they are measurements which lie between $23\frac{9}{16}$ and $23\frac{11}{16}$ inches. If the distance is so near an end of the interval, say $23\frac{9}{16}$, that we cannot determine whether it is less than, or greater than, or for that matter exactly, 23_{16}^{9} we have equal justification for recording the measurement as $23\frac{4}{8}$ or $23\frac{5}{8}$. The arbitrary rule which is usually followed includes the lower end of the interval but not the upper. Then all distances 23_{16}^{9} and above but less than 23_{16}^{11} are recorded as $23\frac{5}{8}$. We would, of course, record 23_{16}^{11} as $23\frac{6}{8}$ under this rule.

In the foregoing situation the instrument used, the yardstick, imposes a limitation on the closeness with which we can approximate. We can make a measurement *to the nearest eighth of an inch*, the smallest unit of length with which we can deal. We could, of course, use the instrument to make measurements to the nearest inch or nearest foot but not to the nearest thousandth of an inch.

The smallest unit of measure used in a measurement determines its *precision*. The smaller the unit the greater the precision. The manner in which an approximate number is written should indicate its precision. For example, $23\frac{1}{2}$ inches is to be interpreted as precise to the nearest $\frac{1}{2}$ inch. It is the measure of a distance which is $23\frac{1}{4}$ inches or more but less than $23\frac{3}{4}$ inches. Note that in the foregoing statement both $23\frac{1}{4}$ and $23\frac{3}{4}$ are exact numbers. If our measurement is $23\frac{1}{2}$ inches to the nearest eighth of an inch it should be written as $23\frac{4}{8}$ inches.

When decimal notation is employed we may indicate precision in any one of three ways:

(1) The last significant digit of the number (see Section 12.4) indicates the smallest unit of measure and thus the precision. For example, the approximate number 12.7 pounds is precise to the nearest tenth of a pound, but 12.70 pounds is precise to the nearest hundredth of a pound.

(2) We may indicate precision by indicating the possible correction. If we write 12.7 $\pm$ .05 we indicate that the true value approximated may be as low as 12.65 and as high as 12.75. This is the same degree of precision as was implied in (1). But the second method has broader application. For example, 12.7 $\pm$ .3 means the true value may deviate from 12.7 by not more than .3; it lies between 12.4 and 13.

(3) We may indicate precision by explicitly stating the degree of refinement of the measure; for example, 12.7 pounds to the nearest tenth pound.

The degree of precision of two measurements cannot be compared unless they are of the same kind. One cannot say $15\frac{1}{2}$ hours is

more or less precise than $6\frac{1}{8}$ inches since we cannot compare the sizes
of $\frac{1}{2}$ of an hour and $\frac{1}{8}$ of an inch. The measurements need not be made
in the same units, however, if they are the same kinds of unit. We
know that 105 inches is more precise than 5.16 miles because, both
being units of length, we know one inch is less than $\frac{1}{100}$ of a mile.

Precision is not the sole criterion upon which we may evaluate a
measurement. A measurement of 3 inches, precise to the nearest inch,
is far more precise than one of 516 miles precise to the nearest mile.
But in another sense 516 miles is a closer approximation than 3 inches.
The possible divergence from the true value, $\frac{1}{2}$ mile, is much smaller
compared to the total measurement of 516 miles than is $\frac{1}{2}$ inch compared
to 3 inches. The ratio of maximum variation to the total measure
determines the *accuracy* of the measurement. The smaller the ratio
the more accurate the measurement. The accuracy of 516 miles is

$$\frac{\frac{1}{2}}{516} = \frac{1}{1032} \, .$$

The accuracy of 3 inches is

$$\frac{\frac{1}{2}}{3} = \frac{1}{6} \, ,$$

which is far less accurate than 516 miles.

Since accuracy is a ratio, a pure number, and not feet or pounds
or seconds, the accuracy of any two measurements can be compared.
We see that $15\frac{1}{2}$ hours is less accurate than $6\frac{1}{8}$ inches because

$$\frac{\frac{1}{4}}{15\frac{1}{2}} = \frac{1}{62}$$

is larger than

$$\frac{\frac{1}{16}}{6\frac{1}{8}} = \frac{1}{98} \, .$$

Which of the two properties, precision and accuracy, is the more
important? In making measurements should we strive for precision
or accuracy? That depends on the situation. There are times when
precision is of over-riding importance. The situation may call for a
high degree of precision but not much accuracy. At other times a high
degree of accuracy is desired but precision is important only to the
extent that it gives the requisite accuracy. For example, if a car-
buretor requires a jet opening .005 inch in diameter, this is a high
degree of precision. But if the tolerance is .0005 inch the opening may
vary from .0045 to .0055 inches. Here the accuracy is low, the
relative error being $\frac{1}{10}$. On the other hand, the accepted distance to

the sun, 93,000,000 miles, is precise only to the nearest million miles. Yet the percent of error is only slightly more than $\frac{1}{2}$ of 1 percent.

Exercises

1 What determines the precision of a measurement?

2 What determines the accuracy of a measurement?

3 Give an example of an approximate number that is not a measurement.

4 Why must measures be of the same kind if they are to be compared as to precision?

5 Which measure of each of the following pairs of measures is the more precise?
(a) 1400 feet—4.6 miles
(b) 32 ounces—.127 pounds
(c) 156 pounds—1.56 pounds

6 Which measure of each of the pairs of measures in Exercise 5 is the more accurate?

7 A measurement which is recorded as 12.4 yards is the measure of an object whose length lies within what range?

8 What is the percent of error of a measurement of 125 pounds?

12.3 ERRORS

Measurements must be approximate because of the presence of unavoidable errors. A mistake usually results in error but an error is not necessarily due to a mistake. Our concern here is with those errors which do not result from mistakes. Errors may be *constant*. For example, a 100-foot steel tape may have been made 0.2 inches too short. If we are aware of constant errors which cannot be eliminated we can compensate for them. Errors may also be *random*. Such factors as imperfect alignment, temperature changes (which will cause a steel tape to expand and contract), and the estimating essential to reading the instrument are possible sources of random errors in making linear measurements. Random errors may be positive or negative; they tend to cancel each other out.

The error introduced by virtue of the fact that there must be a smallest unit in any measurement is called its *absolute error*. It is one half the smallest unit of measure. It is the maximum amount the true value can vary from the measurement. The measure $6\frac{1}{8}$ inches has for its smallest unit $\frac{1}{8}$ inch; its absolute error is $\frac{1}{16}$ inch since this is the maximum amount the measurement can be off. *Relative error* is the ratio of the absolute error to the measurement. *Percent of error* is simply 100 times the relative error.

We state precision in terms of the smallest unit rather than absolute error; $6\frac{1}{8}$ inches is precise to the nearest $\frac{1}{8}$ inch. Relative error is a direct measure of accuracy. The relative error of $6\frac{1}{8}$ inches is $\frac{1}{98}$. This means that our measurement can differ from the true value not more than one part in 98.

12.4 SIGNIFICANT DIGITS

The concept of *significant digits* is an important consideration in connection with both precision and accuracy. The digits of an approximate number are significant if they serve a purpose other than merely helping to place the decimal point. All nonzero digits are significant. A zero may be significant or nonsignificant. A nonsignificant one is not therefore insignificant, unimportant, or useless. It serves solely as a place holder. Zeros situated between significant digits are always significant. In the number 506.3 the zero is a place holder; it gives the 5 its correct position relative to the decimal point. But it does more; it tells us how many groups of ten are present—there are none.

On the other hand, if 5000 is an approximate number precise to the nearest thousand none of the zeros are significant. Their only function is to give the 5 its correct position, or—what amounts to the same thing—they place the decimal point. There is no reason for writing fifteen, correct to the nearest unit, as 15.0. If 15.0 is correctly used the zero is used to specify that to the nearest tenth we have no tenths. If we know nothing, or wish to say nothing, about the number of hundredths of a unit in the measurement we should not write 15.00.

Terminating zeros in a fraction are used solely to specify that we know there are no units of that particular size. They do not help place the decimal; that has already been done. But they serve a role other than that and therefore are significant. On the other hand, initial zeros in a fraction are never significant. In the number .05 the zero merely places the decimal. But is it not true that it tells us we have no tenths? It is true that we have no tenths but we do not need the zero to tell us. The fact that the 5 is the first nonzero digit tells us that it stands in the position corresponding to the largest unit in the measurement. We do not write 56 as 056. There are no hundreds present but we do not need the zero to tell us.

All digits of a mixed number are significant. Consider 5000.0. The final zero specifies there are no tenths of a unit. If we know how many tenths of a unit are present we must of necessity know how many units, tens, and hundreds are present. The zeros in the integral part are between significant digits and are thus significant.

Consider the number 560 out of context. Is this a number correct to the nearest ten or the nearest unit? It might be either. If we want to indicate a number correct to the nearest ten the zero is not significant. On the other hand, if we want to indicate that to the nearest unit we have 560, we know there are no units present and the zero is significant. This ambiguity may be cared for from the context in which the number is used. If we have a group of like measures 17, 19, 20, 23 it is reasonable to assume the 20 is a measure to the nearest unit just as the others are. We may also eliminate the ambiguity by stating the absolute error or by indicating it as 20 ± 5. Finally, we may indicate that a terminating zero in an integer is significant by underscoring it, 20. In the number 5000 we indicate a measure of five thousand correct to the nearest ten; the first two zeros are significant and the last one is not. In the absence of any indication that terminal zeros in an integer are significant they should be considered non-significant.

In summary we may say all digits are significant except (1) terminal zeros of an integer which are not by one of the above means designated as significant, and (2) initial zeros of a pure fraction.

The last significant digit of a number indicates its precision. Of two numbers the one with the greater number of significant digits is the more accurate. For example, 100.0 is more accurate than 931,000 because the relative error is $\frac{1}{2}$ the smallest unit divided by the measure, and the position of the decimal point is of no consequence. The relative error of 100.0 is $.05/100.0 = 5/10000$ and that of 931,000 is $500/931000 = 5/9310$. In fact, we may say that of two measures that one whose significant digits represent the greater number is the more accurate. For example, .00531 is more accurate than 530.

12.5 ROUNDING OFF

When we compute with approximate numbers our results frequently contain digits which indicate unjustified precision. If for this or other reasons we wish to reduce the precision of a number the process is known as *rounding off*.

If we round off an integer, each digit discarded must be replaced by a zero. We round off 1523 to the nearest hundred and get 1500 because 1523 is nearer 1500 than 1600. If the number is a fraction the discarded digits must *not* be replaced by zeros. The fraction .03745, when rounded to two significant digits, becomes .037. If the 4 and 5 were replaced by zeros we would still have four significant digits. The two above rules are combined when we round off a mixed number. Discarded digits of the fraction are not replaced with zeros but if digits to the integer are dropped they are.

EXAMPLES.   174.33 = 174.3 to four significant digits.

174.33 = 170 to two significant digits.

If the highest digit dropped is 0, 1, 2, 3, or 4, the lowest digit retained is left intact. If the highest digit dropped is 5, 6, 7, 8, or 9, the lowest digit retained is increased by one.

EXAMPLES.

9342 = 9300 to two significant digits because 9342 is nearer 9300 than 9400. But
9372 = 9400 to two significant digits because 9372 is nearer 9400 than 9300.

There is one exception to the above rule. If the highest digit dropped is a terminal 5, as 165 or .325 to be rounded to two significant digits, or a 5 followed by zeros as 1.7500 to be rounded to two digits, the rule is altered. In these cases we have no evidence to indicate which rounded number we are nearer. For example, 165 is, to the extent of our knowledge, equally close to 160 and 170. Here we must adopt an arbitrary rule of procedure. Our objective is to minimize the error in the final result. The rule most frequently followed requires that the lowest digit retained be kept or increased by one, whichever is necessary to give an *even* digit:

EXAMPLES.   1.650 = 1.6 to two digits
1.750 = 1.8 to two digits
1.850 = 1.8 to two digits

The justification for this process lies in the fact that our result will have a positive error about half the time and a negative error the other half. The two sets of errors will tend to cancel each other out over a large number of cases.

Exercises

1 A distance between two points is measured to the nearest eighth of an inch and then to the nearest thirty-second of an inch.

(a) Which measurement has the greater absolute error?

(b) Which measurement has the greater relative error?

2 Find the number of significant digits in each of the following approximate numbers.

(a) .6070

(b) 43.0000

(c) 0.036

(d) 32.004

(e) 200.00004

3 If a number is exact what may we say about its significant digits?

4 Justify the statement that the maximum amount the true value can vary from a measurement is $\frac{1}{2}$ the unit of measure.

5 Express the maximum error, the relative error, and the percent of error of the following in base ten.

(a) 32.6_{eight} (b) $.043_{five}$ (c) 1659_{twelve}

6 Round off each of the following to three significant digits.

(a) 35096   (d) 8.9521

(b) 1.1320   (e) 368005

(c) 4525.00

12.6 COMPUTATION WITH APPROXIMATE NUMBERS

Suppose we attempt to add the following weights: 500 pounds, 1.5 pounds, and 136 pounds. These weights represent values between 450 and 550 pounds, 1.45 and 1.55 pounds, and 135.5 and 136.5 pounds respectively. The sum of the minimum values is $450 + 1.45 + 135.5 = 586.95$ pounds. The sum of the maximum values is $550 + 1.55 + 136.5 = 688.05$ pounds. The true value lies somewhere between the two. Then we are not certain of the value even to the nearest hundred pounds. The maximum value is slightly closer to 700 pounds than the minimum is to 600 pounds.

The maximum error of the 500-pound measure, 50 pounds, is several times as great as the 1.5-pound entry. It is of little value to know the 136-pound item to the nearest pound. The limit of precision imposed by the 500-pound measure places the same limitation on the sum.

When we add or subtract, the measurements must be not only the same kind—we cannot add 15 pounds and 25 feet—they must be in the same units. If they are the same kind of measures they can be converted to common units which will also be common to the sum. We can compare the addends and the sum in terms of precision. The least precise addend sets the limit as to the precision with which the sum can be obtained. *A sum of approximate numbers should be expressed to the same degree of precision as that of the least precise addend.* The same situation holds for subtraction. In addition or subtraction we are not concerned with accuracy, for the least precise addend may be the most accurate or the least accurate.

One rule for adding approximate numbers requires that we round off each addend to the degree of precision of the least precise one, then add. A variation of this rule requires that we round to within one place of the least precise addend, add, then round off the sum one place. Still another variation permits the addition of the numbers without rounding off. We then round off the sum to the precision of the least precise measure. The first procedure is the easiest, the last minimizes the error. Frequently all three rules will give the same final result but occasionally the results may differ slightly.

EXAMPLE. Add $12.6 + 120.31 + .073 + 2.436$
By the first rule

$$
\begin{array}{r}
12.6 \\
120.3 \\
.1 \\
2.4 \\
\hline
135.4
\end{array}
$$

By the second rule

$$
\begin{array}{r}
12.6 \\
120.31 \\
.07 \\
2.44 \\
\hline
135.42 \rightarrow 135.4
\end{array}
$$

By the third rule

$$
\begin{array}{r}
12.6 \\
120.31 \\
.073 \\
2.436 \\
\hline
135.419 \rightarrow 135.4
\end{array}
$$

EXAMPLE.   Add 3.49 + 133 + 2.38 + 16.6

By the first rule

$$
\begin{array}{r}
3 \\
133 \\
2 \\
17 \\
\hline
155
\end{array}
$$

By the second rule

$$
\begin{array}{r}
3.5 \\
133 \\
2.4 \\
16.6 \\
\hline
155.5 \rightarrow 156
\end{array}
$$

By the third rule

$$
\begin{array}{r}
3.49 \\
133 \\
2.38 \\
16.6 \\
\hline
155.47 \rightarrow 155
\end{array}
$$

When we multiply, one factor must be an abstract number. We cannot multiply 3 feet by 59 gallons. We do say that we multiply feet by feet to find area in square feet. But we actually multiply square feet by an abstract number. Consider finding the area of a 3-by-4 rectangle:

We may consider this by rows as 3 rows of 4 square feet each. Then the area is 3×4 square feet $= 12$ square feet. Or by columns, we have 4 columns of 3 square feet each. And the area is 4×3 square feet $= 12$ square feet. Notwithstanding this fact, the dimensions are linear measure and the product is a measure of area. Consequently the precision of the product is not comparable to the precision of the factors.

Suppose we wish to find the area of a rectangle the dimensions of which are 6.1 feet by 23.4 feet. Should the area be expressed to the nearest tenth of a square foot? Perhaps it should be to the nearest hundredth since a square $\frac{1}{10}$ foot by $\frac{1}{10}$ foot has an area $\frac{1}{100}$ of a square foot.

If we take the minimum value which the measurements may represent we get $6.05 \times 23.35 = 141.2675$ square feet. But maximum values give $6.15 \times 23.45 = 144.2175$ square feet. All we know about the exact area is that it lies somewhere within this range. We are certain of the result only to the first two digits. We may say the area is 140 square feet, a two-significant-digit result. We are certain that the area is between 135 and 145 square feet. The factors 6.1 and 23.4 had two and three significant digits respectively. A product can be no more accurate than the least accurate factor. *A product of approximate numbers should be expressed with the same number of significant digits as are possessed by the least accurate factor.* Similarly, in the division the quotient should contain the same number of significant digits as possessed by the dividend or divisor, whichever has the least. If one factor is exact the product should contain the same number of significant digits as that of the other factor.

A very satisfactory rule for multiplying approximate numbers is: Round off all factors so that they will have one more significant digit than the factor containing the least. Multiply, then round off the product so as to have the same number of significant digits as possessed by the least accurate factor.

In summary, a sum or difference should never be more precise than the least precise part of the data used. A product or quotient should never be more accurate than the least accurate part of the data involved. Otherwise we are indicating that we know more about the result than we do.

Exercises

1 Interpret the meaning of the following approximate numbers:

(a) 12.5 feet
(b) $\frac{2}{3}$
(c) .67
(d) 12.50 feet
(e) $4\frac{0}{8}$ inches

2 Determine which of the following pairs of numbers is the more precise and which is the more accurate:

(a) 126 inches; 126 miles
(b) 5 pounds; 250 tons
(c) $\frac{1}{3}$ yard; 1 foot
(d) 56 gallons; .00056 gallons

3 Is it possible for two like measures to have the same precision and accuracy? Can the more precise be the more accurate? Can the less precise be the more accurate? Can they have the same precision and different accuracy? Can they have the same accuracy and different precision? Illustrate each of the above to which your answer is *yes*. Explain why those to which your answer is *no* are impossible.

4 Distinguish between errors of measurement and mistakes.

5 Find the absolute error, the relative error, and the percent of error in the following measurements:

(a) 126 ± .5 miles
(b) .025 centimeters
(c) ¼ centimeter
(d) 25,000 miles

6 Determine the number of significant digits in each of the following:

(a) 100.50
(b) 10,050
(c) 100,50$\underline{0}$
(d) .00100$\underline{5}$0
(e) 9340
(f) 93.40

7 Round off the following to two significant digits:

(a) 8463
(b) 92.50
(c) 37,210
(d) .006750

8 Use each of the three rules given in the text to add the following approximate numbers:

$$326 + 451.3 + 5\underline{0} + 27.45$$

9 Find the maximum and minimum areas enclosed by a rectangle whose sides are measured to be 150.4 feet and 27.3 feet.

10 Use the rule for multiplying approximate numbers to find 150.4×27.3. Compare the result with the result of Exercise 9.

11 In finding relative error why do we not use the ratio of the absolute error to the true value instead of absolute error to obtained measurement?

12 Find the absolute error and the relative error when we use .67 as an approximation for the exact number $\frac{2}{3}$.

12.7 SCIENTIFIC NOTATION

This is the age of the astronomically large and the infinitesimally small. Astronomers use as their unit of length the light year, which is the distance traveled by light in one year or approximately 6,000,000,000,000 miles. Physical scientists use a unit of length, the angstrom unit, which is .0000000001 meter. In spite of such tremendously large and unbelievably small units scientists still have need for a more compact way of writing very large and very small numbers. Scientific notation fills that need.

An approximate number is written in scientific notation if it is written as a number 1 or more but less than 10, multiplied by an integral power of 10. The number between 1 and 10 must indicate the significant digits of the number. Unless the number in ordinary notation has nonsignificant digits nothing is gained by using scientific notation.

We can convert a number to scientific notation by shifting the decimal point to *standard position*, that is, to a position such that one and only one nonzero digit stands to its left, then multiply by the power of ten necessary to shift the decimal point back to its original position.

For example, to express 137,000,000 in scientific notation we first place the decimal point in standard position and drop the nonsignificant terminal zeros. This step yields 1.37. If we were to move the decimal back to its original position it would be equivalent to multiplying by 10^8. Then $137,000,000 = 1.37 \times 10^8$. In effect, we have divided by 10,000,000 by shifting the decimal point, then multiplied by $10,000,000 = 10^8$.

We follow the same procedure with very small numbers. To express .0000016 in scientific notation we first place the decimal point in standard position, giving 1.6. This amounts to multiplying the number by 1,000,000. Then, to divide by 1,000,000 we multiply by 10^{-6}, giving 1.6×10^{-6}.

The idea of scientific notation is an obvious extension of the positional character of our base-ten number system. Recall that shifting the decimal point one place to the right increases the value of each digit tenfold. Similarly, shifting one place to the left decreases the position of each digit by one, ones become tenths, tens become ones, and so on. Then shifting the decimal point to the left one place is equivalent to dividing by ten. The integral exponent on ten in scientific notation indicates the number of places and the direction the decimal point must be moved in order to go back to ordinary notation. A negative exponent implies a shift to the left; a positive exponent implies a shift to the right.

The value of scientific notation is more than mere shortening of the symbolism. It is easier to grasp the magnitude of a very large or very small number when it is written in this form. The form also facilitates computation with approximate numbers.

EXAMPLE.   Evaluate $\dfrac{179400 \times .00053}{7600 \times .0000226}$

First, we write in scientific notation, rounding all numbers to two significant digits:

$$\frac{1.8 \times 10^5 \times 5.3 \times 10^{-4}}{7.6 \times 10^3 \times 2.3 \times 10^{-5}} .$$

Combining powers of 10 we get

$$\frac{1.8 \times 5.3}{7.6 \times 2.3} \times 10^3$$

which simplifies to $.55 \times 10^3 = 5.5 \times 10^4$.

Exercises

1 Write the following in scientific notation:
(a) 86,300
(b) 150×10^6
(c) 1.7×10^{-5}
(d) .000830
(e) $.007 \times 10^3$

2 Write the following in ordinary notation:
(a) 5.6×10^8
(b) 1.1×10^{-5}
(c) 221×10^4
(d) 2.34×10^0
(e) 4.3×10^{-1}

3 Use scientific notation to evaluate the following approximate computations:
(a) $76900000 \times .000063$
(b) $186000 \times 3600 \times 24 \times 365$
(c) $\dfrac{.015 \times 9371}{43.8 \times .0006}$

Suggested Supplementary Readings

Andrews, F. E., "Revolving Numbers," *The Atlantic Monthly*, Vol. 155, February 1935, pp. 208–211.

Bakst, Aaron, "Approximate Computation," *Twelfth Yearbook*, National Council of Teachers of Mathematics. New York: Teachers College, Columbia University, 1937.

Banks, J. Houston, *Elements of Mathematics*, Second Edition. Boston: Allyn and Bacon, Inc., 1961. Ch. IX.

Butler, Charles H., and F. Lynwood Wren, *Teaching of Secondary Mathematics*. New York: McGraw-Hill Book Company, Inc., 1951. Pp. 280–289.

Guttman, Solomon, "Cyclic Numbers," *The American Mathematical Monthly*, Vol. 41, March 1934, pp. 159–166.

Mueller, Francis J., *Arithmetic, Its Structure and Concepts*. Englewood Cliffs, N.J.: Prentice-Hall, Inc., 1956. Chap. VI.

Principles of Measurement

CHAPTER THIRTEEN

IN THE STRICT SENSE OF THE WORD, the science of arithmetic is in no way dependent upon measurement and such allied topics as graphical and tabular representation of data. However, a surprisingly large proportion of both adult and child application of arithmetic is related to measurement. Fifteen of the 29 items on the check list of mathematical competence contained in the final report of the Commission on Post-War Plans are definitely related to some aspect of measurement.[1]

Competence in the abstract arithmetical processes is necessary but not sufficient for gaining the arithmetic goals of social utility. Furthermore, situations from the child's experiences which involve aspects of measurement provide some of the best motivation for introduction of new arithmetical processes. We may properly think

[1] Commission Post-War Plans of the National Council of Teachers of Mathematics, *Guidance Pamphlet in Mathematics for High School Students* (New York: The Mathematics Teacher, 1947), pp. 4–5.

of measurement as representing a significant part of *applied* arithmetic. The two, application and theory, should proceed together. We cannot assume that the skills and concepts of measurement will be mastered incidentally.

13.1 NATURE OF MEASUREMENT

The most basic concept concerning measurement is the idea that a measurement is a comparison, a comparison of magnitudes. The rudiments of measurement are present in many of the child's earliest experiences. In such phrases as "this is too big," "a short time," "it fits just right," "real fast," "slow," "a long way," "too late," there is an implicit comparison with some reference unit. The referent of a small child is often inappropriate, at least from the adult standpoint. To a six-year-old, a 150-pound forty-year-old man is indeed "real big" and "real old." Parenthetically, even to most adults there are times when $5.00 looks like a lot of money. The appropriateness of such indefinite comparisons, where the reference unit is merely implied, is a relative thing. Its appropriateness depends upon the past experience of the observer as well as the particular situation. The speed of a propeller-driven airplane is slow if the implied referent is a supersonic jet. But compared to a man on a bicycle it is quite fast. The referent which the young child uses is of necessity limited by his experience. An ordinary apple would appear quite large to one who had never seen anything but crabapples.

Opportunities should be provided, beginning in the earliest grades, for development of more appropriate and more precise referents, including the standard units of measure. Definitions alone are of little value in developing the child's conception of the standard units such as pound, foot, minute, and mile. Even though one has a fairly precise conception of a foot, it is not too much help in visualizing a mile to know it contains 5280 feet.

Development of such concepts must be an outgrowth of experience. Concepts of *inch, foot*, and *yard* can be developed from use of the foot rule and yardstick. But something more than the measuring instrument is needed to help the child form concepts of *ounce, mile, acre*, and the like. An elementary-school child will gain a better notion of an acre if he knows it is about the size of a football field than if he knows it is $\frac{1}{640}$ of a square mile.

Nonstandard units, such as a pace, the surface covered by the hand, the time it takes to play a phonograph record, and a glassful can be used to advantage in developing such concepts as distance, area, time, and capacity. They may also be used to advantage in demonstrating such properties of measurement as: (1) All measurements are comparisons, (2) No measurement is exact, (3) Objects may be compared with each other indirectly by comparing each with a measuring unit, (4) The preciseness of a measurement, (5) The desirability of standard reference units.

13.2 UNITS OF MEASURE

In the past a great amount of time and effort were devoted in arithmetic instruction to memorizing innumerable tables of measures. Modern arithmetic texts contain such tables in varying amounts. They are carried in an appendix and are presumed to be used for reference.

The question of memorizing tables of measures is somewhat similar to that of memorizing the basic addition and multiplication facts. We may never require the latter to be memorized in serial order. However, there are arguments in favor of it.[2] In any event, the ultimate goal is automatic response. Ideally, this goal is reached through meaningful development of the facts coupled with sufficient familiarity through use.

A similar point of view may be adopted with regard to tables of measure. But there are important differences. We should not take the position that it is unnecessary to know any measure facts simply because they can be found in reference sources. One should not have to use a reference source to find that 12 inches equal 1 foot, 4 quarts equal 1 gallon, or 60 minutes equal 1 hour. On the other hand, it is hardly worth the effort for the child to commit to memory such facts as 4 inches equal 1 hand, 40 rods equal 1 furlong, or 1 ton of hard coal equals 35 cubic feet. By contrast with the multiplication facts, 7×8 should be recognized on sight even though it may not be needed as frequently as 6×5.

A sensible goal is automatic recall of the most commonly used facts plus competence in the use of reference sources to find the less

[2] Herbert F. Spitzer, *The Teaching of Arithmetic*, 2d ed. (Boston: Houghton Mifflin Co., 1954), p. 139.

familiar ones. This poses the difficult question as to which facts belong in which category. In this respect it is impossible for the text to be an adequate guide. Some facts are so universally used as to require automatic recall regardless of locality. Others may be in this category in some localities but not in others. Rural children have more need to know that 4 pecks equal 1 bushel, or that 1 cord of wood equals 128 cubic feet, than do city children. The teacher's responsibility does not end with those scales of measure which are extensively used in all parts of the country. Grades of cotton staple are extremely important measures in cotton-producing areas, but they are seldom encountered in midwestern metropolitan areas. On the other hand, it is much more important for the midwesterner to know how many pounds there are in a bushel of wheat. The duration of a spring tide is more significant information to the sea coast dweller than to the mountaineer. The teacher must assume responsibility for inclusion of those facts which are significant for the particular area but are not included in the textbook.

The metric system of measures has many ardent advocates. There are many individuals who feel that our refusal in the United States to abandon our present system of weights and measures in favor of the metric system is not far short of a calamity. An entire professional yearbook has been devoted to descriptions the metric system and discussions of its superiority.[3]

The advantages of the system come, in the main, from two sources. First of these is its decimal nature. We can convert from one unit to a different-size unit of the same kind by merely shifting the decimal point. The fact that ten is the base of the system is not important. The fact that it employs the same base as our system of notation is of extreme importance. The second characteristic is the manner in which linear measure, capacity, and weight are interrelated. There is no denying the fact that use of the metric system would greatly simplify computation. Common fractions would become obsolete fractions. Other claims for the system are somewhat exaggerated. For example, as is well illustrated by American industry, it is possible to obtain just as high a degree of precision under our present system. The system also has disadvantages. Our anatomical predisposition to *ten* as a frame of reference for counting

---

[3] The National Council of Teachers of Mathematics, *The Metric System of Weights and Measures* (New York: Teachers College, Columbia University, 1948).

does not carry over to measurement. The human race has shown a decided preference for both *two* and *twelve*. Subdivisions into a half, half of a half, half of a half of a half ($\frac{1}{2}$, $\frac{1}{4}$, $\frac{1}{8}$), and so on, are easily visualized. *Twelve* is superior to *ten* in that we are as apt to be concerned with any one of the fractional parts, $\frac{1}{3}$, $\frac{1}{4}$, $\frac{1}{6}$, as we are with the part $\frac{1}{5}$.

Regardless of the merits of the argument the teacher must take into account the situation as it is and as it is apt to become within a generation. In the United States we operate under a dual system. The metric system is legal; in fact the units of the older system are legally defined in terms of metric units. We use both systems side by side. We use both Centigrade and Fahrenheit temperature scales. We use both cubic centimeters and fluid ounces. Calories are probably more widely used and understood than B.T.U. With increasing frequency one hears reference to such units of measure as kilograms, liters, kilometers, and megacycles. Incidentally, we are not alone with regard to dual systems. Many countries who have adopted the metric system officially use it in foreign commerce but continue to use their native system in everyday affairs.

The situation is not apt to change materially in the foreseeable future. The proponents of the metric system have about the same chance of success in obtaining its adoption to the exclusion of other systems as the advocates of the duodecimal number system have in replacing our present base-ten notation. The arithmetic program certainly should not ignore the metric system although an exhaustive study of it is hardly justified. A minimum program should include something of its decimal nature and familiarity with systematic use of prefixes to indicate multiples and submultiples of the basic units. It should also include knowledge of the approximate English equivalents of the most common metric units. For example, a yard is slightly less than a meter, a liter is between a liquid quart and a dry quart, a kilometer is a little over $\frac{1}{2}$ mile, and a kilogram is a little over 2 pounds.

There are other widely used units of measure which most children may never have occasion to put to direct use. But they are so ingrained in our culture the child should know what kind of unit they are and have some conception of their magnitude. Included in this category are a number of compound units such as foot pound, light year, passenger mile, knot, acre foot, and kilowatt hour. Typical of other units which might be included are carat (weight of precious stones), radian and mil (angle), wire gauge, nail size, square (100 square feet of roofing), vision ratio, horsepower, volt, watt, ampere, and nautical mile. Although direct experience with most of these units is highly unlikely for most elementary-school children, they can be used to advantage in problem material.

13.3 MEASURING INSTRUMENTS

Children will be aided in learning many measurement concepts through carefully directed use of measuring instruments. For this reason, as well as the fact that it is a legitimate educational aim in its own right, children should be provided with the opportunity to learn their proper use. The simple task of reading a clock or watch must be learned. The great majority of first-grade children have not learned it. There is much for the child to learn about the correct use of a yardstick. Apparently there are many adults who cannot read a simple device such as an electric meter. Some rural electric cooperatives do not read the customer's meter every month. The customer is asked to send the reading in. A facsimile of the face of the meter is printed on a card and the customer is asked to draw in the hands in the correct position.

Any measuring instrument contains a smallest unit, a smallest graduation. This fact should be emphasized in developing the approximate nature of measurement. A child can make linear measurements to the nearest inch with a yardstick as soon as he can read the numbers. After the concept of fractional parts has been developed he can use the same instrument with greater precision; he can measure to the nearest eighth of an inch. But in either case he is confronted with the necessity of estimating the nearest whole unit, be it an inch or an eighth of an inch. If he desires still closer results the instrument is inadequate. The approximate nature of measurement may also be emphasized by measuring the same object, using two different scales of measure. Suppose a distance is measured with both a yardstick and a meter stick. If we then convert the results to the same scale we will not get exactly the same number of yards or the same number of meters.

The existence of a limit of precision inherent in the instrument brings to focus the appropriateness of the unit of measure, as well as the instrument, we select. One would not attempt to weigh either a carload of coal or a precious stone on ordinary bathroom scales. The width of this page is most appropriately measured in inches, the dimensions of a room in feet, the distance between cities in miles, and the distance to a fixed star in light years.

There is of course a limit to the measuring instruments which can be used in the classroom. But the child should be provided with practice in making measurements of length, time, temperature, capacity, angles, and weight. Improvised instruments and units of measure should be used in conjunction with the standard ones. An unmarked stick or a length of string can be used to make linear measures. This will help in bringing to focus both the nature of measurement and the arbitrary character of standard units of measure. When we measure we compare the unit with the thing measured. We must count the whole number of times the unit, unmarked stick or length of string, is used and we must estimate the fraction of a unit needed to complete the measurement. We use a *standard* unit so that different measurements may be compared. We measure the room at home for a new rug. We use a standard unit in order that the measurements may be duplicated in the store where the rug is bought. But how long is a yard? Why is it the same in Maine and California? A yard is three feet, and a foot is 12 inches. But what is an inch? Such questions may be used to show that any scale of measure must have a basic unit. All other units in the scale may be defined as multiples or fractional parts of the basic unit. But how is the size of the basic unit determined? To the extent that time permits, the story of the development of measurement is excellent enrichment material. But we certainly should not fail to bring out the fact that the size of the basic unit in any scale of measurement is arbitrarily selected and established by law.

Weight and *mass* are not identical. The weight of an object is the measure of its gravitational pull, a quantity which varies with altitude and atmospheric conditions. Mass is a measure of the quantity of matter contained by the object. It is constant. The two measures are practically identical numerically. In fact, when we commonly refer to the weight of an object we actually mean its mass. The two types of scales in common use are the spring balance and the platform balance. The former measures weight, the latter mass. The platform balance should be used in developing the concepts of weight measurement and the standard units of weight. A workable balance can be constructed easily. All that is needed is an upright stand, a balance arm pivoted at its center with pans (small ash trays will do) suspended at its ends:

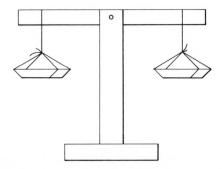

Children are familiar with the principle involved from their experience with a see-saw. When the see-saw is pivoted in the middle the heavy child goes down. The children must be of approximately the same weight if the see-saw is to work (unless the distances from the pivot are altered).

When using the balance, checkers, buttons, loose counting beads, and bottle caps make good reference units. The object to be weighed is placed on one pan and sufficient reference units placed on the other to counterbalance it. Here again we may emphasize the comparison aspect of measurement, we compare the pull of the object weighed with that of the reference units. We must use enough reference units to match the pull of the object. (Parenthetically, the distinction between weight and mass need not concern the children. Merely to clarify the distinction which has been stated we observe that the scale is in balance when each pan contains the same weight. But we measure mass because the constant mass of the reference units is known and, at the same time and place, equal weights have equal masses.) Experiments with the balance also emphasize the measurement concepts of precision, error (inexactness), and indirect comparison. If the balance is sufficiently sensitive, that is, free to move about its pivot, we find the need for reference units of different sizes. A tablet may not weigh 4 checkers, or 3 checkers and 1 button, but 3 checkers, 1 button, and 2 bottle caps. Thus the notion of a least unit of measure or precision. In fact, we may not be able to bring the scale into perfect balance with the reference unit at hand, showing the presence of error. We can illustrate indirect comparison or substitution by weighing a quantity of modeling clay which balances the reference units, then showing the clay and the tablet balance each other.

Experiences involving standard units of weight should also be provided. We may know the relationships between units, 16 ounces = 1 pound and 2000 pounds = 1 ton, without having any conception of just how heavy a pound is. Children enjoy helping find heights and weights for their health records. Practice in estimating lengths, weights, and areas should be provided. The habit of estimating before measuring gives meaning to the units of measure. It also provides a valuable check on the results of measurement.

Time measurement does not end with ability to read a clock or watch. Young children's concept of time is hazy. Participation in planning the daily schedule—when we rest, when we play, how long we have for lunch, when it is time to go home—is helpful in sharpening the concept of an interval of time. The order of the days of the week and months of the year must be learned. In the lower grades a valuable class project consists of making a large calendar for the bulletin board each month. Special school events and holidays for the month may be indicated, with discussion of days and weeks until an event and between events.

In the middle grades determination of age in years, months, and days should be included in the work with denominate numbers.

Standard time and time zones are topics which should be included in the study of the measurement of time. Although the reason for time zones is properly a part of geography or natural science, unless it is understood arithmetic work in this area can only lead to confusion. Discussion of television programs, network and local, and study of a map showing time zones are helpful aids in fixing the ideas. Since the sun travels from east to west (or appears to) sunrise occurs in New York before it does in California. Then at any given time the clock indicates an earlier hour farther west. As we go west we advance our watches one hour each time we enter a new time zone.

For the upper grades a study of the history of the development of timepieces and the calendar make excellent enrichment materials. Such devices as a burning candle, three-minute timers of the hour glass type, and a second pendulum are easily obtained. They may be used effectively as illustrations of methods which have been employed to measure the passage of time. In studying the history of the calendar the interrelationships of days, weeks, months, and years may be emphasized. This type of activity might well include the need for calendar reform and a study of the currently proposed World Calendar.

13.4 INDIRECT MEASUREMENT

A surprisingly large proportion of measurements are made indirectly. An indirect measurement is one which is obtained from some other direct measurement. The direct measurement may and may not be of the same kind. Linear measure is direct if the standard unit is applied directly to the object to be measured. Many linear measures are made indirectly from other direct linear measures. The solution of a triangle by numerical trigonometry is an example of indirect measurement. So also is the application of proportion to similar triangles as in shadow reckoning. The height of the house is obtained indirectly from the direct measurements of the height of the post and the length of the two shadows.

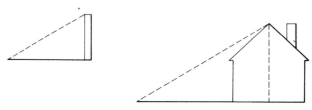

Measurement of areas and volumes are almost invariably indirect. We make direct linear measures from which we obtain measures of area and volume. On the other hand, capacity is more often determined directly. If we wish to find how much a jar holds we can fill it with water, then measure the water in a measuring cup. This is direct measurement. If the jar is cylindrical we can measure its inner diameter and height, from which we can compute its capacity. This is indirect measurement.

The ease with which we can find area as an indirect measure constitutes a threat to meaningful learning. We measure two consecutive sides of a rectangle and multiply their lengths to obtain the area. "Feet times feet equal square feet." There is nothing in this procedure to suggest what a square foot is. The measurements were linear, why should not their product be linear also? As a matter of fact, if we multiply two line segments geometrically the product is a line segment, not an area.

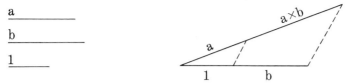

Before any area formulas are taught, the child should (1) have an opportunity to learn what "area" means and (2) see *why* the formula gives the correct result.

How many pairs of hands are needed to cover the desk? How many tiles (if the floor is tiled) does it take to cover the floor? Experiences suggested by such questions will develop the idea of area as surface covered. We find area when we find how many units of area, hands, dominoes, tiles, are needed to cover the surface.

Preliminary to the development of the formula for the area of a rectangle the selection of the unit of area should be considered. We cannot completely cover the desk top with hands unless there is overlapping. How many checkers does it take to cover the page? A circle cannot be our unit because circles will not fill the surface about a point. The class is asked to find how many different shapes the unit may take so as to fill the surface about a point. Triangles, rectangles, and squares probably will be suggested. These and the hexagon are the only possibilities. If we select from these the ones that will completely fill a rectangle we have only rectangles and squares. Further experimentation can show that a rectangular unit of area which will fill one rectangle will not fill a dissimilar one.

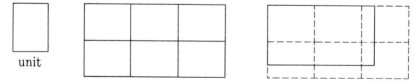

Of course, the unit square may not fill the rectangle either. But we can succeed in filling it with smaller squares. The incommensurable case should be ignored in elementary school instruction. For that

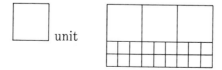

matter, it is not pertinent in the context of measurement. Since measurement is approximate we may with justification assert that any two lines are commensurable, for we can always find a length that will measure both lines to any desired degree of accuracy.

Having selected the square as our unit of measure we find the area of a rectangle by finding the number of unit squares required to

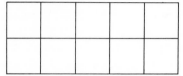

cover it. When we multiply the length by width we are multiplying the number of squares per row (column) by the number of rows (columns). It is well to require drawing solutions early in the study of area. A drawing solution should continue to be required occasionally as a check.

There is much less need for the formula for the area of a parallelogram than for a triangle or circle. It should, however, be included as an aid in the meaningful development of other formulas.

A nonrectangular parallelogram cannot be filled with squares, no matter how small. In spite of this we can find its area by finding that

of a rectangle which has the same amount of surface. If the formula for the area of a parallelogram is to have a meaningful basis the concept of congruent figures, as well as that of a unit of area, is essential. In the figure the right-hand triangle has the same area as the left, even though neither can be filled with unit squares. This is so because if one is superimposed on the other they fit, they cover the same surface. It is advisable when deriving the area for the parallelogram to challenge the class to cut up a cardboard parallelogram and rearrange the parts in such a way that the area can be found.

Once the area of the parallelogram is accepted, that of the triangle follows from the fact that any triangle may be considered half a parallelogram with the same base and altitude. Here again we cannot

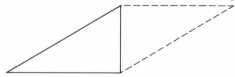

demonstrate the formula by covering the triangle with unit squares. Some writers advocate the inductive approach. With this approach the class estimates the number of unit squares necessary to cover the triangle. This approach has serious limitations; granted that a reasonably good estimate can be made. There is no particular reason why this should be related to half the product of base times height. The procedure provides no clue to the desired generalization. On the other hand, if the child can be led to discover the relationship between the triangle and some other figure whose area can be found then the generalization is easy.

The relationship between the radius and the circumference of a circle should be established before its area is considered. This will have to be done empirically. By actual measurement of circular objects we can obtain the ratio of circumference to diameter. A number of such observations should be made. The results will not be identical, but they will show that $\frac{22}{7}$ (or 3.14) is a good representative value. Care should be exercised to emphasize that the ratio is obtained from measurement and hence our result is only approximately correct. This applies not only to the individual results but to the chosen representative value as well.

We may now show the area of the circle as the equivalent of the sum of the areas of many triangles, all of which have the radius of the circle as altitude and the sum of whose bases equals the circumference. Then the area of the many triangles is found by the formula

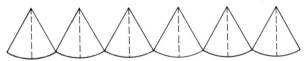

$\frac{1}{2} \times c \times r$, where c is the circumference and r is the radius of the circle. But since $c = \frac{22}{7} \times 2r$, we have for area $\frac{1}{2} \times \frac{22}{7} \times 2r \times r = \frac{22}{7}r^2$.

As the exceptionally observant pupil will note, no matter how many parts the circle is cut into they never actually become triangles. Any kind of formal discussion of the limit process even in Grade 8 would be inappropriate for all but the most gifted pupils. The following is one way out of the dilemma presented. It is quite true that the circular sectors never become triangles. But neither is the ratio of circumference to diameter exactly $\frac{22}{7}$. After relatively few divisions the sectors so nearly approach triangles the error is well within the limits of precision imposed by our measurements. This approach is an evasion of the point at issue, the limit process. But it is in keeping with the fact that $\frac{22}{7}r^2$ is not an exact expression of the area. We have already evaded the issue when we accept $\frac{22}{7}$ as the value of π.

13.5 COMPUTATION WITH MEASUREMENT NUMBERS

Formal rules similar to those discussed in Chapter Twelve for computation with approximate numbers are seldom included in the elementary arithmetic curriculum. This does not relieve the elementary teacher of all responsibility relative to the matter.

The ability to round off numbers is an invaluable aid when one's work is checked by approximating the answer as well as when finding trial divisors. Children should learn how to round off whole numbers early in the arithmetic program. It is recommended that the rule for dropping a terminal five not be used at this stage. That is, the last digit held is increased by one if the digit immediately to its right is 5, 6, 7, 8, or 9, including those cases when it is a terminal 5. The concept can easily be extended to fractions and mixed numbers when decimal fractions are studied. This does not imply that elementary-school children should or must learn the meaning of significant digits. Rounding off will consist of rounding to a named digit. For example, 17,863 is to be rounded *to the nearest hundred* rather than to three significant digits.

If the concept of precision in measurement has been emphasized consistently when measurement is studied, rounding off in the manner indicated above should cause no great difficulty when extended to measurement. Measurements will be rounded to a named unit of measure, a named degree of precision. For example, we round 17,863 miles to the nearest hundred miles rather than to three significant digits. Similarly, 12 years 8 months 17 days can be rounded to the nearest month as 12 years 9 months or to the nearest year as 13 years. It is not unreasonable to expect seventh- or eighth-grade children to understand both the meaning of and the justification for the rule which requires the sum to have the same precision as the least precise addend. The safest and simplest procedure is to require each addend to be rounded to the precision of the least precise measurement, then add. This procedure will avoid "ragged decimals"; it is in keeping with the notion that only like things can be added, inches to inches, feet to feet, and so on; the sum automatically has its justifiable precision, it requires no rounding off.

Multiplication of approximate numbers poses a more difficult situation. Here we are concerned with accuracy rather than precision. The concept of significant digits is unavoidable. If the concepts of accuracy and significant digits are not developed the child should be given some kind of guidance and direction as to the proper way the result should be left. For example, in posing the problem the precision required of the product can be specified: Find the area of a rectangle 2.3 feet by 3.5 feet, *to the nearest square foot*, or *to the nearest tenth*. In dealing with measurement computation common sense should be the guiding rule. The child should be helped to determine the appropriateness of his answer. We do not know the area of the 2.3-by-3.5 foot rectangle is 8.05 square feet. The child unaided is not apt to see the inappropriateness of this answer.

13.6 AVERAGES

An average is a measure of central tendency of a group of measures. It is a single measure which best typifies the group. There are many kinds of average; the three most commonly used are the *arithmetic mean*, the *median*, and the *mode*.

The arithmetic mean, which is defined as the sum of the measures divided by the number of measures, is often referred to merely as the average. Instruction in arithmetic all too frequently is confined to the mechanics of finding the arithmetic mean, with too little regard for the significance of the measure.

The teaching of averages should include development of the concept of an average. It should also include the more specific concepts of arithmetic mean, median, and mode. That is to say, an average is the one measure which is the most representative of the group. The three different averages are the most representative from three different points of view. The median is by definition the midscore. It is the most typical in the sense that there are an equal number larger and smaller than it is. It is the middle measurement when they are arranged in order of size. The mode is by definition the measure which appears most frequently in the group. The arithmetic mean is not necessarily one of the group of measures. It is the result we would obtain if we decreased the larger ones and increased the smaller until they were all the same size.

The arithmetic mean may be considered the most representative from the standpoint of size. The magnitude of each measure in the group helps determine its size. The median is the most representative from the standpoint of position. It is unchanged if the large measures are made larger and the small ones made smaller. If there are extreme measures the mean is the better average in case we wish to take into account how extreme the extremes are; the median is better if we do not. The mode is the most representative from the standpoint of frequency; it is the measure which occurs most often. Neither its position in the group nor the size of the members of the group has any bearing upon its value.

When studying averages major emphasis should be on interpretation rather than computation. Only the arithmetic mean requires any appreciable computation. As has been mentioned elsewhere, determination of the arithmetic mean is an example of partition division—the sum is equally distributed over the measures. Children should have the opportunity to examine situations which illustrate conditions under which each of the three is the most appropriate.

13.7 RELATED TOPICS

Topics rather closely related to measurement include scale drawings, charts, graphs, and tables. A casual perusal of the daily newspaper is sufficient evidence of their importance from the standpoint of social utility.

Major instructional emphasis should be placed on reading and interpreting these items rather than on construction. This does not imply that no attention should be given to construction of scale drawings, graphs, and tables. If for no other reason, children should have experience in their construction because such experience brings out quite clearly the basic ideas necessary to intelligent use.

Since a scale drawing is a miniature the basic ideas are the ratio of lengths and preservation of shape. Children will have had experience with scale drawings from their study of maps in social science, where the "scale of miles" is given as a line equal a given number of miles. The ratio factor is sometimes given as, for example, "scale 1/15." Still another means of indicating ratio is the substitution of units, such as "1 inch equals 1 mile." This is probably the best method for developing the ratio concept. We employ the idea that the small unit in a drawing "stands for" the large unit in an object.

Instruction in the use of scale drawings should begin with a situation in which the class has a real interest, in which a need for the drawing is apparent. For example, the class is to go to some member's home for a picnic. Discussion of how to find the place suggests the drawing of a map to scale. A picture of the route is drawn, one inch in the drawing takes the place of one mile (or block) on the route.

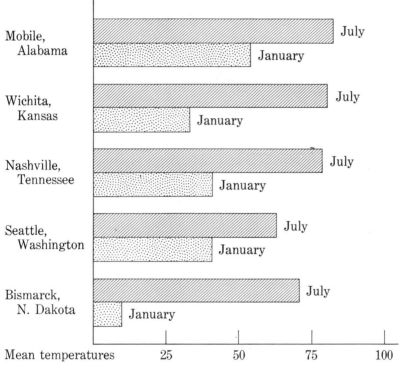

COMPARATIVE MEAN TEMPERATURE IN SELECTED CITIES. UNIT OF BAR LENGTH IS SUBSTITUTED FOR DEGREES OF TEMPERATURE.

Practice should be provided in reading and interpreting floor plans, road maps, and diagrams such as drawings of a basketball court or baseball diamond. There are three essentials to interpretation of a scale drawing: (1) orientation as to direction, (2) awareness of the preservation of shape, and (3) knowledge of the ratio employed.

Substitution of units is also basic to the construction and reading of graphs. The substitution is usually of a more general kind. In a scale drawing a small *linear* unit is substituted for a larger *linear* unit. When a bar graph is used, the linear unit employed in determining the length of each bar may be used to represent either a count or any kind

1900	
1915	
1930	
1945	

CATTLE PRODUCTION IN THE UNITED STATES. PICTURE OF COW IS THE SUBSTITUTION UNIT. ONE COW REPRESENTS 15,000,000 HEAD.

of unit of measure. When a pictograph is used, each picture represents a specified number of the pictured objects. Temperature is indicated on a continuous-line temperature chart by the height of the curve above the base line. Thus, a linear unit represents a given number of units of temperature. But the linear unit is not the length of the line itself. The arithmetic program should provide competence in the

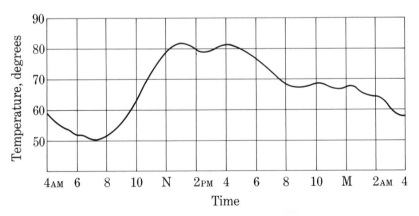

FLUCTUATIONS IN TEMPERATURE. ONE HORIZONTAL UNIT IS SUBSTITUTED FOR TWO HOURS OF TIME. ONE VERTICAL UNIT IS SUBSTITUTED FOR TEN DEGREES OF TEMPERATURE.

construction and interpretation of bar graphs, circle graphs, picto-graphs, and line graphs. Graphs are used primarily to show com-parisons, trends and fluctuations, and relationships. The best type of graph to use will depend upon the kind of information it is to convey. The bar graph and pictograph are used primarily to show compari-sons. The circle graph is used to advantage in comparing the various parts with the whole. The line graph best shows trends, rise and fall, and rate of change of a changing quantity.

Two related sets of things are pictured in a graph. If the graph shows the wheat production of the nations of the world, the nations constitute one set and the quantity of wheat produced in each nation the other. On the other hand, we may have a graph showing the wheat production for the state of Kansas over a period of years. In this case one set of things is the years and the other the quantities of wheat for each year. Wheat production by nations is best shown with a bar graph. But wheat production in Kansas should be shown with a bar graph if we wish to read from the graph a comparison of specific years. A line graph would be more meaningful if we wish to picture the manner in which production has changed with the passage of time.

One of the sets of things shown in the graph may be geographic locations, makes of automobiles, seasons of the year, or types of house construction—sets of things which may not be comparable numeri-cally. Associated with each member of the first set there is a member of another set of things which are numerically comparable. The graph gives a pictorial representation of the set of pairs of things. In the graph showing wheat produced by nations the pairs of things shown are the nation and its wheat production. Each bar represents one nation-production pair. The temperature chart pictures time-temperature pairs. Each point on the line represents one such pair. Intelligent reading of a graph requires that we correctly identify the nature of the pairs of things represented and that we correctly identify the substitution unit or units employed. When constructing a graph, care should be exercised to assure that this information is provided.

A table gives essentially the same information as a graph. In a table the pairs are simply written down in some systematic fashion, frequently in two columns, the members of each set of things in a column and paired by rows. Thus we may think of a graph as a picture of a table.

Exercises

1 List units of measure which are very important in some localities but unimportant over the country as a whole.

2 List strengths and weaknesses of a pictograph.

3 The article "Toward Better Graphs" by Edwin Eagle in *The Mathematics Teacher* (March 1942) lists a number of attributes a graph should possess. List those that should be emphasized in the study of graphs in the upper grades.

5 If a small picture of a house is used in a pictograph to represent 100,000 homes, why should we not represent 200,000 homes by a picture whose dimensions are twice those of the other?

6 In the article "When Size 9 Is Size 10" in *The Metric System of Weights and Measures*, reference is made to the fact that there is great lack of uniformity in clothing sizes. Is this a valid argument for the adoption of the metric system by the clothing industry?

7 List arguments both for and against the exclusive use of the metric system.

8 Contrast (a) scale drawings and graphs, and (b) graphs and tables.

9 Under what conditions will the arithmetic mean be misleading as a measure of central tendency of a set of measurements?

10 List the major measurement concepts which should be developed in the elementary school.

11 Describe the skills and concepts which a second-grade child must use in making a linear measurement with a yardstick.

12 Describe the probable extent to which a beginning first-grade child will have already developed the concepts basic to measurement.

13 Is a table of measures a table in the sense used on page 401? Explain.

14 Is the measurement of time by a watch direct or indirect measurement?

15 List instances of indirect measurement aside from those in the text.

16 Should a child be taught that feet times feet equals square feet? Is there any difference between this and the teaching of compound units such as foot pounds—feet times pounds equals foot pounds? How would you explain this difference to a seventh-grade class?

17 Buckingham (see Suggested Supplementary Readings, page 457) states: "Accordingly, every measurement number is incommensurable or irrational." Explain what he means. Do you agree?

Suggested Supplementary Readings

Banks, J. Houston, *Elements of Mathematics*, Second Edition. Boston: Allyn and Bacon, Inc., 1961. Ch. VIII.

Buckingham, B. R., *Elementary Arithmetic: Its Meaning and Practice*. Boston: Ginn and Company, 1947. Pp. 456–735.

Eagle, Edwin, "Towards Better Graphs," *The Mathematics Teacher*, March 1942. Pp. 127–131.

Larsen, Harold D., *Arithmetic for Colleges*. New York: The Macmillan Company, 1950. Pp. 162–185.

Morton, R. L., *Teaching Arithmetic in the Elementary School*. New York: Silver Burdett Company, 1938. Vol. II, pp. 411–453.

National Council of Teachers of Mathematics, *Selected Topics in the Teaching of Mathematics*. New York: Teachers College, Columbia University, 1928. Pp. 149–222.

——, *The Metric System of Weights and Measures*. New York: Teachers College, Columbia University, 1948.

Sanford, Vera, *A Short History of Mathematics*. Boston: Houghton Mifflin Company, 1930. Pp. 351–377.

Spencer, Peter L., and Marguerite Brydegaard, *Building Mathematical Concepts in the Elementary School*. New York: Henry Holt and Company, 1951. Pp. 256–296.

Wheat, Harry G., *How to Teach Arithmetic*. Evanston: Row, Peterson and Company, 1951. Pp. 365–396.

Problem Solving

CHAPTER FOURTEEN

THE TERMS "WORD PROBLEM," "stated problem," "story problem" are used to describe "problem" as it is used in the present context. By problem we mean a quantitative situation, described in words, in which a quantitative question is raised without an accompanying statement as to the arithmetical operations required. Thus, $45 \div 15 = ?$ is not a problem in the present sense of the word; it is an exercise in division.

14.1 FUNCTION OF PROBLEM SOLVING

Skill in problem solving is not the sole objective of arithmetic instruction. Nor is problem solving a separate topic of arithmetic. It should be a vital part of all phases of the subject. Meaningful problems should serve to introduce each new arithmetical topic. The problem should establish a need for the new skill. For example, problems most efficiently solved by division should be used as a preliminary to learning the division algorithm. They enable the pupil to appreciate the usefulness of the process.

Problems should also be used to lend variety to drill. The additional time required is a good investment in terms of pupil interest. Furthermore, drill in the form of problems does not merely fix the skills involved, as is apt to be the case with mere drill exercises; it gives meaning and significance to the practiced skill.

Problems should be used to help the child equip himself to solve his own real-life problems. This does not imply that prestructured textbook problems can be relied upon wholly in teaching the child to attack successfully unstructured real-life problems. But it is unrealistic to assume that sufficient familiarity with the situation and sufficient practice can be provided by depending upon actual problems from the experiences of the children. For example, how many real problems involving installment buying can an average eighth-grade class be expected to provide? We make a mistake when we assume that seventh- and eighth-grade children have adult interest in such things as insurance, taxation, buying a home, and so on.

The role played by problem solving is not the same in the early grades as in the upper grades. Major responsibility for mastery of the fundamental processes with integers and common and decimal fractions rests with the first six grades of elementary school. This is not to imply that instruction beyond that point need not be concerned. Provision must be made for remedial drill and systematic review if the secondary-school pupil is to maintain a satisfactory degree of functional competence in arithmetic. Schorling has found that 50 percent of a sample of twelfth-grade pupils could not perform 67 of 100 simple arithmetic tasks.[1] More recent experimental evidence is of the same vein. Brown has found that, as a group, the 947 high school seniors tested showed unsatisfactory proficiency in each of the four areas of "(1) consumer problems, (2) graphs and tables, (3) symbolism, equations, etc. and (4) ratio, tolerance, etc." into which he classified

[1] Raleigh Schloring, "The Need for Being Definite with Respect to Achievement Standards," *The Mathematics Teacher*, XXIV, No. 5 (1931), pp. 311–329.

the 29 items of the *Check List of Functional Competence*.[2] Similar results are reported by Ohlsen[3] and others.

Although the job does not end there, the first mathematical objective of Grades 1 through 6 should be the development of the skills—and attendant concepts, meanings, and appreciations—with the fundamental operations. The main purpose of problem solving should be to aid in carrying through this objective. Problem solving as a means of fostering the social utility of arithmetic should play a secondary role. In the upper grades relatively few new arithmetical topics are introduced. The emphasis is on application. Here social utility should dominate the selection and use of problem material.

The validity of the argument that problems should simulate real-life situations of the child depends upon the purpose for which the problem is to be used. If the purpose is to illustrate and to illuminate a mathematical principle, puzzle problems, pseudo-real problems, and even fantastic problems may serve better. Welch has produced evidence to show that pupils have a preference for fantasy problems over those describing real-life situations.[4] He found that attention to the ridiculousness of a situation such as "A strong man lifted 4750 pounds with one hand and 8817 pounds with the other" not to be a distraction. Performance on the unreal problems was as good as on the real ones.

If the purpose of the problem is to give practice in solving the kinds of problems one encounters in real life, the "tailor-made" problems of the textbook are far inferior to those that come from school, home, and community activities. A real-life problem differs from a textbook problem in many ways. Real-life problems come unstructured. We must decide what variables are pertinent to the problem. We must determine what data are relevant and we must find the data. We must pass on the reliability of the source and on the accuracy of the data. We must determine the degree of accuracy a satisfactory solution must have. We must determine what assumptions are implicit in the solution. Frequently the problem does not

---

[2] Robert C. Brown, "Functional Competence in Mathematics of Louisiana High School Seniors" (unpublished Ph.D. dissertation, George Peabody College for Teachers, 1956), p. 61.

[3] Merle M. Ohlsen, "Control of Fundamental Mathematical Skills and Concepts by High School Students," *The Mathematics Teacher*, XXXIX, No. 8 (1946), p. 365.

[4] Ronald Welch, "The Relative Merits of Two Types of Arithmetic Problems" (unpublished Masters thesis, University of Iowa, 1950).

yield a pat textbook answer; there are alternative solutions. Consider, for example, what is involved in the solution of the real-life problem of a family in need of more living space. The problem is to decide whether to enlarge the house, sell and buy a larger house, or sell and rent a larger place.

14.2 SOURCES OF DIFFICULTY

Some sources of difficulty in problem solving are immediately apparent. A lack of command of the required mathematical operations precludes the correct solution of the problem. This deficiency may be either inability to perform the necessary skills or insufficient insight as to the significance of the operations to determine which is required.

Reading difficulties may be a major source of trouble. Good general reading ability is no guarantee of ability to do the kind of reading demanded for success in mathematics.[5]

Poor problem-solving techniques are often stumbling blocks to success. Discovery of poor practices is not an easy matter. Mere examination of the pupil's written work is sufficient to discover what he did wrong, but it frequently gives no clue as to *why* he did it. The "think out loud" technique has been used with varying degrees of success. The pupil is given a problem to solve and urged to vocalize all his thoughts as he attempts a solution. Just how good a picture of his actual thought processes one obtains in this manner is problematical. We are in the dilemma of the introspection psychologists. The very act of reporting one's thoughts alters them. There is some question as to whether a child can relate the thought processes whereby he reaches a solution. If a complete record of the child's vocalization were available for careful study after the interview, it could reveal a good bit of information as to how he attacked the problem.

Dwight employed an ingenious method for studying the problem-solving habits employed by seventh-grade pupils. He used the interview technique. The individual pupil was given a set of problems to solve and encouraged to "think out loud" throughout his solution.

---

[5] Leo J. Brueckner and Guy L. Bond, *The Diagnosis and Treatment of Learning Difficulties* (New York: Appleton-Century-Crofts, Inc., 1955), p. 290.

A tape recorder was used to record all words spoken by the pupil and the observer. The observer also kept notes. After the interview the pupil's work, the tape, and the observer's notes were studied for evidence of the pupil's problem-solving behavior. The following behaviors were considered good procedures because they seemed to aid the pupils in obtaining correct solutions:

1. Evaluated solutions by:
   (a) Checking answers with the conditions of the problems
   (b) Checking answers as to reasonableness
   (c) Checking processes chosen
   (d) Checking computation
   (e) Re-reading problems after obtaining a solution
2. Used label for each part
3. Used word cues in relation to the setting of the problem
4. Interpreted punctuation correctly
5. Made statements about the problem precise and complete
6. Gave critical thought to the "required" before computing
7. After obtaining an impression of the problem as a whole, re-read the problem to note details and to check interpretation
8. Stated "given" and "required"
9. Planned the solutions and outlined the processes to be used
10. Determined the relationships of the data in the problem
11. Used drawings and figures when possible
12. Noted and discarded irrelevant data
13. Obtained comprehension of problem before performing computation.[6]

The following behaviors seemed to lead to incorrect solutions:

1. Used multiplication process rather than the appropriate division process to obtain quotients
2. Used incorrect arithmetic language
3. Used number cues as a basis for the selection of process
4. Lacked critical thought on "required" before computing
5. Used single word cues to determine processes
6. Interpreted punctuation incorrectly
7. Incomplete statements about parts of the problem
8. Incorrect procedures in the fundamental processes
9. Performed operations without properly relating the data

[6] Leslie Alfred Dwight, "Problem Solving Behaviors of Seventh Grade Pupils in Selected Schools" (unpublished Ph.D. dissertation, George Peabody College for Teachers, 1952), p. 201.

10. Experimented in order to obtain solutions to problems
11. Manipulated numbers in solutions of problems
12. Chose processes by eliminating others
13. Added and subtracted unlike denominate numbers
14. Worked mentally without being able to write down the solution.[7]

14.3   READING IN MATHEMATICS

Many of the above "good procedures" indicate skill in mathematical reading, just as many "poor procedures" indicate reading difficulties. Mathematics requires special reading skills. Some of the current practices in the teaching of reading, such as rapid reading and scanning, may be actually detrimental to effective mathematical reading.

Much of the difficulty with reading in mathematics stems from a lack of awareness of the purpose of the reading. The same material might be read on different occasions for entirely different purposes and will imply different kinds of reading. Upon first reading of new material the purpose should be to get the over-all picture in broad outline, to get the story, a rough framework with the details to be filled in later. This should be followed by a more careful, slower reading for the details. The same material may require a number of subsequent readings. For example, suppose the pupil cannot solve a problem illustrative of the material he has studied. He then re-reads in search for what he has missed. He reads with the question before him "What in this material bears upon the problem at hand?" This implies scanning to locate the passage wanted and intensive, critical reading of the passage. At other times the same material may be re-read in search for specific facts, which will again imply the ability to scan. Or it may be read for review. In this case the purpose will be to relate the content to other material, to place it in a larger perspective, to make it a part of a larger whole.

The type of reading which causes the most difficulty is that which requires careful attention to every detail. This requires slow reading, but not the slow reading of the slow reader. It requires a reflective, questioning, critical frame of mind. Critical toward what is read, critical toward one's own comprehension of what he reads, and critical toward the teacher's explanation of what he has read. As he studies, the pupil should mark any statement he does not understand,

---

[7] *Ibid.*, pp. 202–203.

see the justification for, or believe. At the completion of the reading some questions will have been answered. Upon re-reading others can be answered. The pupil should then have for ready reference those specific points which need further clarification. The teacher can contribute greatly toward developing ability to read critically by curbing the tendency to tell the pupil what he should have gotten from reading—in other words, to do his reading for him. This is the easy way out for both pupil and teacher. But it is not conducive to intellectual toughening and growth. We are prone to spend so much time "teaching" our pupils they do not get the chance to learn for themselves.

The language of mathematics has characteristics which complicate the problem of reading. One of these is its conciseness. Rapid reading may well prove to be a handicap. The omission of a word, a mathematical symbol, or a punctuation mark may change the entire meaning. Think of the difference in meaning of the following statement if a single letter f is omitted: "Sale, 25 % off list price." Reading of formulas and equations requires attention to every detail. Too rapid reading might easily cause "tan $1 = x$" to be read "tan $x = 1$" since the latter is much more frequently encountered. Consider the two questions "Fifteen is 25 % of what?" and "What is 25 % of 15?" It requires attentive reading to make the distinction between the two.

Technical mathematical terms must convey precise meanings if they are to evoke the desired concept in the mind of the reader. One could hardly find technical terms more descriptive of their correct meaning than "numerator" and "denominator." Yet to the child whose vocabulary does not include "numeration" and "denomination" they will not automatically convey the correct concept. If the typical fourth-grader associates "denominator" with "denomination" he will probably think it has something to do with what church the fraction belongs to. The correct meanings of many technical terms can be inferred from kindred words: such as "monomial" from "monologue," "binomial" from "bicycle," "percent" from "cent" or hundredth of a dollar, "tangent function" from "tangent line." But there are many other terms which also have a nontechnical meaning (or meanings) that may serve as effective barriers to the correct mathematical meaning. Consider, for example, the mathematical and nonmathematical meanings of the words "function," "irrational," "power," "product," "root," "imaginary," "precise," and "accurate."

It is amazing what misconceptions a child can logically form if the correct meanings of technical terms have not been established.

Another source of difficulty with words, though a minor one, is the fact that we sometimes use the same word to convey different technical meanings. There is nothing unusual about a word having many and diverse meanings but it seems unfortunate that this is true of technical language. We use "remainder" in connection with both subtraction and division. It is a logical choice in both cases; we are referring to what is left. But it can be confusing. "Parameter," "homogeneous," and "analytic" each has a number of different meanings in mathematics. "Congruent" is another good example. The word has multiple meanings and to further complicate the picture there are two different congruency signs, $\cong$ and $\equiv$. The latter sign is also used to indicate a definition and to indicate an identity. Or consider the word "ounce"; it is $\frac{1}{16}$ of a pound sometimes and $\frac{1}{12}$ at others. But the pounds are different and so are the ounces. If the youngster ever gets this straight he may suddenly discover that sometimes "ounce" does not refer to weight at all, it refers to capacity.

In the language of mathematics we use, in addition to English words, some of which have special technical meanings, innumerable mathematical signs. These signs are not always used in isolation, but often as an integral part of grammatically correct sentences. For example: "Since in the equation

$$ax^2 + bx + c = 0, \qquad a \neq 0,$$

the discriminant, $b^2 - 4ac > 0$, we know the roots are real and unequal." If the correct mathematical thought is to be conveyed the sentence must be viewed in terms of the correct grammatical structure.

Consider the division sign. Sometimes we see the conventional $\div$, at other times the horizontal bar as in $\frac{3}{4}$, at still other times an oblique bar as 3/4, and occasionally two dots, 3:4. They all imply division which, in the strict abstract mathematical sense, has but one interpretation, the inverse of multiplication. $a \div b$, a/b, $\dfrac{a}{b}$, $a:b$ all mean "that number which multiplied by b yields a." But in terms of its applicability to a concrete situation $12 \div 4$ expresses how many 4s there are in 12, but it also tells how large each part is when 12 is separated into 4 equal parts. It tells how many times as large 12 is than 4. It is a ratio of two numbers, and it is a number. Sometimes $\frac{3}{4}$

means $\frac{3}{4}$ of 1, sometimes it means $\frac{1}{4}$ of 3, and sometimes it means the ratio of 3 to 4. The child must read with care and reflection and place such symbols as these into context before he can determine which interpretation is the correct one.

Words and signs are merely mental pegs on which to hang ideas. Needless to say, to the extent that the reader does not have clear, concise referents for these symbols he cannot read them. Then improving reading is a matter of concept building. The child who is befuddled by the fact that the product of two fractions is smaller than either one of them does not have the correct concept of a fraction nor as complete a concept of multiplication as is needed.

Concepts do not come as flashes of insight nor are they acquired in the manner of memorizing history dates. They grow and unfold slowly. The development of a concept must have its beginning in familiar surroundings. The new must grow out of that which is already established. The child's concept of addition grows out of counting concrete objects, then pictures of the objects, then tally marks to stand for the picture of the objects, and finally to the abstract symbolism. We build the concepts of zero and negative exponents on the foundation of the familiar positive integral exponents.

How is one to know whether the child has the correct grasp of the concepts symbolized in his reading? The best way to find out is to ask him. You will then be confronted with the eternal "I know it but I can't say it." Let us grant that one may know much that he cannot verbalize. But the odds are pretty good that those things we "know but can't say" are at best vague, fuzzy concepts. There is no better way to clarify and sharpen ideas than to have the child talk about them. It is sheer folly to attempt to build new concepts on others that are incorrectly or inadequately mastered. Students are almost unanimous in saying that the most difficult part of calculus is the algebra. We may learn our algebra in calculus class but we cannot learn the calculus until we learn the algebra. We cannot fathom the mysteries of limits if we do not know what a function is.

Another kind of difficulty with reading in mathematics stems from special kinds of reading which must be done in mathematics, reading of formulas, tables, and graphs. These are means of representing functions. The first task is to determine what the variables are. This information should be given in the title. In the case of the formula the pupil should be able to translate it into a verbal statement in a manner showing the relationship of the variables. This implies a necessary knowledge of the units of measure involved in the formula. The essential thing to know in reading a table or graph is how to pick the paired values of the related variables, given either member of the pair how to find the other. Here again, efficient use of a table or graph presupposes knowledge of the purpose for which one reads. For example, one might be seeking many different kinds of information from a graph. One might be seeking to determine trends of variation, maximum or minimum values of either variable, or the value of one variable corresponding to a given value of the other.

Children's ability to read in mathematics can be improved by doing two things: (1) help them to develop their own correct referents for the symbols, and (2) help them determine the purpose for which they read and to adapt their reading to their purpose.

14.4 IMPROVEMENT OF PROBLEM-SOLVING ABILITY

A number of methods have been proposed for teaching problem solving. No one of them is a panacea. Each constitutes a useful technique for attacking a problem. Their relative effectiveness is a function of both the problem and the individual using it. The pupil should understand and practice the use of each of them. But the child who succeeds in problem solving should not be required to use a specific method. The various methods should be regarded as available aids. No method should be considered necessary to an acceptable solution. Frequently more than one method can be used to advantage on the same problem.

The *analysis method* is held in high favor by many arithmetic textbook writers. It consists of a formal sequence of steps: Read the problem to determine (a) what is given, and (b) what is required. (c) Determine from the relationships between the quantities, given and required, what operations are necessary. (d) Estimate the answer. (e) Solve by performing the operations in (c). (f) Check the answer.

The method places emphasis on the purpose for which the problem is read, that is, to find the statement (given) and the question (required), and to find the manner in which the quantities are related. Estimating the answer in advance of the solution and checking afterwards are most valuable habits. Too great emphasis on the formal aspect of the method, writing down each labeled step in sequence, is apt to place undue emphasis on the method rather than the problem itself. The method is not an end unto itself. It is a means to the solution of the problem. One of the most important requirements for successful problem solving is the ability to translate to mathematical symbolism the stated and implied relationships between given data and between given and required data. This is essentially step (c) of the analysis method. But the method provides no suggestions for help in making this step. It is here that the analysis method may well be supplemented by other methods.

The following problem and solution illustrate the analysis method:

PROBLEM.   Mr. Roberts traded cars this year. The new car cost $1250 plus the old car. He averaged 16 miles per gallon of gasoline with his old car and 20 miles per gallon with the new one. Find how much Mr. Roberts saved on gasoline the first year he drove the new car if he drives about 15,000 miles per year and gasoline costs an average of 32 cents per gallon.

SOLUTION:

(a) *Given:* Gasoline mileage with each car. Difference between cost of cars. Miles traveled per year. Cost of gasoline per gallon.

(b) *Required:* Saving in cost of gasoline for first year.

(c) *Operations required:* We must *subtract* the annual cost of gasoline for the new car from the annual cost for the old one. The total miles per year *divided* by the miles per gallon determines the gallons of gasoline used. The number of gallons *multiplied* by the cost per gallon gives the total cost.

(d) *Estimate the answer:* The old car required about 1,000 gallons and the new one about 750 gallons. At approximately 30 cents per gallon the saving was about $250 \times .30 = \$75.00$.

(e) *Solution:*

$$\frac{15000}{16} = 938 \text{ gallons used by old car}$$

$$938 \times .32 = \$300.16 \text{ cost of gasoline for old car}$$

$$\frac{15000}{20} = 750 \text{ gallons used by new car}$$

$$750 \times .32 = \$240.00 \text{ cost of gasoline for new car}$$
$$\$300.16 - \$240.00 = \$60.16 \text{ saving on gasoline bill}$$

(f) *Check:* Compare the result with the estimate, $60.16 with

$75.00. This is not too convincing, but it is not out of reason in view of the approximate nature of the estimate. The problem may be checked by reviewing the computation. The most satisfactory check consists of using a different approach in solving the problem. The old car required $\frac{1}{16}$ gallon per mile and the new one $\frac{1}{20}$ gallon per mile. Then the new car saved $\frac{1}{16} - \frac{1}{20}$ gallon per mile. The total gallons saved is $15000 \times (\frac{1}{16} - \frac{1}{20})$. The total dollars saved is $.32 \times 15000 \times (\frac{1}{16} - \frac{1}{20}) = \$60$.

The time and effort required to write out the complete analysis is a good investment so long as it is used to establish the habits of purposeful reading of the problem, and estimating and checking the solution. It is not justified as a procedure to be used permanently. The ultimate objective in problem solving should be the development of confidence and competence, independent of any set procedure.

The *method of analogies* consists basically of relating the problem to a simpler analogous one. The simplification may consist of substitution of simpler numbers. For example, consider the problem "If one yard equals .89 meters, 17.3 meters is equivalent to how many yards?" An analogous problem is "If one foot equals $\frac{1}{3}$ yard, 100 yards is equivalent to how many feet?"

The simplification may be from an unfamiliar to a familiar setting. Many third-grade children who cannot solve the problem "Find the number of days in 6 weeks" can without hesitation find the cost of 7 ice cream cones at 6 cents each.

The method of analogies enables the pupil to see the relationships involved in the data by projection from a familiar to an unfamiliar setting. It should be used only when the need for it exists. The analogy is an analogy of relationships. The child should guard against attempts to reason by analogy simply because of other superficial resemblances between the two problem situations. A number is divisible by six if it is divisible by both two and three, since two times three equals six. By analogy, a number is divisible by eight if it is divisible by both two and four, since two times four equals eight. This illustrates the danger of reasoning by analogy if the full significance of the relationships is not apparent.

The *method of dependencies* consists of reasoning from the required to known facts. We illustrate the method with the problem on page 415. The amount saved on gasoline depends on the annual cost of gasoline for each car. The cost for each car depends upon the number of gallons of gasoline used and the cost per gallon. The

number of gallons used depends upon the distance driven and the
rate of gasoline consumption. But the distance driven and the rate of
consumption are given for each car. We can now retrace the steps of
reasoning in reverse order, thus leading to the solution.

This method is very effective for determining the relationships
involved in the problem. Note that the chain of reasoning in no way
involves the cost of the new car. The method can be very useful in
helping to identify superfluous or insufficient data.

The *graphic method* is much more appropriate for some problems
than for others. This method consists of using a diagram or graphic
picture of the situation presented in the problem as an aid in discovering the relationships between the quantities. The following diagram
of the above problem illustrates the method:

$$\begin{array}{c|cccc} \text{cents} & 32 & 64 & 96 & \\ \hline \text{miles} & 16 & 32 & 48 & \overline{15000} \end{array} \text{ old car}$$

$$\begin{array}{c|cccc} \text{cents} & 32 & 64 & 96 & \\ \hline \text{miles} & 20 & 40 & 60 & \overline{15000} \end{array} \text{ new car}$$

The contention that the relationships must be understood in
order to draw the picture contains an element of truth. However, the
act of drawing the picture frequently clarifies and sharpens the conception of the relationships. For example, the above diagram may
suggest a different approach to the problem. The old car gets $\frac{1}{2}$ mile
per cent of gasoline and the new one gets $\frac{5}{8}$ mile per cent. The old car
requires $15000 \div \frac{1}{2}$ cents of gasoline. The new one requires $15000 \div \frac{5}{8}$
cents. The saving is $15000 \div \frac{1}{2} - 15000 \div \frac{5}{8} = 6000$ cents or \$60.00.
Admittedly, this is an awkward solution from the standpoint of the
required reasoning. The important point is that a study of the diagram frequently reveals other aspects of the basic relationships.

14.5 SOME QUESTIONS CONCERNING PROBLEM SOLVING

(1) *Should the child be taught to use word cues and number cues in
problem solving?*

Dwight lists the use of cues as both a good procedure and a bad
one. It all depends on how the cue is used. Such practices as dividing
the large number by the small one, multiplying at the sight of the

word "of," assuming subtraction is implied when "greater than" is seen, and expecting the required to be stated in question form at the end of the problem, are obviously poor practices. If cues are to be used they are better thought of as *clues*. The cue must be interpreted in its context. Cues should never be used to avoid thinking through the problem.

(2) *Should problems containing insufficient or superfluous data be used?*

It is argued that, since in real-life problems we must determine for ourselves what data are and are not relevant, some problems containing insufficient and superfluous data should be used. There is, however, some doubt as to whether this will be of much help in the gathering and selection of data. It in no way approaches a life situation to have one or two bits of superfluous information placed in our path as "bait." On the other hand such problems do serve to emphasize the necessity of reasoning through the problem and not merely attempting to use all the numbers in the problem in some combination which will yield the answer.

Customarily the pupil is forewarned that the problems may contain insufficient or superfluous data. This practice robs the technique of much of its value. The pupil should have the opportunity to discover from an analysis of the relationships that more information is needed or some information has no bearing on the problem. An occasional problem in which the answer is explicitly given also serves to challenge the pupil to read critically.

(3) *Should any emphasis be placed on oral solutions?*

In former years "mental arithmetic" had a prominent place in the elementary-school curriculum. In the main it has suffered the same fate as oral spelling. This is lamentable. Although nearly all need for spelling occurs in connection with written work, the same is not true of arithmetic. A sizable portion of the practical applications of arithmetic are made without benefit of pencil and paper. This is true not only of problem solving but simple computation as well. Furthermore, Spitzer has cited experimental evidence in support of the proposition that oral problem solving is a valuable technique for improving problem-solving ability.[8]

[8] Herbert F. Spitzer, *The Teaching of Arithmetic*, 2d ed. (Boston: Houghton Mifflin Company, 1954), pp. 189–191.

(4) *Should problems be solved by type?*

This depends upon the purpose for which the problem is studied. If problems are to be used to illustrate a particular mathematical operation then it is quite appropriate to use a list of problems taken from a variety of situations all of which illustrate the one mathematical principle. On the other hand, if the purpose of the problem is social utility it is much better for all the problems in a given list to emanate from a common problem situation but to require different mathematical principles.

14.6 LEARNING THEORY AND PROBLEM SOLVING

Problem solving is learning. It is a more complex kind of learning than is acquiring of facts or development of motor skills. Recent curricular trends place much more stress on the mathematical structure of arithmetic than was true in the past. The validity of this change in attitude toward the teaching of arithmetic is obvious when one considers the needs of the future mathematician and scientist. Though it may be less obvious, its value is no less real for the other ninety odd percent of pupils.

Development of genuine problem solving ability in arithmetic requires mastery of arithmetic as a coherent, complete body of knowledge. It is through concrete, practical situations that the child develops such mathematical abstractions as the meaning and significance of the operations of arithmetic and such number properties as the commutative, associative, and distributive laws. Conversely, when the abstract system is mastered the specific problem falls into place as a model of the abstract structure.

Both common sense and experimental evidence point to the fact that learning is facilitated by *active* participation. We can tell children how to solve problems as long as we like. But we have no assurance that from this the child will ever learn how to solve problems. This is one of the most serious pitfalls for the conscientious teacher, telling the child how to work a problem. This tendency, from the standpoint of both teacher and pupil, probably stems from preoccupation with getting the "right answer." What could be of less consequence to the child's future welfare than getting the right answer to problem 6 on page 137? If he gets the wrong answer we certainly should be concerned with why. But the right answer is important only to the extent that it indicates (incorrectly, in many cases) that the child sees the mathematical structure inherent in the problem and has the requisite skill in carrying through the computation.

In teaching children how to solve problems the children should take an active part in determining the mathematical structure underlying the problem. The teacher's role should be that of guide and counsellor, pointing out faulty reasoning, helping with unfamiliar vocabulary, and leading to more efficient methods. It definitely should not be telling the child how to work the specific problem. Discussion of the problem situation should include seeing the whole situation in relation to its parts, establishing the relationship of what is known to what is required, expressing the relationship in symbolic mathematical language, and estimating the answer.

There are those who question the present trend toward earlier introduction of the terminology of set theory and of algebra into arithmetic. It is granted that the important thing is to develop the concepts. But we should not forget that labeling a thing makes it easier to remember and to use in a problem situation. There is no virtue in the child's being able to say "subtraction is the inverse of addition." But giving it the name will help the child *know* that $3 + 6 = n$ and $n - 6 = 3$ require the same replacement for n to make the two sentences true.

Nothing in the present movement should be interpreted as relegating problem solving to a secondary role in arithmetic instruction. Problem solving remains its *raison d'être*.

Exercises

1 Describe a good classroom procedure for the study of oral problem solving.

2 Is the ability to solve problems or the ability to compute the more important? Give arguments on both sides of the question.

3 Find from a history of mathematics what the Rule of False Position is.

4 Make up a problem and solve it by the Rule of False Position. Compare your solution with the modern approach to problem solving.

5 Find and evaluate arguments for and against the use of problems with insufficient and superfluous data.

6 Make up a problem which can best be attacked by each of the methods described in Section 14.4.

7 Contrast the arithmetic problems one meets in life with textbook problems.

8 Contrast the role of problem solving in the early grades with its role in the upper grades.

9 List uses of arithmetic you encounter in a typical day which do not involve problem solving.

10 List major difficulties which pupils encounter in problem solving.

11 What in your opinion is the best method for attacking a problem?

12 Why is it usually harder to identify pupil difficulties with problem solving than difficulties with computation?

Suggested Supplementary Readings

Brownell, William A., "Problem Solving," *Forty-first Yearbook*, National Society for the Study of Education. Bloomington, Indiana: Public School Publishing Company, 1942.

Brueckner, Leo J., "Improving Pupils' Ability to Solve Problems," *Journal of the National Education Association*, June 1932, pp. 175–176.

————, and Guy L. Bond, *The Diagnosis and Treatment of Learning Difficulties*. New York: Appleton-Century-Crofts, Inc., 1955. Pp. 290–301.

Chase, V. E., "The Diagnosis and Treatment of Some Common Difficulties in Solving Arithmetic Problems," *Journal of Educational Research*, December 1925. Pp. 335–342.

Eves, Howard, *An Introduction to the History of Mathematics*. New York: Rinehart and Company, Inc., 1953. Pp. 38–40.

Henderson, Kenneth B., and Robert E. Pingrey, "Problem Solving in Mathematics," *Twenty-first Yearbook*, National Council of Teachers of Mathematics. Washington: 1953. Pp. 228–270.

Committee on the Function of Mathematics in General Education, *Mathematics in General Education*. New York: Appleton-Century-Crofts, Inc., 1940. Pp. 59–89.

Morton, Robert Lee, *Teaching Arithmetic in the Elementary School*. New York: Silver Burdett Company, 1938. Vol. II, pp. 454–493.

Spencer, Peter L., and Marguerite Brydegaard, *Building Mathematical Concepts in the Elementary School*. New York: Henry Holt and Company, 1952. Pp. 297–330.

Spitzer, Herbert F., *The Teaching of Arithmetic*, 2d. ed. Boston: Houghton Mifflin Company, 1954. Pp. 178–203.

Stokes, C. Newton, *Teaching the Meanings of Arithmetic*. New York: Appleton-Century-Crofts, Inc., 1951. Pp. 187–219.

Wheat, Harry G. *The Psychology and Teaching of Arithmetic*. Boston: D. C. Heath and Company, 1937. Pp. 212–228, 363–372.

Answers to Exercises

Section 2.4, page 31

1 (a) ℐℐℐℐℐℐℐ∩∩∩∩∩|

   (b) MMMCCLI

   (c) 二 干 = 百 五 十 一

2 (a) ℐℐℐℐℐℐℐℐℐℐℐℐ∩∩∩∩||

   (b) MMCMXLII

   (c) 二 干 九 百 四 十 二

3 (a) 𓏤𓏤 |

  (b) MCI

  (c) – 十 – 百 –

4 (a) 43 (b) 1782 (c) 257 (d) 947 (e) 906

5 (a) MCMLIX (b) MMI (c) MDCCLXXVI (d) CCCXLVII

6 (a) 𓏤𓏤𓏤𓏤𓏤𓏤∩∩∩∩∩∩∩|||||||||

  (b) 𓏤𓏤𓏤𓏤𓏤𓏤𓏤𓏤𓏤𓏤𓏤𓏤∩∩||

  (c) 𓏤𓏤𓏤𓏤∩∩∩||||

  (d) 𓏤𓏤𓏤𓏤𓏤𓏤𓏤∩∩∩∩∩∩∩∩||||||||||

7 Egyptian is simplest.
  Chinese is usually most compact.

8 MLXXIV

9 (a) 𓏤∩∩∩∩∩∩∩||||

  (b) – 十 七 + 四

10 CCXXVI

11 𓏤𓏤𓏤𓏤𓏤𓏤𓏤𓏤𓏤𓏤𓏤𓏤𓏤𓏤𓏤𓏤𓏤∩∩∩∩||||

12 MMMCXXIV

13 四 十 五 百 = + 四

14 None. None.

15 No, not to represent a positive whole number. One shows there are
  no hundreds by merely not using the symbol for 100.

16 Yes, they are useful when two distinct numbering systems are used
  together, as for example, page numbers and chapter numbers in a
  book. Roman numerals are more widely known and easier to print.

17 Common fractions, yes. Decimal fractions, in the sense of positional
  fractions, no.

18 21

Section 2.5, page 34

1 (a) 1000 (b) 262144 (c) 36 (d) 512 (e) 7 (f) 1 (g) 1/216
  (h) 4 (i) 1 (j) 83 (k) 1/9

2 (a) 5^9 (b) 9^2 (c) 8^3 (d) 1

3 (a) $4 \times 10^2 + 6 \times 10^1 + 8 \times 10^0 + 2 \times 10^{-1} + 3 \times 10^{-2}$
  (b) $1 \times 10^3 + 3 \times 10^0 + 4 \times 10^{-2}$
  (c) $7 \times 10^2 + 7 \times 10^0 + 7 \times 10^{-2}$

4 (a) 274 (b) 427 (c) 43.4 (d) $1099\frac{2}{3}$

5 (a) 6583 (b) 405 (c) 7206.8 (d) 309.07

Section 2.7, page 39

1 Roman – M, Chinese –千, Hindu-Arabic – 1000
2 $8 \times 10^2 + 7 \times 10^1 + 6 \times 10^0$
3 $1 \times 8^3 + 5 \times 8^2 + 5 \times 8^1 + 4 \times 8^0$
4 Both abacus and Roman system use addition to indicate how many of each size group are present, both provide a special means of indicating half the base, 5, 50 and so on. Both abacus and Hindu-Arabic systems have place value.

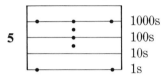

5   1000s
     100s
     10s
     1s

6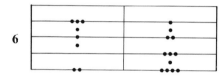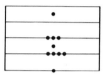

7 We must have a means of indicating same when powers of ten are missing in order that other digits have their proper place.
8 Each power of ten has its own symbol. Place value is not used. If a power of ten is missing we merely leave it out.

Section 2.8, page 45

1 1651
2 $637_{(eight)}$ $415_{(ten)}$
3 474
4 1111011
5 10101101
6 520
7 252
8 1010
9 3011
10 210201
11 Twelve. Each power of twelve will appear from zero to eleven times in each number.

Section 2.9, page 49

1 $\times \, \# \, \#$, $\square \oplus \#$, $\times \oplus \# \, \# \, \#$, $\square \square \# \, \#$

2 $\oplus \square \# \, \#$, $\oplus \# \, \# \oplus$, $\square \square$, $\oplus \# \times \square \#$

3 Addition

$1 + 1 = 2$	$2 + 2 = 4$	$3 + 3 = 11$	$4 + 4 = 13$
$1 + 2 = 3$	$2 + 3 = 10$	$3 + 4 = 12$	
$1 + 3 = 4$	$2 + 4 = 11$		
$1 + 4 = 10$			

Multiplication

$1 \times 1 = 1$	$2 \times 2 = 4$	$3 \times 3 = 14$	$4 \times 4 = 31$
$1 \times 2 = 2$	$2 \times 3 = 11$	$3 \times 4 = 22$	
$1 \times 3 = 3$	$2 \times 4 = 13$		
$1 \times 4 = 4$			

4 1033_5

5 30032_5

6 111110

7 10001111

8 1263_8

9 20604_8

10 No, 43_b cannot be even. $4 \times b$ is even regardless of whether b is even or odd, and $4 \times b + 3$ is odd. Yes, if b is odd 53_b is even.

11 Six.

12 Yes, if b is odd. No, 42_b is even because $4 \times b$ is even regardless of b.

13 Base four – 302

14 27

15 Six.

16 (a) base an odd number
(b) base an even number
(c) none
(d) none

17 113

18 3224

19 1575

20 (a) odd   (b) odd   (c) odd   (d) odd   (e) even

21 No. Any power of one is equal to one.

22 $39843_{(ten)}$

23 1032
  313
  ̄ ̄ ̄
  113

24 (a) Base four, sum of missing digits 4.

  (b) Base eight, sum of missing digits twelve.

25 (a) twelve (b) eight (c) five (d) two

26 No. In base seven $321 = 168_{(ten)}$.

Section 2.10, page 55

1 (a) 1/3 (b) 1/2 (c) 14/25 (d) 15/49

2 (a) .7 (b) .5 (c) .64 (d) .242 (e) .13

3 (a) .132 (b) .321 (c) .44

4 Yes. Two, the only prime factor of 8 is a factor of 10.

5 $.44_{(eight)}$ $.100100_{(two)}$

8 No. Five is a factor of ten.

Section 2.12, page 60

1 Seven.

2 If five is base there is no symbol 6.

3 (a) 11.75 (b) 51 13/64 (c) 61/64 (d) 15/16

4 (a) $260.\overline{6314}_8$ (b) 15.72_8

5 Yes. Yes. Two is a prime factor of both eight and ten.

6 Not necessarily. Yes.

7 Disadvantage.

8 (1) Take 2 from 16 (2) Take 18 from 25 (3) Take 14 from 23.

9 The play is the same with one exception, never force the opponent to play to a 1–1 combination.

10 Yes, all but locating the decimal point.

11 Yes.

12 When the number ends with 1.

14 Advantage to first player. Take 14 from 18.

15 $10 - 8 - 2$

Section 3.2, page 75

5 (a) 9 ones (b) 9 hundreds (c) 9 thousands (d) 9 tens.

13 Five symbols.

14 Four.

15 One hundred twenty four. 400.

Section 3.6, page 82

1 (a) four million three hundred eighty six thousand two hundred
     seventy four ten millionths.
     (b) one hundred thousand two millionths.
     (c) three hundred thirty three thousandths.
     (d) one and twenty seven ten thousandths.
     (e) one hundred and twenty seven hundredths.
     (f) one hundred twenty seven thousandths.

2 (a) 1.7 (b) 100.7 (c) 10.7 (d) .132 (e) 100.032 (f) 1.00032
     (g) .001002 (h) 1000.000002

3 (a) seven hundred and two thousandths
        seven zero zero point zero zero two
     (b) seven hundred two thousandths
        point seven zero two

4 (a) a symbol to identify the empty set
     (b) a point on a scale
     (c) a place holder

6 One thousand million three hundred thousand six hundred two

7 1000,300602

Section 4.1, page 94

1 Tie ten knots in it.

3 (a) in our society, (e)

4 $4 \times 3 \times 2 \times 1 = 24$

Section 4.3, page 98

1 1 3 5 ... $2n - 1$ ...
     ↕ ↕ ↕   ↕
     1 2 3 ... n ...

2 If a_i corresponds to c_i in the first correspondence and b_i corresponds
     to c_i in the second, then a_i matched with b_i will give the desired
     correspondence between A and B.

3 5 10 ... $5n$ ...
     ↕   ↕   ↕
     1/1 1/2 ... 1/n ...

5 By showing that they cannot be placed in one-to-one correspondence.

6 Show a one-to-one correspondence between the set of natural numbers and the set of natural numbers greater than 10.

7 $\aleph_0$

8 No. If we remove a countably infinite set from a countably infinite set the result might be anything from a countably infinite set to the null set.

9 $1/n$ corresponds to $10n$.
The unit fractions and multiples of ten.

Section 4.4, page 102

1 $A \cap B = \{2, 4, 6, 8, 10\}$
$A \cup B = \{1, 2, 3, 4, 5, 6, 7, 8, 9, 10, 12, 14\}$

3 Yes. No.

4 {Tom, Dick, Harry}, {7, 8, 9}, {red, blue, green} are three such elements. There are infinitely many other correct answers.

5 No. There is a difference in kind between 1 and {1}.

6 A is a set of five elements. B is a set of two elements, one of which is a set of three elements and the other a set of two elements.

7 C is a set of four elements. D is a set of two elements, each of which is an ordered pair of the elements of C.

8 3, 3, 1, 5

9 5, 4, 4, 5

10 3, 4, 0, 7

11 $A \cup B = \{2, 3, 5, 7, 11, 13, 17\}$
$B \cap A = \phi$

12 $A \cup B = B \cup A = \{5, 8, 16, 19, 22, 23\}$

Section 4.5, page 106

1 (a) None.
  (b) Transitive.
  (c) Symmetric, transitive.
  (d) Symmetric.
  (e) None.
  (f) Reflexive.
  (g) Transitive.
  (h) None.
  (i) None.
  (j) Symmetric.
  (k) Reflexive, symmetric, transitive.
  (l) Transitive.
  (m) Transitive.
  (n) Symmetric, transitive (if three integers are different).

2 Mapping $A \leftrightarrow B$ corn $\leftrightarrow$ apples
                            potatoes $\leftrightarrow$ oranges
                             wheat $\leftrightarrow$ prunes
                              hogs $\leftrightarrow$ people

   Mapping $B \leftrightarrow C$ oranges $\leftrightarrow$ Jones
                              people $\leftrightarrow$ Smith
                              prunes $\leftrightarrow$ Brown
                              apples $\leftrightarrow$ Roberts

   This establishes the mapping $A \leftrightarrow C$ (through B)
                              corn $\leftrightarrow$ Roberts
                            potatoes $\leftrightarrow$ Jones
                             wheat $\leftrightarrow$ Brown
                              hogs $\leftrightarrow$ Smith

3 How about "knows the name of" applied to persons not suffering from amnesia?

4 "Is a factor of" applied to whole numbers.

5 "Greater than."

6 (a) $=$ is symmetric   (b) $>$ is transitive   (c) reflexive
   (d) $=$ is reflexive   (f) "brother of" is transitive
   (g) $=$ is symmetric and transitive   (h) "brother of" is transitive but not symmetric.

Section 4.6, page 110

1 (a) Not closed, $5 \div 2$ is not a counting number.
   (b) Not closed, $9 - 7$ is not an odd number.
   (c) Not closed, $7 - 9$ is not a counting number.
   (d) Not closed, $7 + 9$ is not a one digit number.
   (e) Not closed, apt, pat, tap are words but tpa is not.

2 $b, c, d.$

3 $b, c.$

4 (a) A, A (b) ϕ, A (c) $\phi \cap \phi$ is the set of all elements in both the empty set and the empty set, that is, no elements. $\phi \cup \phi$ is the set of all elements in either the empty set or the empty set, still no elements.
   (d) If ϕ has no elements, ϕ has no elements in common with itself.

5 Yes, 1.

Section 4.9, page 118

1 (a) 4   (b) -45 (c) -8 (d) 22   (e) -34 (f) -46 (g) 46   (h) -65

3 (a) 21   (b) 21   (c) 21   (d) -14 (e) -14 (f) 11   (g) 11

Section 4.10, page 122

2 (a) 76   (b) 76   (c) -58 (d) -58

4 (a) 90   (b) —73   (c) 46   (d) —69   (e) 6   (f) —25

7 *b*

Section 4.11, page 124

1 (a) a loss   (b) a distance south   (c) loss of population since last census   (d) a distance north   (e) a deceleration   (f) feet below sea level   (g) a date, B.C.

2 (a) 32° below   (b) zero   (c) 3° below   (d) 2° above

Section 4.12, page 130

1 (a) 4   (b) 4   (c) 4   (d) 3, 0   (e) 1   (f) 5, 2   (g) 6

3 0 and 3 are their own inverses, 1 and 5 are inverses, 2 and 4 are inverses.

4 (a) 2   (b) 2   (c) 0   (d) 2, 1   (e) 3, 5   (f) 4, 2   (g) 5

5 Yes, no, yes. *b* is its own inverse.

6 Yes. No. In the case of the circle of six divisions some number other than 0 is its own inverse, that is, 3 is its inverse.

Section 6.1, page 182

1 (a) $\{(a, 1), (a, 2), (b, 1), (b, 2), (c, 1), (c, 2)\}$
  (b) $\{(1, a), (a, a), (x, a)\}$
  (c) $\{(1, 2), (1, b), (1, z), (a, 2), (a, b), (a, z), (x, 2), (x, b), (x, z)\}$
  (d) $\{(1, a), (1, b), (1, c), (2, a), (2, b), (2, c)\}$

2 (a) 3, 2, 6   (b) 3, 1, 3   (c) 3, 3, 9   (d) 2, 3, 6

3 8, 9

4 If $n(A) = a$ then $n(A \times A) = a^2$.

5 the empty set

6 $\{(a, a)\}$

Section 6.2, page 189

1 $\{(1, 0), (1, y), (a, 0), (a, y), (x, 0), (x, y)\}$

2 $\{(0, 1), (0, a), (0, x), (y, 1), (y, a), (y, x)\}$

3 $\{(1, x), (1, y), (a, x), (a, y), (x, x), (x, y)\}$

4 $\{(1, 0), (1, x), (1, y), (a, 0), (a, x), (a, y), (x, 0), (x, x), (x, y)\}$

5 Because B and C are not disjoint.

6 Yes. No. No.

7 (a) Distributive property.
  (b) Multiplication is commutative.
  (c) Any cardinal number times 0 equals 0.

(d) Addition is associative.

(e) Addition is associative and commutative.

8 Equality is a symmetric and transitive relation, multiplication is commutative.

Section 6.3, page 190

1 There is no replacement for a, hence there are no ordered pairs.

2 There are no first elements of the ordered pairs of $A \times B$.

3 Because 5 has no integral divisors except 1 and 5.

4 The number of elements of $A \times B$ must be a multiple of 3.

5 $\{x, y\}$

6 $r \div p = m$

7 $p \times m = r,\ r \div m = p$

8 Division by 0 is undefined.

Section 6.5, page 193

1 (a) 2   (b) 2   (c) 270   (d) 270   (e) 144   (f) 144

3 (a) 15   (b) 21   (c) 51   (d) −12

4 (a) 4   (b) −3   (c) 3   (d) −5

5 (a) positive   (b) negative   (c) negative   (d) positive

7 (a) -2×-4 (b) 1×-2 (c) 2

8 negative

11 (a) −5   (b) 10   (c) −4

Section 6.6, page 202

1 1 is its own inverse, 2 and 4 are inverses, 3 and 5 are inverses, 6 is its own inverse.

2 5

3 3

4 (a) 6   (b) 6   (c) 3   (d) 3

5 No. 6 is its own inverse.

7 Yes.

8 All odd numbers are congruent to either 1 or 3 modulo 4. $1^2 \equiv 1 \bmod 4$, $3^2 \equiv 1 \bmod 4$.

9 0, 0, no, no.

10 1, 5, 7, 11. Each is its own inverse.

13 $493 \equiv 7 \pmod 9$,
$871 \equiv 7 \pmod 9$
$639 \equiv 0 \pmod 9$
$7 + 7 + 0 \equiv 5 \pmod 9$
$2003 \equiv 5 \pmod 9$

14 $463_8 \equiv 6 \pmod 7$,
$721_8 \equiv 3 \pmod 7$
$542_8 \equiv 4 \pmod 7$
$6 + 3 + 4 \equiv 6 \pmod 7$
$2146_8 \equiv 6 \pmod 7$

15 (a) $543 \equiv 3 \pmod 9$,
$657 \equiv 0 \pmod 9$
$3 \times 0 \equiv 0 \pmod 9$
$356751 \equiv 0 \pmod 9$
(b) $321 \equiv 6 \pmod 9$,
$47 \equiv 2 \pmod 9$
$6 \times 2 \equiv 3 \pmod 9$
$15087 \equiv 3 \pmod 9$

16 (a), (b)

17 $0^3 = 0$, $1^3 = 1$, $2^3 = 8$, $3^3 = 27 \equiv 0 \pmod 9$,
$4^3 = 64 \equiv 1 \pmod 9$, $5^3 = 125 \equiv 8 \pmod 9$,
$6^3 = 216 \equiv 0 \pmod 9$, $7^3 = 343 \equiv 1 \pmod 9$,
$8^3 = 512 \equiv 8 \pmod 9$

18 (a) $18546 \equiv 6 \pmod 9$
$8328 \equiv 3 \pmod 9$
$10218 \equiv 3 \pmod 9$
(b) $63524 \equiv 2 \pmod 9 \equiv 11 \pmod 9$
$3760 \equiv 7 \pmod 9 \equiv 7 \pmod 9$
$59764 \equiv \qquad 4 \pmod 9$

19

	0	1	2	3	4	5	6	7	8
0	0	0	0	0	0	0	0	0	0
1	0	1	2	3	4	5	6	7	8
2	0	2	4	6	8	1	3	5	7
3	0	3	6	0	3	6	0	3	6
4	0	4	8	3	7	2	6	1	5
5	0	5	1	6	2	7	3	8	4
6	0	6	3	0	6	3	0	6	3
7	0	7	5	3	1	8	6	4	2
8	0	8	7	6	5	4	3	2	1

3   6

20 (a) $543 = 88 \times 6 + 15$
$\qquad 3 \equiv 7 \times 6 + 6 = 48 \equiv 3$
(b) $2974 = 10 \times 278 + 194$
$\qquad 4 \equiv 1 \times 8 + 5 = 13 \equiv 4$

21 Modulo tables should be the same except that only ones digit is shown. This is because in base seven the ones digit is the residue modulo seven.

22 7, 19, 31 are the smallest three.
5, 12, 19 are the smallest three.

23 6×11

25 mod 5

26 (a) 2 or 289.

Section 6.7, page 206

1 2, 3, 5, 7, 11, 13, 17, 19, 23, 29, 31, 37, 41, 43, 47, 53, 59, 61, 67, 71, 73, 79, 83, 89, 97

2 $40 \times 63 = 2 \times 2 \times 2 \times 5 \times 3 \times 3 \times 7$
$35 \times 72 = 5 \times 7 \times 2 \times 2 \times 2 \times 3 \times 3$

3 $2^4 \times 3^3 = 432$

4 (a), (b), and (d) are prime.

5 Yes, because a is a factor of a^2.

6 No, n can have a as a factor without its being a repeated factor.

Section 6.8, page 212

1 (a) remainders are 1, 2, 1, 2, and 6
(b) divisible by 2, 3, 5, and 9; remainder 1 when divided by 11.
(c) divisible by 2 and 11, remainders are 2, 2, 8 when divided by 3, 5, 9.
(d) divisible by 2, 3, 5, 9, 11.

2 (a) divisible by 2, 4, 8.
(b) divisible by 2, 4, 8.
(c) divisible by 2, remainder 2 when divided by 4, remainder 6 when divided by 8.
(d) remainders are 1, 1, 5.

3 Because 2 and 3 are relatively prime, but 2 and 4 are not.

4 Each digit must be multiplied by the following congruences, modulo 13.
$10^0 = 1 \equiv 1, 10^1 \equiv -3, 10^2 \equiv (-3) \times (-3) = 9 \equiv -4,$
$10^3 \equiv (-3) \times (-4) = 12 \equiv -1, 10^4 \equiv (-3) \times (-1) = 3,$
$10^5 \equiv (-3) \times (3) = -9 \equiv 4, 10^6 \equiv (-3) \times (4) = -12 \equiv 1,$
$10^7 \equiv (-3) \times 1 = -3,$ etc.

5 A number is divisible by 12 if it is divisible by 3 and by 4.

6 No. Yes. Only the last two digits determine divisibility by 4. 14 is not divisible by 4. All digits enter in determining divisibility by 3 and by 7.

7 A number is divisible by 22 if it is divisible by 2 and by 11.

8 The sum of the odd placed digits differs from the sum of the even placed digits by a multiple of eleven, and the sum of the digits is a multiple of nine.

9 (a) Cannot be made divisible by 4 or 5. Divisible by 2 for all replacements. Divisible by 3 and by 6 for 1, 4, or 7. Divisible by 9 for 7. Divisible by 11 for 0.

10 Yes, $10 \equiv 3 \bmod 7$.

Section 6.9, page 214

1 36

3 $7 \equiv 13 \bmod 6$

4 No. The modulus would have to be a common factor.

7 2

9 Yes.

10 $13_{\text{(eight)}}$

Section 6.10, page 216

2 (a) No (b) Yes (c) no, yes (d) yes, yes

3 Yes, no.

4 Yes, yes.

5 No, yes.

6 If the base is five (or any odd number) each odd digit represents an odd number and each even digit represents an even number. The sum of an even number of odd addends is even.

7 If it has an odd number of odd digits.

8 Ends in 0 or 3. Ends in 0, 2, or 4. Divisible by 4 if units digit plus twice sixes digit is.

9 Is divisible by 8.

10 Select an odd base. Then any two digit number, with the higher digit odd and the ones digit even, will be odd. For example 34_7. Now make the ones digit odd and the number is even. For example 35_7.

11
$$1^2 \equiv 1 \pmod 5 \qquad\qquad 2^2 = 4 \equiv -1 \pmod 5$$
$$3^2 = 9 \equiv -1 \pmod 5 \qquad 4^2 = 16 \equiv 1 \pmod 5$$
$$5^2 = 25 \equiv 0 \pmod 5$$

Section 6.11, page 222

1 True—order of successive divisors can be changed.

2 True—multiplication distributive with respect to subtraction.

3 False

4 False

5 True—special case.

6 True—multiplication of dividend and divisor by same number does not affect quotient.

7 False

8 True—special case.

9 True—division obeys right distributive law.

10 True—special case.

11 True—successive division may be performed by dividing by the product of the divisors.

12 False

13 True—multiplication is distributive with respect to subtraction.

14 True—special case.

15 False

16 True—successive subtraction may be performed by subtracting the sum of the subtrahends.

17 True—the quotient is unchanged by dividing both dividend and divisor by the same number.

18 False

19 True—subtracting the same number from both minuend and subtrahend does not change the remainder.

20 False

21 False

22 False

23 True—division obeys the right distributive law.

24 True—successive subtraction may be performed by subtracting the sum of the subtrahends.

25 False

26 True—multiplication is distributive with respect to addition.

27 True—successive division may be performed by dividing by the product of the divisors.

28 True—the same number may be subtracted from minuend and subtrahend without changing remainder.

29 True—division obeys right distributive law.

31 (c), (d).

32 Yes.

Section 8.1, page 273

1 (a) 5, 9
(b) 6, 9, 21, 8, 28
(c) 5, 15, 4, 20, 12, 20

2 (c), (e)

3 (a) 3 (b) 3 (c) 9 (d) 5/2

4 329 miles, 11 13/47 hours

5 Jim $30, Tom $45, Bob $75

6 33 feet

7 A 300, B 500, C 700

Section 8.2, page 276

1 Because $0 \times k = 0$ for any k.

2 An equivalence class has for its elements all equivalent elements, whether there be a finite or infinite number of them. On the other hand, the infinite set of equivalent elements does not necessarily include all of them.

3 2

4 Yes, No.

5 $1/\sqrt{2}$

6 $1:3:5$

7 Yes, $2:\sqrt{3}$.

8 $4/10$, $6/15$, $2\sqrt{2}/5\sqrt{2}$, 200/500, 1/2.5

9 Yes.

10 $3:1$, $3 \div 1$. The classification of a number as a fraction has to do with its form. Although 3 is not a fraction 3/1 is, it is an improper fraction.

Section 8.6, page 285

7 (a) 8/15; 8/15
(b) 9/14; 9/14
(c) 15/16; 15/16

A quotient is unaffected if both dividend and divisor are multiplied (or divided) by the same number.

8   (a) 34/55   (b) 5/140   (c) 6   (d) −1/11

10   No.

11   (a) 3/4, −4/3   (b) −3/5, −5/−3   (c) −2/5, 5/2
        (d) −a/2b, 2b/a   (e) − −b/2a, 2a/−b

12   No. Because the square of any rational number is positive.

Section 8.7, page 289

1   (a) simple, improper
        (b) complex, proper
        (c) complex, improper
        (d) simple, proper

2   (a) 20/6   (b) −9/5

4   Since b and d are positive we can reduce to a common denominator
        and have $ad/bd > bc/bd$. The denominators are positive, hence we
        can compare numerators and have $ad/bd > bc/bd$ if and only if
        $ad > bc$.

5   The denominators must also be positive. Apply the result of
        Exercise 4.

6   3/5, 20/31, 2/3, 21/31, 21/30, 5/7

7   29/70 is one of infinitely many correct answers.

8   (a) 15/12   (b) 1/17   (c) 4   (d) 1/7

Section 10.2, page 331

1   If $N = .24\overline{9}\ldots$ then $100N = 24.\overline{9}\ldots$ and $1000N = 249.\overline{9}\ldots$
        $1000\,N - 100\,N = 249.\overline{9}\ldots - 24.\overline{9}\ldots$
        $$900\,N = 225$$
        $$N = \tfrac{225}{900} = \tfrac{25}{100} = .25$$

2 $.123 = \tfrac{123}{1000}$
        If $N = .\overline{123}\ldots,\ 1000\,N = 123.\overline{123}\ldots$ and
        $999\,N = 123$
        $$N = \tfrac{123}{999}$$

3 $.\overline{123} = \tfrac{123}{999}$
        Let $N = .1\overline{231}\ldots$, then $10\,N = 1.\overline{231}\ldots$
        and $10000\,N = 1231.\overline{231}\ldots$
        $10000\,N - 10\,N = 1231.\overline{231}\ldots - 1.\overline{231}\ldots$
        $$9990\,N = 1230$$
        $$N = \tfrac{1230}{9990} = \tfrac{123}{999}$$

4 $.\overline{142857}$

5   They are the same.

6 The product 142857×2 may be obtained by shifting the digits 14 to the extreme right, thus 142857 gives 285714. Similarly for the other multipliers 3 through 6.

7 $.99\overline{9}$ ... and $1.00\overline{0}$ ... are the same number.

8 Consider any one digit number N.
$\frac{1}{81} \times 9 \times N = \frac{1}{9} \times N$. The repeating form decimal for $\frac{1}{9}$ is $.11\overline{1}$ ...

9 $\frac{1}{16}, \frac{9}{40}, \frac{10}{128}$.

10 $\frac{1}{16}, \frac{1}{9}, \frac{10}{128}$ in base 12. None in base 5.

11 $.312_8$

12 $.01100101_2$

13 To be a terminating decimal the common fraction, when reduced to lowest terms, must have only powers of 2 and 5 in its denominator. The higher exponent in the denominator is the number of digits in the expansion.

14 No.

15 Repeat, terminate, repeat

16 4/7 in base fourteen
2/5 in base fifteen
5/6 in base twelve

19 None in base seven. In base nine, $\frac{2}{3}$ terminates.

20 (a) 7/8 (b) 53/32 (c) 342/343 (d) 433/25

Section 10.5, page 336

2 17.3 is a terminating decimal, it means the same as $17\frac{3}{10}$.
$17.\overline{3}$ ... is a repeating decimal with a repetend 3, it means the same as $17\frac{1}{3}$.
17.3 ... may be anything from $17\frac{3}{10}$ to $17\frac{4}{10}$. It is an endless decimal but the rule for forming the sequence of digits is not given.

3 Assume $\sqrt{3} = \dfrac{a}{b}$, a, b relatively prime. Then $\sqrt{3}b = a$ and $3b^2 = a^2$.

From this we may infer a^2, and hence a, has the factor 3. Replace a by $3c$. $3b^2 = (3c)^2 = 9c^2$. Then $b^2 = 3c^2$. Therefore b^2 and b have the factor 3 also. But this contradicts the assumption that a and b are relatively prime.

4 If $4b^2 = a^2$, we cannot infer that a has the factor 4.

5 In this case $2b^3 = a^3$. If a^3 has the factor 2, so must a. Continue as before.

6 Assumed $\sqrt[3]{4} = a/b$ then $\sqrt[3]{4}b = a$ and $4b^3 = a^3$. If a^3 has the factor $4 = 2 \times 2$, then a must have the factor 2. Replace a with $2c$. $4b^3 = (2c)^3 = 8c^3$ $b^3 = 2c^3$. But this implies b has the factor 2.

7 Construct a unit square. Using its diagonal and unity as sides, construct a rectangle. The diagonal of the rectangle is the required length.

8 The first ten approximations, to 3 digits are 4.00, 2.67, 3.47, 2.90, 3.34, 2.98, 3.29, 3.02, 3.26, 3.05.

9 Deficiency.

10 .67

Section 12.2, page 370

1 The position of the smallest position valued significant digit.

2 The number of significant digits.

3 When used for π, 3 1/7 is approximate but not a measurement.

4 Precision is a unit of measure, not just a number.

5 (a) 1400 feet   (b) .127 pounds   (c) 1.56 pounds

6 (a) 4.6 miles   (b) .127 pounds   (c) same

7 12.35 yards to 12.45 yards

8 .4%

Section 12.5, page 374

1 (a) the first   (b) the first

2 (a) 4   (b) 6   (c) 2   (d) 5   (e) 8

3 All digits are significant.

5 (a) 1/16, 1/428, .23%   (b) 1/250, 1/46, 2.17%   (c) 1/2, 1/5322, .02%

6 (a) 35100   (b) 1.13   (c) 4530   (d) 8.95   (e) 368000

Section 12.6, page 377

1 (a) A length which may be any value between 12.45 feet and 12.55 feet.

   (b) Represents a length which may be any value between $\frac{3}{6}$ and $\frac{5}{6}$.

   (c) Between .675 and .665.

   (d) Between 12.495 feet and 12.505.

   (e) Between $4\frac{1}{16}$ inches and $3\frac{15}{16}$.

2 (a) 126 inches more precise—same accuracy.

   (b) 5 pounds more precise—250 tons more accurate.

   (c) Same precision and accuracy.

   (d) .00056 gallons more precise—same accuracy.

3 Yes to all questions.

4 Mistakes are one kind of error—a misuse of the measuring instrument is a mistake.

5 (a) .5 miles, $\frac{1}{252}$, .4%

   (b) .0005 cm., $\frac{1}{50}$, 2%

   (c) $\frac{1}{8}$ cm., $\frac{1}{2}$, 50%

   (d) 500 miles, $\frac{1}{50}$, 2%

6 (a) five   (b) four   (c) six   (d) five   (e) three   (f) four
7 (a) 8500   (b) 92   (c) 37,000   (d) .0068
8 The three results are 854, 855, and 855.
9 Maximum 4114.8075, minimum 4097.0375.
10 4110
11 There would be no need to measure if we knew the true value.
12 $\frac{1}{300}, \frac{1}{200}$

Section 12.7, page 380

1 (a) 8.63×10^4 (b) 1.5×10^8
   (c) 1.7×10^{-5} (d) 8.30×10^{-4}
   (e) 7×10^0

2 (a) 560,000,000   (b) .000011
   (c) 2,210,000   (d) 2.34
   (e) .43

3 (a) 4.9×10^3 (b) 5.9×10^{12}
   (c) 5×10^3

Index